JUDY LIGHT AYYILDIZ has taught creative writing to all education levels for 30 years. Prior to that, she was a musician and music teacher. She has been an instructor and presenter at literary workshops, international conferences on poetry, writing and women's studies. Internationally published, she was an editor of *Artemis, Artists and Writers from the Blue Ridge* for 13 years and was a Blue Ridge Writers Conference founder. Her published books are *First Recital, Smuggled* Seeds, *Mud River* (poetry), *Skyhooks and Grasshopper Traps, Creative Writing across the Curriculum, Easy Ideas for Busy Teachers, The Writers' Express* (writing texts), *Nothing but Time* (memoir of triumph over trauma) and *Some of My Ancestors are Ottomans and Turks* (children's picture book illustrated by Vedii Ayyildiz). Literary publications include *New York Quarterly, Mickle Street Review, The New Renaissance, Sow's Ear, Pig Iron Press, Hawaii Pacific Review, Black Water Review, Northeast Journal, Kalliope*. Among others, honors include "YWCA Women of Achievement in Education 2010", Va. Com. Of Arts, various poetry short story prizes (www.judylightayyildiz. com) Daughters of Ataturk, Turkish Forum, College Bookstores Best Book Finalist, Gusto Poet Discovery Winner, VCCA Fellow. Her essay, "Weaving This Woman's Life and Work" with excerpts from her books was included in the 2008 international anthology, *Women in Dialogue: (M)uses in Culture*. She won the "Nazim Hikmet 2009 Poetry Festival Prize. Judy currently works on a memoir about growing up in WVA. She has been a leader in various creative civic organizations, is a mother of three children and two grandchildren and has been married for half a century to her Turk.

D1157764

BLURBS FOR *FORTY THORNS*

Ms. Ayyildiz does it again. Her new book, *Forty Thorns*, is a lovingly written biography of her mother-in-law Lady Adalet. *Forty Thorns* is also a lesson in history of a region as well as endurance. Set during the turbulent times of WWI in the Balkans and the War of Independence in Turkey, it takes the reader on a whirlwind journey. She pieces together the collective history of her mother-in-law and her relatives, intermingled with customs that are so different than her own. A much needed book that will familiarize the reader with history and customs of the region as well as love and respect in families of different backgrounds.   **Sema Karaoglu,** Founder, Daughters of Ataturk

I was so taken when reading: An American wife and her Turkish husband come back from the United States to Istanbul, after many years, to bury and pay their last tribute to the man's mother, Adalet, and to remember the story of her eventful, rich, tragic, and inspiring life – life, lived to the fullest, against the grand setting of war-torn Turkey of the twentieth century, and marked fatally by the decisive moments of the country's modern history. Adalet's life connects exemplarily the public and private spheres of human existence, and the strength, generosity, and liberality of her spirit provide for her loved and loving American daughter-in-law a cherished and unlimited source of motivation, encouragement, and muse. It is a strong text indeed.
Klara Kolinska, Ph.D. Anglophone Studies, Metropolitan University, Prague, Anglophone Literatures and Cultures, Charles University, Prague. Studies in Literature and Culture. Charles University, Prague, Shakespeare and His Collaborators Over the Centuries. Cambridge Scholars Publishing

Forty Thorns is a sensual feast, bright, colorful, and exotic. Based on the life of Judy Light Ayyildiz' beloved Turkish mother in law, Adalet shines forth as a heroine for all times, and all women.   **Katie Letcher Lyle,** *Friends In High Places,* and 20 other books

Judy Light Ayyildiz has created an unforgettable portrait of a feisty, patient, and tenacious heroine that evokes the indomitable spirit of Turkish women – even under oppression. It takes us into the heart of the Republic Era invoking sepia images of Turkey's past.
Alev Lytle Croutier, the author of *Harem: the World Behind the Veil* and *Seven Houses*

Forty Thorns is a fascinating account from a woman's point of view of a nation's history at two levels. From a national level, it describes the momentous changes in Turkey's history in the early 1900s as the Ottoman Empire is ending and the new Turkish Republic is being born out of its ashes. At the personal level, it is a woman's ordeal in her private life dealing with love and suffering at the hands a restless and straying husband. There is a parallel as Adalet gradually takes control of her fate and Turkish women gain their rights through the reforms of the new Republic established by Kemal Ataturk. The mores and customs of the times are described in meticulous detail. The book describes the flow of the events in the same breathless fashion as they occurred during those extraordinary times: Many wars, death, suffering, exile and then peace followed by reforms and the birth of modern Turkey. These measures are intertwined closely with the many occurrences in Adalet's life, which gives the book a very personal and warm touch.
Oya Bain, Trustee, Assembly of Turkish American Associations

JUDY LIGHT AYYILDIZ

Judy Light Ayyildiz

3-12-13

Forty Thorns

*For Peggy and Steve
with best
wishes —*

Remzi Kitabevi

FORTY THORNS / Judy Light Ayyildiz

© Judy Light Ayyildiz, 2011
© Judy Light Ayyildiz, Remzi Kitabevi, 2011

All rights reserved. Reproduction, modification,
storage in a retrieval system or retransmission, in
any form or by any means, electronic, mechanical
or otherwise, is strictly prohibited without prior
written permission.

The poem, "Ritual" was published *Turkish Torque,* 2004;
Turkish Times, April 2003; *McGuffin Magazine,* June 2000

Chapter 25 was first published by Rubbettino Editore 2007
as a short story translated into Italian titled, "Pears" in the
anthology, *International Women Writing Today.*

The poem, "Adalet" was printed with permission of K. Kamal
Ayyildiz and is from his Istanbul collection, *The Cistern,*
Citlembik Publications, 2004

Editing: Leyla İsmier Özcengiz
Cover design: Ömer Erduran

ISBN 978-975-14-1474-8

FIRST EDITION: December 2011

Remzi Kitabevi A.Ş., Akmerkez E3-14, 34337 Etiler-İstanbul
Tel (212) 282 2080 Faks (212) 282 2090
www.remzi.com.tr post@remzi.com.tr

Printed and binded: Remzi Kitabevi A.Ş. basım tesisleri
100. Yıl Matbaacılar Sitesi, 196, Bağcılar-İstanbul

For my family...

This is a novelized account based on Adalet's oral memoir,
actual history and loosely on my personal memory.
For privacy, I have changed names and characteristics
of those living at the time of this writing.

Acknowledgements

I am indebted first of all to Adalet for being who she was and for wanting me to write a novel based on her life; and then, to my husband, Vedii, who became my right hand during the writing of this novel. I also salute Ates Oner, who translated Adalet's oral memories, Deniz Yesim Isik, Nihal Ayyildiz, Bilgen Bengu and Golgen Bengu. There are so many Turkish people who showed interest in my project and gave freely of their time and knowledge that I could not mention them all. Some of them were strangers. I hope not to have forgotten anyone who has done me particular favors and ask forgiveness if I have left anyone out. The novel has progressed over ten years of notes and research in books and written literature, visits throughout Anatolia and Thrace and in interviews with many people who gave me information. Particularly, I wish to remember the hours of discussion with me, and the gift of his writing and books from the historian and writer of Kirklareli, Nazif Karacam. Special thanks to Professor Talat Halman, Doctor Fuat Umay's daughter, Esen and her son Engin Kevenk, the novelist Erendiz Atasu, Professor Gunseli Isci and also, the female Turkish novelists of Adalet's generation, Cahit Ucuk, as well as Munnever Ayasli, Ruhittin Saylik's daughter Nermin and her brother, Tunc, Sabri's son, Salahattin, and his sons and daughter-in-laws, as well as Mustafa's sons, Ozhan and Ertan, and Sabri's daughter Meral, the Mayor of Merzifon, Cahit Toprak and the Kaymakam Yasar Donmez of Gumishacikoy. Thanks also go to writer friends who read certain drafts of some chapters and encouraged me, especially the "Good Ole Gals" workshop group, and the writer and my mentor for many years, the late Walter

James Miller as well as Kenneth Reckford and Charlotte Roth. I am grateful that I was awarded an Artist Assistance Grant by the Virginia Commission for the Arts to study novel writing at the Iowa Summer Workshops and also for two fellowships at The Virginia Center for Creative Arts where I was able to begin and finally complete the first full draft of this work. Were it not for the belief in this novel first by Kalem Agency and then my competent and enduring editors, Omer Erduran and Oner Ciravoglu of Remzi Kitabevi, this book would not have come into being. Last but not least, I thank my skillful Turkish translator and English copy editor, Leyla Ismier Ozcengiz, readers everywhere and women and men of a great spirit to whom we continue to look for hope that leads us along this journey.

Foreword

Forty Thorns began at a kitchen table in Istanbul where my mother-in-law Adalet enticed me to come and spend the summer recording her oral biography. Her lucid memory was astounding to me as a writer. She was a sparkling storyteller, insisting, "I'm not important, but my story is. Write my book." She died at age 92 the following year. I had known Adalet since her early sixties. Her humor, intelligence, illuminated grace and faith in tomorrow impressed me greatly. Plus, she proved to be a good friend to me. How had she survived with those qualities considering the turmoil and tragedy through which she had lived? To write Adalet's story, I would have to discover from where that strength grew. What motivated her not only to survive – but also survive well? A wise and open-minded woman, she was a creative wit with a curious attachment to the West. Yet, she was rooted in the mystic and ritual of the East and was a devoted progressive Muslim. I spent the next ten years off and on researching the conglomerated and erratic Turkish history. After that, novelizing Adalet's oral biography became an obsession for me. The dynamic changes following the 10 years of continuous wars in Adalet's early life from 1912-1923 engulfed and molded her survivor's instinct. The New Republic would move her all across Anatolia and Thrace with her husband and children from 1923-1945. Once I was deep into the manuscript, I felt her spirit's presence guiding the action as I wrote. I was further stimulated when I began to realize how her own trials, beginnings, deaths and betrayals paralleled the emergence and growth of the Turkish Republic. Burhan the blacksmith's son stole Adalet's heart and set her on the course to lose her family inheritance. Although peace in her personal realm became a constant challenge, the founder of the Turkish Republic, Kemal Ataturk – with his visions and insistence on a new era of equality, fraternity and justice for both men and women – won her spirit and gave her hope. Today, Turkey plays a key role on the world's stage. Adalet was right. As a female and survivor, her epic story is important. Great republics are built on the strength of such uncommon women.

JLA

RITUAL

[for Adalet]

*After your death at age ninety-two, I return
to Istanbul, where you spent your final years.
I dust your treasures: red gone to ochre
silk flowers, a chipped vase on an oak chair
split at the back, a marble Russian swan
with head caught preening a folded wing,
a crumpled prayer book, a plastic turtle
balanced on the* Kredi Bankasi *candy dish.*

*I wash your fingerprints from corners
where you made your way from bedroom,
bath and kitchen, your soft smudges
at knee-level, where your hands steadied
against gravity. You were determined
to walk alone long after time had warped
and twisted you down. You pulled up
with a strength that had carried you past
broken Ottoman relics into the fires of love,
devastation, revolution, the loss of two
of your seven children and betrayal again.*

*You said your prayers five times a day,
chuckling at aggravations in between,
or weeping for the ironies and inadequacies
of a third-world system and second-rate love.*

Yet, you believed in the magic of ritual:
fat ripe figs in hand again, Turkish coffee,
seeing good fortunes in dregs, feeding seagulls
come in from the shores at night – seagulls sidling
near to eat stale bread you would not throw away,
for bread is sacred. But, there were always hungry,
orphaned spirits waiting at your moonlit ledge.

I squeeze water from the rag, see your mornings
and evenings clarify in streams below the drain,
think you pleased, knowing how you loved clean
space. The traces of your last pains are gone,
stains that your Tracian eyes did not see. Walls
merely served to hold you forward into light.

JLA

Forty Thorns

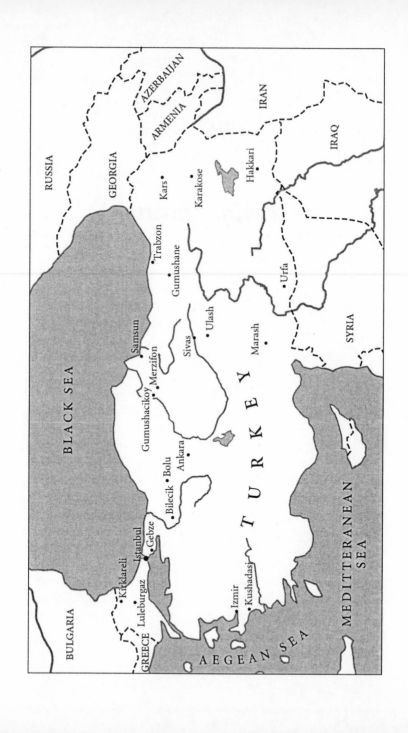

ONE

Separation

Nuri had been expecting his mother to die for a long time, but somehow pictured her as being alive forever. These past two years, I'd stir as Nuri eased out of bed in the middle of the night to dial his mother across the oceans. In the last six months, Adalet's voice had sounded hoarse, but she was in her full mind until the end. "Did Lee finish my book yet?" she'd ask him. "Still sharp as a tack," Nuri would say, climbing back into bed. Two nights ago, that jarring ring startled us.

Istanbul, September 1993

At some signal I don't catch, the mourners all at once make a surge toward the wall. My husband, Nuri, tugs our son's shoulder and says, "Over there." I follow them to join the rows of bodies quickly forming at the base of the concrete platform.

The heavy-bearded imam appears in a white cap and black robe to conduct the rites. Stationed above and behind the bier, he raises his hands toward the cloud-straggled sky. A breeze furls his gown like Moses in *The Ten Commandments*. His oboe voice waffles over the concrete pedestal and across the compound's garden. A gust ruffles the Arabic script on the green and white mantles draped across the coffin. The recital mingles with Istanbul's engines and horns.

"People don't understand Arabic," Mother Adalet said a year and a half ago, telling me how her leader changed the prayer calls

to Turkish after he became president of the new republic and how they were later changed back to the old language in 1950.

She clapped her hands beneath a toothless grin and added, "Ataturk was our everything." After that, she brought her palms to her face, whispered a prayer into them, winged her hands out and up, and then continued just as if she hadn't paused. "Why should Turks pray in a foreign tongue? Allah understands Turkish."

"Leee – no! Come!" Nuri's youngest sister is gripping me by the arm.

"What?" I reply, dumbfounded and tugging loose.

When I turn, I see I'm stalled between men at the altar and women clumped back under some trees.

The sister, grabbing and propelling me with an air of authority, flicks her head as she indicates my place with the females. I am doubly stunned with confusion and jet lag but am irritated at the idea of being siphoned-off because of my sex. I yank back against her pull, cross my arms and give her a message in international body language by my stance: I don't understand your rules. She tightens her lips. But, I have to remember where I am. I shrug and uncross my arms and turn, facing the bier. But I don't take a step; stay stuck between the two groups. I hear the swish of her skirt as she leaves me. I'm silently calling after her, *What happened to "Justice," the literal meaning of your dead mother's name – and equality, the reason she gave for joining the revolution? Is the reform warped and withered inside that box?* I stare at my husband's back. He's unaware of my dilemma. They say that the older women usually stay home from funerals. Small wonder.

Across my shoulder at the edge of the courtyard, my eyes are drawn again to the concrete hut, where earlier today, a woman had cleansed Adalet's body. At noon, after we drove in from the airport, the family was together. For the first time, the reunion was sad, clustering around that hut. Nuri and I along with our twenty-seven-year-old son, Kurt, joined the nieces and nephews and the middle sister and her husband. The older sisters didn't come then, either. When the woman finished, the females were invited inside to view the body. The nieces pulled back and the younger sister walked away crying.

"I'll go," I said.

I went to the niece in from the States, a professor who has taught economics there for ten years. She was sitting on the steps with her sister. "Come with me to see your grandmother," I said, knowing that if any one of them would go, it would be her. The red-eyed and silent others weren't moving.

"I'm afraid to see her this way," she told me.

I tightened my gaze on her sun-glassed eyes. She took a breath and wiped her eyes under her glasses. "There are not enough women like Grandmother in the whole world," she said, taking my arm. We walked toward the heavy wooden door with the green paint scabbing on it. Only a few years after she came to the States, she was teaching undergraduates at Purdue. This was her first trip back.

The hut felt as damp and cool as a springhouse. Adalet's body lay bound in white linen with only her face exposed. Extra strips were tied at her legs and beneath her breast. She looked as if she was meditating, as if she was some Egyptian bird goddess lost in a trance. Perfumed oils, soap, dank walls and mildew mingled in the gray light of a naked bulb hung at the end of a black wire. Her cheeks were drawn, eyelids dark and shallow, nose rigid and protruding like a beak above her shriveled mouth. Her spirit was not in that place. There was just her wrapped-up form looking too small to really be hers. The peasant woman caring for the body lowered her head and whispered, "Allah give you grace."

I ran my fingertips over the sheet at the outline of Adalet's hands, remembering them soft as dough. The lump was cold and set.

"I can't touch her," my niece whispered in a foggy voice. "But don't you think she will know I made this trip back for her?"

I couldn't answer but nodded yes. She stepped away and ducked out the open door, her black ponytail swishing back and forth.

A white muslin scarf framed the ruddy face of the peasant woman, the ends tied in a knot at the top, the same as my Virginia mother used to wear for cleaning, and a style common for Adalet in the house. To show that she was sharing the grief, the woman swayed side to side three times, then paused, waiting. Still red and puffy from the cleansing, her hands rested, cupped on her abdomen. I remembered when I had washed Adalet's bent back:

Summer before last, I had come home to the apartment after an all-day jaunt with one of my friends. We had gone up to the village beach at Kilyos on the lip of the Black Sea where it enters the Bosphorus Strait. On the way back from the beach, I spotted Ottoman wooden stools with woven hemp tops scattered around tables in front of a shop.

When Adalet was on her new bath stool ready to be lathered in olive oil soap, she whispered to me, "My body is old. Don't look."

"Your body is very good," I answered. Adalet loved getting bathed. She had me shampoo and rinse her hair three times, just like they'd done in the old hamams. I scrubbed her gnarled hump with a rubbing cloth until it was as red as tomatoes.

As the Arabic preaching goes on and on, I loosen my stance and wander back under the tendrils of the willow, feeling the women's eyes on me. I rub the arm where Sister caught me, thinking: Sure, the unbeliever –the Gentile– embarrassing the family in front of the guests.

I stare across the yard to the wall of jackets. The men arch their necks. The imam looms above the coffin. A few of the men have on skullcaps, but most of the heads are bare. It feels wrong that patriarchy should dominate an equal-minded woman's final ritual. But, either way, she is gone. Adalet's prayers for all of us five times a day are sunk into a hush. Her strong will, her chuckle and my earthly bond with her. I envision her and me on a couch in our den years ago eating popcorn and watching a Hallmark special of *King Lear*, both of us weeping in all of the right places. Back then, her bulky frame moved in a grace of subdued slow motion, though she could dart after a child at the drop of a hat. Adalet was forever down on her plump knees swashing the floor with a rag. Or concocting at the stove, her straight hair wound into a loose salt and pepper colored bun. Always hoping company might drop in, the guest, a gift from God. The hump that developed over the next twenty-some years was hardly noticeable then. Only her smooth skin never changed – and the light in her eyes. Dead, as gone as those fresh figs we bought from the side of a road: *quickly peeled and slurped up while Nuri drove down that bumpy Anatolian highway. Splitting back the miles. Slinging purple skins out the windows. Above the Aegean Sea. Transparent wind and sun. The leaves of the olive groves making sparkling mirrors on the hillsides.* Finding ourselves out of those famous Smyrna figs, we turned and retraced our route until we found them. Adalet insisted on it, saying that you hardly ever found something that good anymore. We missed the ferryboat at Bandirma landing and gave Nuri's younger brother Vedat a two-hour wait – although he heartily agreed with what we'd done and didn't mind when we let him share the figs.

Staring over to the coffin, I tell myself that it's a blessing to die at age 92 when your body's completely worn out. And then, I recall with a jarring reality check that my slender husband standing across the court has lost his dear mother. Glancing at him, I feel a wavering in my stomach. I have her oral memoir in my office back home. But, how can that ever come close to being the same as her live voice? Adalet and I managed to connect in spite of our broken languages – and on a level that the people in this yard could find confusing. A mixture of broken Turkish and English along with lots of gestures. That was our way. The others around might think that I'm making too much of my grief, like the professional mourners do. Mothers-in-law are not exactly treasured subjects by their daughters-in-law, here. Through the years with our coming and going and Adalet's visiting us in Virginia, I've told myself that I've absorbed Nuri's culture. But, what do I know, really? For instance, I'm at a loss to know how to deal with this Muslim funeral. When I asked Nuri's youngest sister why the service is held here in the courtyard, I was politely informed, "Well, of course, death is not taken into a mosque. Mosque is for life." Sure will be strange to return to this country from now on without Adalet's pillowed giggles warding off the wounds of travel.

As I loosen the knot under my chin, I think, Headscarves – in this stifling heat. I dug Adalet's headscarf out of a drawer at the apartment today. We arrived from the airport one minute and were told the next that we had to hurry to the compound to view the body. They told me to grab a scarf.

The women are restless. One niece has her hands linked behind her back, scanning the others' shoes as if she is ready to make an offer on a pair. So much Arabic that few of them understand seems forced. Catholics do it. We say the Latin's ethereal. It's all what you're used to.

The chant staggers across the courtyard. Eyes closed, I can almost hear Adalet's thin voice chirping, chiming the stories of her life to me a summer ago, laughing about love and loss, faltering on her husband, Burhan's, name, claiming how she never really cared that much for him and then admitting yes, she guessed she did. Even after the shock that he'd really leave her flat after she'd had to go away from him for the sake of the children so many times before – and yet, of all that she'd lost, one thing was clear to her. His leaving was not the worst.

A stirred-up breeze brushes against my face and I look up and see one of those little brown wrens, its claws surely holding it balanced on a willow branch. The wind swirls. My head tilts toward a wide sky beyond the skinny-leafed tree. The silk scarf slides down onto the back of my neck. Its embroidered tassels flick on my chin. The air lifts the sweat from my hair as I watch the single little female wren flit from the branch, away from the knoll and on out of sight.

TWO

The Wedding

Kirkkilise, Thrace, 1914

Little remained of Bedre village that Emin Aga governed. Wailing winds shifted ashes on scattered stones that were once homes. The only trace left of the mansion was the chimney's spine. They had even taken the floor tiles. The hundreds of sharecroppers had vanished, and Emin Aga would not speak of trying to rebuild.

It had been a dismal winter. When he could be sure that the Balkan Wars had exhausted themselves, Adalet's father, Ahmet, brought his wife Zehra and three of their four children back from Istanbul to Thrace. The children and their mother Zehra stayed in a rented house. One month ago, Ahmet moved his family into a fine house that he had built on the edge of Kirkkilise, a town about seven miles from what had been the village of Bedre, where Adalet had flourished for the first ten years of her life as the aga's grandchild.

Twelve and a half-year-old Adalet stood looking out of the second floor window of the harem, the women's part of the house. Greens, blues and pinks on that June day hid the ruin that had come to Kirkkilise the past several winters. At least, it had not been utterly destroyed. Springtime was nursing the earth back to health. The two cows, two horses and two goats, which her father Ahmet had regained in the Bulgarians' retreat, had given birth. Everyone hoped for an end to wars.

She spun from the window toward that high lilt dancing

through the women's quarters. Aunt Azime had just come into the sitting room where Adalet's only and older sister Nefise was being dressed. "Sweetheart, our beautiful bride!" Aunt Azime said, eyeing Nefise.

Sister brought both hands to her cheeks at this praise; but she smiled and hoped it was true. Their mother Zehra swept across the floor and took Nefise's wrists and removed the bride's hands from her face. Everyone ooohed as Zehra placed Sister's arms down to the side of the fitted satin gown. It ruffled at her ankles like foamy wavelets and hugged at her neck and wrists like white lilies. The neighbor Seniye, Zehra's good friend, stepped closer and fingered the clusters of pearls that dotted the bodice. "Bridegroom Captain Prince Tevfik certainly showed good taste in choosing this gown," she said. Seniye turned to Zehra. "Did you have to alter it?"

"Not much," Zehra answered, "The Prince was captivated by my daughter's tiny form the day she served him tea in the palace in Istanbul when we were regrettably there during the Balkan Wars. This material is from London, and the dress was made by the very finest tailor in Pera – the European section of Istanbul, you see." Zehra signaled the maid Hanifey to come pin up a lock of Nefise's hair that had worked itself loose. "His mother," Zehra continued, "the very sultan's sister-in-law, herself, began to design it only three months ago when the marriage agreement was signed."

Adalet smiled to reference to the two years in Istanbul. After her mother and her older sister, younger brother and she had returned last winter, the governor of the province, her parents' friend, had come to the house that her father had rented while this one was being built. The governor came to give Nefise an examination on her studies. He brought a lute to Adalet. The governor recalled that Adalet had been taking music lessons before the Wars. The lute had been found among the ruins of a building. No one had claimed it. Fate obviously meant the lute for her, who had the fingers for it. He told Adalet that someone's misfortune must come to life as her good luck. "Let it sing again," he added. The smooth pear shape fit into her arms like a baby. In fact, she hoped to be asked to play it tonight at the wedding festivities.

The governor brought more than examination papers and a lute with him that day last winter. He also brought a soldier who had visited at the Aynalikavak Palace in Istanbul where Zehra and her children stayed during the Balkan Wars. The soldier was none other than Captain Prince Tevfik. The captain's father was the security commander in Sultan Mehmet Reshad's huge and modern Dolmabahce Palace on the Bosphorus Strait.

Last winter, when the governor and Prince Tevfik sat in their rented house, Nefise served her parents and the gentlemen high tea on a silver tray that had survived the Wars' plunder. That tray, two years before, the maid Hanifey had hurriedly buried under the floor of the barn along with other valuables in the hour the family fled Bedre village to escape the rage of the Bulgarian soldiers. After that February day, along with the Officer and the prince, the governor's wife called on Father Ahmet and Mother Zehra. In the name of the prince, the governor's wife asked for Nefise's hand. "She isn't even sixteen, too young for our daughter to leave home," Ahmet stated. "But, gladly, I'll will bring in the groom. " This was a common practice in Thrace.

Today, fifteen-year-old Nefise would become a princess. She and the prince would live with Adalet's family in this new house. It showed quite nice enough even for a prince –though not as large as Emin Aga's mansion in Bedre had been– burned to the ground with the rest of the village. There was not enough wood to create a mansion such as the aga's anyway. The Bulgarians had torched most of the forests. But men had been found to trim new stones, lay them between the wooden frames and cover them smooth and tight with sandy mud. Father ordered red shingles and beveled glass shipped in. The windows stood tall and rounded at the top like the ones that Adalet had seen in Sirkeci Train Station in Istanbul, but not nearly so grand.

Hanifey's voice sparkled. "We added another liter of pearl sequins! The gown shines." She took Nefise's hand and pulled her around. "Nefise dear, show them the bows we created for the bustle."

"Adalet," Zehra continued, "bring us the box of jewelry brought from Istanbul." The wooden box sat on the inlaid marble top of the mahogany chest of drawers that Father ordered made last December to please Mother at the New Year holiday – or as Mother said, "To quell my despondency over the loss of the furnishings in the mansion."

She skipped across the room, imagining her own elegance. Adalet, like all the other women, wore wedding black to mourn the giving over of the virgin daughter. Maid Hanifey had sewn Adalet's soft lacy dress. Never had the girl owned anything so fancy. She was the bride's honored lady.

Picking up the box, Adalet glanced into the chest's mirror encased in its shiny frame. The dark braids that usually hung to her shoulders were fitted across her head. A friend had loaned her a black mantilla to attach at the top with an ivory comb borrowed from neighbor, Seniye. In only two hours, Adalet would no longer be a mere twelve-year-old schoolgirl. Many would be admiring her. A crowd was gathering, including peasants, merchants and gentry – some from Asian and European Istanbul. Hired cooks had been preparing for a week –although numerous necessities were hard to come by now– even coffee and sugar. Music would follow the wedding feast. Perhaps people could forget their sorrows and give way to traditional dancing and laughter. The festivities could last well into the evening, extending on for days. Men would stop talking about politics, enraptured by the loveliness of the ladies. "Let revenge be done with," Adalet said to herself. There was no need of wine for the unbelievers, for it was said that never again would Bulgarians or Greeks join their festivities. It was hard to believe: no gatherings with those Ottomans who had lived in Thrace and Anatolia ever since the Byzance Romans.

However, many Muslims from the district had now returned to Thrace. For example, Mehmet Nuri the Blacksmith and his family were back from Izmit, and again he was working in his shop. Since much of the town was invited, there was a good chance that his sons Burhan and Ruhittin would be among the company. Adalet glanced over her shoulder into the mirror and blushed at the profile of her blossoming bust.

In the next hour, the five women decorated Nefise like a festive cake – after all, her wedding was a holiday. At the hamam yesterday the women had bathed the bride and smoothed henna in her hair and on her hands to keep tradition and to honor the red beard and hair of The Prophet. Today, for the first time ever, Nefise's cheeks and lips were rouged. "Nefise my girl, you are going to marry royalty," Zehra proclaimed. "I will not see you looking like a peasant." Adalet relished the bragging pleasure in her mother's voice, although much of the bridal jewelry had been borrowed from friends and family. Most of it was silver rather than gold, and the stones were not precious. Nevertheless, by the time the women finished decorating her neck, ears, bodice and arms, Nefise shone like a fairy tale princess.

"You must look fetching, Adalet, for you will be our next darling bride," portly Aunt Azime said, stepping back to admire the silver and turquoise earrings she had loaned her to wear.

"Don't be shameless, Azime!" her sister Zehra snapped. "Adalet's a child."

"A female must always think of her future, Zehra," neighbor Seniye added, helping the maid Hanifey to place the white silk scarf brimming with sequins onto Nefise's head.

"I hope my daughter knows that the future is more than a man – unless that man is well-educated, of a high position or wealthy," Zehra retorted. "Fix the scarf so that it will fall on her cape. There will be no bride's face covered in the wedding given by my husband Ahmet Giray." Zehra enjoyed making a point of saying her husband's surname, Giray, one of the last and most illustrious tribes of the Tartars of the Crimea. Mother jammed her hands onto her belly and raised her ample chin as she appraised her masterpiece, the bride.

"Sister," Aunt Azime said, "don't you think it's the occasion to remind your daughters how you dared our parents and eloped with Ahmet?" Zehra starred back at her sister Azime and puckered her lips. Azime's plump face crinkled up like a cherry tree. Nefise and Adalet leaned forward to hear every word. Hanifey and Seniye were smiling too, for the story had been repeated many times in these parts. The girls never grew tired of it. Azime continued, looking first to Nefise and then to Adalet. "Your Father was then employed by Emin Aga."

"Ahmet was a graduate of the Istanbul Theological Seminary," Zehra interrupted, "and he was on his way home to Shumnu in Bulgaria when he stopped in Bedre." Zehra went to the low divan and fluffed several pillows. "Ahmet was my father Emin Aga's house guest," she continued, extending her arms and turning. Zehra plopped back onto the divan like an overripe quince into mud. Adalet snickered under her hand. "But soon he became the plantation's bookkeeper," she added, emphatically shoving a pillow behind her back.

Seniye's hazel eyes flashed while she continued the mirth. Pulling her brown and green striped scarf from under her back and onto her shoulders, she swept to Zehra's side and floated down beside her on the divan. "The part I like the best," she said in a hushed breath, "is where Ahmet was given the honor of calling the faithful to prayers and you fell in love with the sound of his voice."

The daughters giggled to think of somber Father as romantic, although it could be said that they'd heard him repeat often enough: "There is only one beautiful woman in the world and her name is Zehra."

"It was my sound that he fell in love with," Zehra answered, first snapping a look at Seniye and then nodding to Nefise and Adalet. "I used to sing to myself," she continued, cocking her head. Adalet exchanged glances with Nefise and the two moved closer to their mother. "I was quite grown. Seventeen," Zehra revealed – as if her audience didn't already know. "Sometimes I would walk in the rose garden at evening. Unbeknown to me, Ahmet heard my songs and found himself carried away with the sweet texture in my voice. Later, we married."

"Ohhhh, but give the whole story," Azime interjected. She slipped behind Nefise and Adalet, placing her hands on their waists. "Tell the truth – how for a year you secretly flirted with him –although formally engaged to another– a sugar beet plant- er's son."

"You've always been jealous!" Zehra retorted, haltingly pushing up from the divan.

The two girls parted as Azime stepped to Zehra. "Truthful," she said, "is what I am, and yes you did, and you did not want the man our father picked out for you because his nose was big as a bull's."

Zehra's mouth fell open. Catching a breath, she rolled her eyes in reflection. "The overseer and his wife," she said breathlessly, "brought horses for Ahmet and me." Throwing back her head, she began to cackle, and set them all to laughing.

Azime stuttered through her tittering. "And you rode off to be abducted – ran to the groom without a word to the other poor suitor."

"But Father Emin Aga rode after us and all was settled," Zehra said with finality, "for he was quite willing to have such a fine one as Ahmet for a son."

Azime's hands went to her hips. She regarded Zehra with her wizened grin, saying, "And three rams and a goat appeased the planter's pride!"

Handsome Burhan

She naturally wanted to overhear what kind of talk two gentlemen like Doctor Fuat and Burhan would make together.

A bit later, Adalet was sent with the maid Hanifey down to the kitchen to check on the cooks. She wandered alone into the parlor to spy out the window on the guests congregating on the rambling front yard. The blacksmith Mehmet Nuri's son Burhan stood near the large iron barbeque grill. His legs were spread and his arms folded across the breast of his jacket. He held his chin like a man of importance while watching the smoke curl from under the domed lid where the lamb roasted on the coals. Probably, the smell was making him hungry. He looked across at two men rolling cigarettes. Did Burhan smoke? After all, he was nineteen. He certainly wouldn't now, for his father was standing nearby talking with the butcher, whose wife seemed to perch on her husband's shadow. The wife stood draped in a black charshaf with all but her eyes in camouflage. Adalet told herself that she would never consent to be the wife of a man who would have her shrouded as if she didn't exist outside of his needs.

Just beyond Burhan and his father sprawled an expansive wooden table. Its cloth was embellished in the yellow and pink of forsythia sprigs and cherry blossoms. That matchmaker Aunt Azime had made it her business to brag all over town about how Nefise's hands had skillfully applied all of the embroidery on the tablecloth. Father insured that the table would be piled end to end with plenty. Breads, rice dishes, stuffed vegetables, layers of handmade paper-thin dough laced with onions and meats, a variety of fruit and assortment of juices. Everything that this town could still rummage up for feasting sat waiting in the kitchen. Mother ordered some of the delicacies brought in from Istanbul and Izmir.

Burhan looked to be admiring the house. Adalet stepped behind the drapery and squinted from the edge. She felt a rush of gratitude and pride that her family had the reserve to build again so soon after the Wars.

Burhan then turned and starred toward the road. Pulling the sheer curtains back, Adalet watched two servants in brown britches and vests walking from the kitchen adjoining the house. They toted large platters of white cheese, olives, pickles, rolled grape leaves drenched in olive oil plus eggplant, squash and tomatoes stuffed with rice, currants, and pine nuts and fresh oregano from low hillsides. Life was coming back to normal.

A colorful bunch of women sat gossiping like times past under the shade of the round maple tree. Adalet could almost smell the whiff of rose water floating in the air around them. The wide yard was raked clean and scarred by wagon and cart tracks. Young children lingered at their parents' elbows, not speaking unless asked a question. Father Ahmet stood near the steps greeting the striking family of the prince. He began to usher the party over to the side of the house to present them to Emin Aga, who sat rigidly in a wooden chair. Adalet's younger brother Sukru stood by with his hand on Grandfather's shoulder.

In the self-assured way they carried themselves, Prince Tevfik's family seemed rather European. Both the prince and his father wore army uniforms. A long blue dress gathered at the back adorned the mother, who finned a ruffled parasol, no doubt to shade her delicate skin from the sun. Her blue scarf, pinned back from her face, rather resembled a hat. The town guests starred curiously at the royal family, who had only a bit earlier gotten off the train. Even Nefise screamed with excitement when Hanifey told her that the tasseled carriage with her elegant future in-laws was arriving at the house.

At the gravel road on the hem of the yard, Burhan's first cousin climbed out of a phaeton with his young wife, Mediha. The distinguished-looking man was neighbor Seniye's son, Doctor Fuat. The doctor took his wife by the arm as they proceeded to walk up the yard. Mediha had fine brown hair that fluffed at the sides of her flowered scarf. Both she and Fuat handed wicker baskets to one of the servant boys. Most likely the baskets were full of sugary baklava or other cakes or candies. It was known that Doctor Fuat had returned from Tirnovacik to practice medicine in Kirkkilise. Burhan raised his hand when his older cousin looked in his direction. Burhan's brother Ruhittin, across the yard speaking with the imam, raised his head and smiled in Burhan's direction.

Adalet sidled down the front of the table. The doctor bowed, leaving his slender wife with friends, and ambled over to Burhan, pausing briefly to speak with an elderly gentleman. Bending from the waist, he kissed the back of the man's hand and then brought it to his forehead in respect.

Stopping at the far end of the table, with her back to the guests,

Adalet lowered her head to shade her face and began to rearrange a pot of fresh white and gold daisies. She stood in range of Fuat and Burhan's voices. "Hello, good cousin." Everyone knew the doctor. He always had a kind word. His whole family behaved like that. Adalet had overheard Seniye tell Mother that she always reminded Fuat to be considerate of Burhan and Ruhittin. Poor Mehmet Nuri's first wife died in childbirth, leaving him a daughter to bring up alone. No wonder Seniye's interest in them. The brothers' mother had been their father Mehmet Nuri's second wife. The widow Hayriye was Seniye's sister. The sisters' father was the highest imam of the provincial mosque. Naturally, the imam took Mehmet Nuri into his home to live; the widower had made the pilgrimage to Mecca. In almost no time, the imam offered Mehmet Nuri his daughter, Hayriye. Seniye had sighed after telling that family history, and added that she could see that Burhan would tolerate no pity, even though, as bad luck would have it, Hayriye up and died of tuberculosis when Ruhittin was born. Burhan was two years old. So, Mehmet Nuri was compelled to find a third wife. Thus far, she hadn't died. Adalet was slightly acquainted with the two brothers, although they had never paid attention to a girl like her.

Doctor Fuat spoke again. "Burhan, I hear you graduated from high school in Izmit."

"Yes, cousin; and you have established a medical practice in our province." Over her shoulder, Adalet saw Fuat acknowledge by raising both palms in front of him, saying, "Inshallah-God willing." He placed the palms of his hands together at his chest and regarded Burhan with a serious intent.

"Now that high school's completed, surely your father doesn't expect you to become a blacksmith in Kirkkilise?"

Adalet sidled to the foot of the table to see from the corner of her eyes. Burhan was chuckling while readjusting his fez. "A man like my father," he replied, "is hardly one to force a profession on his son." Adalet smiled.

The cousins paused and looked out over the rest of the crowd.

Adalet scanned the attendance as well. There were almost a hundred guests. Mehmet Nuri had gone with the coppersmith to the edge of the field where he appeared to be appraising the man's donkey. The scruffy critter, hitched to a wooden-wheeled cart in which his twin girls sat, absently flicked its ears and tail against gnats.

"You should also consider medical school," Fuat said. He leaned his mustached profile sideways to Burhan.

"Possibly," Burhan answered, tilting his comely head. "That, or political school and represent the state."

"And what do you say about Parliament?" Fuat asked. "Is our country in any better shape than when the despot, Sultan Abdulhamid ruled? Sultan Mehmet Reshat is nothing but a puppet; and General Enver and his Committee of Union and Progress act as if they have lost their wits."

Adalet lowered her head. Fuat was speaking against the regime. "I heard you're a member of the Party," Burhan answered.

"Yes, and I had hopes," Fuat replied. He seemed thoughtful and again scanned the crowd lingering on the yard. Tweaking the upturned end of his stylish crescent-shaped mustache, he added in a hushed voice, "But the Committee's confused and self-absorbed, in my opinion."

Burhan looked surprised. "But the country's in disorder and must have some time to get back on its feet. We've only been out of war for ten months. Look around you, things are coming back together."

Fuat retorted. "Haven't you seen the widows and orphans, the ones who squat in mud huts? Coming together. Ha! And the Serbs and Bulgars will fight us again."

"Why do you say that?" Burhan's face looked strained.

"Serbia wants Albania, Burhan – went to war for that in the beginning, wants the land and sea." The Bulgars also want to get their hands on Salonika as well, and mark my words; they will challenge the Greeks for it. And, there's Austria-Hungary, who's not going to let the Serbs' lust for power grow too wide."

Burhan seemed to hang onto Fuat's every word. No wonder. The doctor was known to go to Istanbul, often where he got news from all over the world.

"You may be right, Fuat," Burhan answered. "I'm just a farm boy, but I read reports of the dissatisfied, saying Parliament continues patching our carpets while the collectors are at the door and the Russian Bear waits for a chance to steal our honey – the Istanbul straits."

Adalet flinched. Could the Russians really steal the Bosphorus? She felt goose bumps sprout on her neck and arms.

"And Arabs, they clamor for independence," Fuat continued. "I question how long the House of Osmanli can stand." Adalet caught her breath at those words. It was impossible to think of not being an Ottoman! Men said such silly things to impress each other.

"Let us just pray that we have a prosperous kismet on our horizon," Fuat continued. Adalet turned and began to ease back up the side of the table. "But it doesn't look hopeful to me," he went on. "The Europeans own us. We have no factories. Nor can we borrow more money to build them. Germany has in mind 'to protect us' from the Russians – but it will not prove to be to our advantage. But what can we do? Our treasury is empty. We are exhausted."

"We sure could not stand another war," Burhan answered.

Fuat's reply burned Adalet's ears as she slipped off in the direction of the side door. "In another war, more powerful countries would jump at the chance to cut us to pieces."

Insult

The people were waiting, speculating on what would happen. Certainly, there was no protocol for this particular development.

Thirty minutes later, just inside the front door, Adalet waited with Nefise. The other women stood behind them. With the ceremony at hand, the door opened slightly so that Adalet could know when to walk onto the stoop. The guests on the lawn began moving toward the front doorway.

Ahmet raised his hands. Adalet's older brother, Captain Sabri, had arrived and was in uniform at Father's side. "Greeting, friends," Sabri called in his soldier's voice, "and welcome esteemed family of the groom – whom we shall soon embrace as ours."

The imam stood at the foot of the steps. His small figure was a mound of brown, from his woolen cap to his robe and shoes. Father Ahmet looked back toward the door and nodded. "It's time," Adalet said to Hanifey. When the maid pulled open the door, the sunlight was almost too heavy for Adalet's eyes to bear; but she beamed as she drifted over the threshold. The day shone so bright that the crowd bobbled in the breeze like a wildflower garden. She blinked and shyly looked down to the foot of the steps. In his new suit and fez, her father stood tall. By his side, Sabri smiled faintly and reached down to pat his younger brother's head. Sukru wrapped his arm around Sabri's leg. Grandfather stood next to Sukru with hands folded on his cane. At the side of the imam, the prince captain's dark eyes snapped. Prince Tevfik's mother gave off the air of confidence in her long blue dress. Her husband's uniform flashed an armor of brass metals, a large one right below his throat.

There was rustling in the hallway inside the door. Mother Zehra whispered loudly. "Hold it, my girl; I must take one last look at you while you're still all mine."

Adalet spotted the enticing Burhan beyond the Palace Commander's head. He stood with Fuat and Mediha. The sun flashed on Burhan's eyes, focused in Adalet's direction – though of course she didn't look directly back at him. In that light, she felt all grown up and beautiful, floating in a thick dream. She stepped aside as Nefise came through the doorway.

Everyone took in a breath at once. Adalet's eyes darted to the face of the prince to catch him breathing in the sight of his princess. His sharp jaw moved slightly. There were several broad seconds of hush.

And then out of the blue, the Prince made choking sounds. He wasn't supposed to speak now. Was he ill? As if pulled tight by an invisible string, the crowd drew forward.

Nefise and Adalet winced as Prince Tevfik continued with the gagging and flung up his hand, pointing in their direction.

"The bride is a camel!" he yelled.

In unison, the crowd let out a gasp. They loosened back. There was a hush again, but this time the silence gaped on faces frozen too heavy to bob. The tension held so tight that were anyone to faint, they would shatter like a goblet. Adalet's shadow tinkled down the stone steps.

And then, Father Ahmet was loudly clearing his throat. The crowd again tightened. He stepped out of the line and wheeled back toward the Prince.

"You say what?" Ahmet's voice was hard.

The prince and Ahmet leaned face to face. The flustered bride-groom shot a glance up at the stoop and then back to the shocked father of the bride.

"She is a camel, I say, not the bride I chose!"

Ahmet whipped around and started for the steps, his hands clinched into fists at his sides. Sabri followed his signal. At the same time, Zehra called from inside the door, " —get back in here!" The crowd began to tumble, looking up into the sky as if it was raining. Adalet stumbled backwards across the threshold.

Inside the front parlor, with the doors shut against the prince and his family and the rest, Father and Grandfather raged about insult while Sabri accosted his mother: "What have you done to the gown?" His voice rang sharp as a thrown saber across the reception room.

"It was ordinary and plain when it came," Zehra answered deeply. She knitted her brows.

From the corner where she stood blubbering into her hand-kerchief, Hanifey's voice warbled like a bird's. "I did it myself," she said.

Sabri shouted, "It is not only the gown! Her face is painted like a harlot."

"I'll not tolerate such a reference to our child!" Emin Aga called.

Ahmet paced up and down the room. "Damn Prince!" he answered, his voice raised to the new rafters. "And my daughter shall not wed that cucumber head!" Her father's curse and calling the royal prince a tasteless name like "cucumber" stunningly surprised the bride's lady.

"Do you realize," Sabri said in a controlled voice, "what it means for a woman to be called a camel?" Ahmet paused and turned. As if they had just discovered that she was a thief, all glared at Nefise, who took in a jerk of air, then burst into tears. Adalet immediately thought how the rouge on her poor sister's cheeks would soon be running in streams, dripping onto that beautiful gown. No one, not even the maid Hanifey, moved to blot Nefise's face or comfort her. Adalet didn't dare. Everyone turned to the oldest son.

"A 'camel'," Sabri explained with a Captain of the Ottoman Army's dignity, "is a woman who is so overlain with jewels and makeup that she resembles those beasts in their embellishments given by the Sultan once a year. I'm sure that you all know about the Gift Caravan to Mecca."

The others held quiet, absorbing what the oldest son said. Ahmet and Emin Aga nodded their heads. So, Adalet thought, the prince was in a shock when he called Nefise a camel. Up until that moment, Prince Tevfik had not seen Nefise with false color on her face and hands. Her usual dress was plain.

Suddenly again her mother and father and Sabri began arguing with each other all at once, so that their words resembled tangled spools of wool tumbling across the floor.

"Our reputation is ruined."

"We cannot let it go."

"Prince Tevfik will have to say he has changed his attitude."

Maid Hanifey had moved to Nefise and taken her to sit in the corner chair. Adalet slipped to the window and glanced through the sheer curtains. The guests now went scattered into small bouquets. She didn't see either the prince or the members of his family but the carriage they had come in was still there by the scrub tree. She eased back to the others in the reception parlor.

Grandfather leaned on his tall cane with the elk-horn handle, listening with a jutted lower lip. Seniye and Azime stepped forth from the shadows when the others grew quiet.

"We wanted to say," Seniye offered, "that if the sequins and bows are the problem, they can be fixed – even removed."

"With Hanifey's help, in no time, we can make the gown a simple one again while you distract the guests," Azime added. Making their voices bright in this despairing hour struck Adalet as gutsy effort of note.

"It is more than that, woman," Ahmet told her. "It is the shame of being publicly insulted!" He cut his glare toward Zehra, who turned, propped an elbow on one hand and brought the other to her face. After a few seconds, she padded toward Adalet.

Zehra stopped and scanned her younger daughter head to toe as if deciding what she might be worth. And then, Zehra turned and parted the company, striding halfway across the room before she paused. She lifted her head and hands and appeared from her back to be looking through the sheer curtains to the distant mountains. After a moment, she began a mysterious flitting her hands like wing tips. Of course, the rest ceased talking and waited in silence. Mother was in her space. At length, her hands came down and clasped.

Zehra whirled around toward the others, proclaiming, "All is well, all is well!" Her voice jittered the small silver spoons in the tea glasses left in haste last hour on the copper tray. In the slanted light, a green glow fumed about her. "Sabri, inform the people that we will join them shortly. Tell them I have gone into a trance."

Open-mouthed, with expectation, stout Sabri and the others froze. The tall and wiry Ahmet began to stroke his beard. When Zehra spoke, his face softened.

"Some spiteful jinni spirit is molesting this event!" she snapped. No one challenged that. Zehra had willed logic back into the room.

Forty Evil Thorns

After the men skirted from the room, Zehra led the women to the harem, where she left them.

Mother Zehra promptly went to her room and shut the door. Hardly speaking or looking at each other, the women bumbled around. Nefise began to sniffle again. Although Adalet was sad for her, she was put off by it. Crying would not help. Sister was just going to ruin the dress and her face. Hanifey and Seniye went to Nefise and coaxed her into her bedroom to freshen up.

When the three of them left, Aunt Azime dropped down on the divan. "I need a stiff shot of raki!" she moaned, flinging her head back on the pillows. Her arms fell limp in her lap.

Adalet went to her. "Aunt, shall I fetch it for you?" The girl knew where Sabri kept some of the forbidden alcohol, put away for the infidels, and him. It was exciting to imagine her aunt's shocking notion of taking the strong drink.

"Come here, my love. Sit," Azime said, slyly smirking and patting the divan seat. "My sister Zehra will resolve the quandary," she whispered, taking Adalet's hands and piercing the girl's eyes with the intensity of her own.

"But our family's pride is ruined," Adalet said. "No husband will want Nefise now. Her honor is tainted." Adalet heard the whining in her own voice, though she frankly disliked the habit of it.

"Men – they don't know what they want. I am the town matchmaker. Listen to me, not to what some foolish man has said in his confusion." Aunt Azime spoke in velvet tones.

"But the prince wanted her. Now he shames her in front of everyone."

Aunt pulled Adalet's face closer with her long fingers. The

sparkles from her eyes seemed to filter into the air between them. "The female bird makes the nest," she warbled. "It is natural for a mere man to lose courage at the sight of a wedding gown."

Adalet pulled up and toward Azime. "Is it courageous to wed?" she asked.

"The hardest thing in the world, because when we give ourselves to another, we fear we will forfeit who we think we are."

"Who does the prince think he is?"

"He thinks he is a brave Ottoman warrior. To capture the warmth of Sister in his wedding bed tonight, he must surrender pretense of invincibility and become soft as butter – so that she will take pity and let him melt into her."

"What can be done?"

"Your Mother is in there," she answered, pointing a red fingernail across the room to Zehra's heavy door, "in a deep trance, to be sure. A solution will be given that will no doubt rally this poor boy's courage once again."

"The prince is a soldier."

"And so, my sister Zehra will create a battle for him to win. You'll see. A touch of drama. Assuredly, Dearie, there will be dancing under the veil of torchlight tonight."

"Are you sure? Is Mother that wise?"

Azime chuckled as if she were enjoying the dilemma. "Zehra now speaks to an ancient web," she said in a voice like a loose string on a lute, "that women long before us were spinning."

"Ah so," Adalet said, "The prince waits for a woman's guidance, although he doesn't know." The girl felt relief. Azime readjusted her hips and smiled into the inquisitive face of her niece, lifting that pale finger to Adalet's cheek.

"Of course," she answered. "And you, Adalet love, you are going on thirteen, began your bleeding with the turn of the moon, I heard." Adalet pulled to move away, but Azime caught her arm and continued. "And when you are fully ripe, your Azime will deliver a prince to you as well." She held her niece's face in her eyes so that the girl could not turn. "He may not be a soldier and he may not be royalty, but you can be certain that he will be handsome and ambitious." Adalet's heart was beating wide and hot. "Of course," Azime whispered, "he will need a clever girl like you to build his nest."

After some minutes, Zehra came forth. Adalet ran to Nefise's bedroom and brought the other three women to her.

"I have had a vision," Zehra told them. That expected low and mysterious rasp coated her words. "There most certainly is a curse on the wedding gown. It has clouded the mind and eyes of the prince."

The women and girl in unison took in the revelation with a gasp and brought their hands to their mouths. Knowingly, Zehra nodded her head as she proceeded to explain the details of what had caused the havoc:

"It seems, as it was while the prince was yet living in Istanbul last year, that there was a cunning Greek servant who was in love with him – without his knowledge, of course. When she saw him bring home the satin material this spring and realized that it was for his bride, that wench convinced a wicked spirit jinni to place a hex, which settled into the gown. The nature of the curse was that whoever should wear its cape would look like a camel in the eyes of the prince."

"No wonder the prince behaved so rudely," Azime said with dramatic awe. Her big black eyes were glistening. She rolled them to glance at the girl.

"Adalet, come with me," Zehra said, taking her to the divan to sit. "The forty evil thorns have clustered in the cape of the wedding gown." In horror, Adalet thought of Sister in the beautiful gown. Zehra wrinkled her eyes and brow.

Azime fetched the cape from Nefise's bedroom and laid it beside Adalet on the divan. Mother Zehra took a breath and continued.

"Only a pure maiden can pluck them out," she whispered. "Adalet, we are depending on you, can you do it? Can you save the name of our family and the happiness of a sister?" Adalet was slow with reluctance. It was as if she had been handed a cotton jacket in the Balkan wintertime and led to the door.

Not picking up on Adalet's hesitation, Zehra placed a silk bag that was for holding yarn in the girl's lap, instructing her that she was to find and extract the thorns embedded in the folds of the cape and place them in the bag. Adalet would be left alone in the room. No one else could or would ever see the ghastly thorns. It was forbidden.

"You must beware the thorns yourself – not to examine them closely," Zehra warned in her far-away voice. "For they are evil. Although," she added quickly, "in your purity you are largely protected."

Before the women left, Zehra emphasized that once all forty thorns were plucked, Adalet was to tie the top tightly. The women would return shortly, when Zehra would give the instructions as to what was to be done next.

Bride Nefise, who had gotten up, fidgeted at the door. "Please, Adalet, you are our only hope," she pleaded. Adalet looked at her swollen eyes, and gave her to know that she would do her best.

"Hanifey, go down and tell the cooks to serve cheese and cakes and hot tea from the samovars from the outside table," Zehra said brightly. "Then, go among the people and spread the news of the revelation."

Mother Zehra brushed across the room to Nefise. "And if more time is needed," she said back over her shoulder as they went toward the room, "tell the boys to pass around the chocolates!"

Devil's Creek

"That one could light a candle with her eyes," Burhan stated. Adalet's ears and face tingled. She did not dare look at the men.

Adalet sat on the hard green divan in the quiet of the room with the cape spread over her lap. The green silk bag lay on top of it. The hem of the cape spilled onto the floor. It felt heavy. Mother Zehra had emphasized that she was to do this job care-

fully; but it must be accomplished quickly, for the evil had affected the gown far too long already. Adalet hoped it was not too late.
She ran her hands over the satin. It did not feel evil, just bumpy
with sequins. Her eyes closed as she concentrated on how hidden
evil might present itself. As she breathed a prayer, a sequin sliced
her finger.

The thin pain spread to her face in a sudden jolt. She sat forward, flinging the hand bitten by the evil thing away from the cape
lest her blood be absorbed! She held up her finger. It throbbed
like a sweat bee sting, but there was no blood. She sucked it and
wiped it on her petticoat, then picked up the cologne bottle resting on the copper tray on the low tripod in front of the divan. She
poured the lemon water onto her palm and worked her hands together. She said another prayer to bless them as they dried, hoping they hadn't soaked up taint. There was no time to brood on
whether she had sliced some of the bride's curse into her own
hand. There remained a task in her lap. No time to waste worry-
ing about what may or may not have happened.

With her eyes squeezed tight, she pinched and pulled and
dropped invisible evil into the bag, each thorn coming with a
wide sliver of breath. Forty times she did it.

When the women came bounding in, Adalet sat with the bag
tied tightly, her lips fixed. She nodded to assure them.

"Put on your bloomers and long jacket, Adalet," Mother
Zehra commanded, "for you must ride with the men to the banks
of Devil's Creek and throw the bag into the hungry jaws of the
water."

So be it. Even with all of the turmoil, Adalet had to admit that
this day was turning out to be more interesting than she could
have imagined in her wildest dreams. Adalet had long been fascinated with the unpredictable powers of that willful stream that
played against the banks of her old home place.

Adalet stepped out the back door and stopped when she saw
the men waiting at the gray barn. They were with horses, ready.

She clutched the silk bag. All of the men's eyes focused on her except Burhan, who was mounting a white mare. The horses were anxious, as if their extra sense let them know about the forty evil thorns. Her fingers tightened on the neck of the bag. The men obviously knew about the curse. By now, the word was out: She was the one, the pure maiden.

Sabri rode over to Doctor Fuat, who leaned across to say something to Burhan, who looked up at Adalet while holding a kind of crooked grin on his lips. Men, whispering to each other, and waiting. How could she be the one? She was the one. Her knees trembled, hidden under her bloomer pants.

The horses at the barn door parted as the stable groom Hassan stepped from the cluster, leading Adalet's horse, Lightning Girl, by the reigns. Lightning's pony-size and the dapple-gray coat made her perfect. Groom Hassan took wide important strides across the lawn with his head held high. His boots shone with polish so fresh it spread through the air.

Adalet straightened and raised the bag slightly. How was she supposed to do this? If it weren't for the fact that she carried her family's reputation on her shoulders, she would run and hide from this stinging burn of eyes. She reminded herself that she was strong, a part of a woman's web. Thracian women: independent, witty, and insightful.

At once, the wind hissed through the yard, snatched the black brimless cap from groom Hassan's baldhead, and flung it into the air. The scar from his ear to his mouth pulsed red.

"Allah, Allah!" someone yelled. A horse whinnied. The cap spiraled down like a crow's wing and landed on the end of a dried-up sapling. Hassan's daughter, Zeyneb, darted from the hut, a bundle of red, yellow, blue skirts and scarf bounding toward the small tree. Adalet glanced toward the hut that Father had added onto the barn for Hassan and his two children. She had neglected Zeyneb, taller now than two years before. Had Adalet heard it rumored that the Bulgarians during their raids had ruined Hassan's wife, who had disappeared, leaving Hassan with now only Zeyneb and her older brother, Alican? Adalet stung with the recall: the lucky "evil eye" that Zeyneb had given to her when she fled Bedre at the outbreak of the Wars. In her haste to come back from Istanbul, Adalet had forgotten to take the "eye" down from where she had pinned it to a drapery. Did her friend Zeyneb still have the locket with Adalet's photo inside?

Zeyneb dashed back to Hassan, and then bent from the waist to her knees. Keeping one arm to her stomach and her head down, she reached a long-sleeved arm out to her father. He took his cap from her fingers with a sweep, and artfully returned it with both hands as if he were crowning himself. Zeyneb took several tiny steps backwards from Hassan, still showing respect, and shy with all of this attention. Adalet hadn't called for Zeyneb since her return from Istanbul. Two years ago, they had been playmates. Hassan's girl folded one hand into the other, her head bowed as she followed her father and walked toward Zehra's girl.

Dusting the lapel of his faded maroon jacket, Hassan looked at Adalet's face, expecting her word. From where Zeyneb had scrubbed it, his collar was threadbare.

"I'm ready," she told him. With his warty knuckles, Hassan held the reins up to Adalet. "My girl Zeyneb is to ride on your grandfather's old horse, Miss, and I'm to say –Doctor Fuat's– that is, his wife, comes to accompany the ladies."

Adalet signaled slightly to Zeyneb, who was stretching around her father. She vowed to make up for the negligence of her friend who stood grinning in the old silly way that she always did, with her face pink as a lokum sweet. She wasn't wearing the locket that Adalet had given her two and a half years ago before the flight.

Adalet was barely acquainted with Fuat's wife, Mediha. She trotted around from the side of the barn. Someone had dressed her in a riding skirt. She had a compassionate face. Her scarf was tied at the back of her head like the peasants in the fields. Sabri trotted up, leading Grandfather's old horse. Adalet started to ask for help onto the pony, but Hassan already stood posed beside the pony, trying to hold her steady. Lightning Girl was prancing to go.

The Ride

She had her own mysteries. Who could guess where fortune
would lead?

They cantered through the center of town ignoring the curious
faces of those who were not invited to the wedding, who lingered
at the market center or leaned against a crumbled stone wall, rode
on out of town between the fields just sprouting green tips of sugar beets, corn and melons; and then, they pushed around the rev-
eling forsythia that flamed out of their twisted winter nests, and
on down the uneven hill where there soon would have been a
sweet-juice-down-the-chin peach orchard had the invading soldiers not chopped it all to pieces for fires.

The fezzes of two men brushed from their heads as they galloped under the patch of walnut trees. Pink blossoms on the
ground buzzed up as hooves swept through. Below the hill they
raced like a spring flood, not slowing for the men gone back for
their hats. They were a torrent quite beyond where the wheat was
beginning to rise up from the sandy soil, riding and riding as if
that race could last a lifetime.

But no elation could last forever; for then, it seemed that all
too soon, they jerked against the reins and stalled the hooves.
They had come to the banks of wild Devil's Creek, whose source,
it was rumored, could not be found. No one dismounted. The
pungent air was thick with horse and human sweat and the sound
of gargling water among big rocks.

The two cousins clopped over under a plane tree and began talking, careless if the others and the girls and woman could
hear them. "Do you think she'll pull it off?" Fuat asked Burhan.
His voice had a teasing tone to it. Zeyneb darted her face toward
Adalet.

Mediha trotted her horse to the girls. "Are you all right?" she
asked. They both nodded. A button had come open at Mediha's
neckline.

Seriously, and toward the water, the one named by her mother stretched her chin, trying to figure out how to soak up the men's fixation on her without showing that she was even aware. Sabri walked his horse over to her.

"All right. This is it," Sabri said, looking his sister in the eyes. He dismounted and then led Lightning Girl and Adalet toward the edge.

The bank was clustered with large smooth stones and boulders washed out of slopes and gullies. No wonder the Greeks had called Bedre as "Petra" meaning "Rocks," Adalet thought. The old and weathered men at the tea garden at Kirkkilise's center said Bedre was washed away by fire.

Sabri helped her down and held her shoulders. She flashed a piercing look into his dark eyes. His eyelids sagged. Under his bristly mustache, his upper lip turned into the pillows of his cheeks. Sabri had often spoken about family loyalty. Adalet took in a deep breath of his protective air.

The weeds were high, and although she was the one, she was afraid of snakes. She must not show her fear. Still, she was mindful of where she planted her feet as she made her way through the unfamiliar, unruly, prickly underbrush.

On the brink of the sloping bank, she untied the bag and tried to imagine how it would be to extend her spirit to the swirl. She wished to be mysterious like Mother. Adalet studied the jagged stream for several seconds. She hesitated, glancing down for the secrecy of the bag. Some might say the pouch was empty. It was filled with confusion. No doubt that's what people thought about evil. In truth, the bag felt light as air.

Behind her, the restless horses shifted hooves in the bramble. She turned her head, and for a quick second, she read a twinkle in Burhan's eyes. He knew she was frightened. How did he know?

Turning to face Devil's Creek again, she gulped in her breath and took a wide step. A prickling sensation ran over her fingers where she held up the bag of poison thorns. She could feel the weight of their eyes fixed on it. With another heave of her breath, she exhaled as she flung the lot. The bag arched high and then dove into the eye of greenish whirling fingers that dragged it into the undercurrent.

The men cheered.

When Adalet returned to the harem, Hanifey had prepared a basin of water to wash away the sweat and dust of riding to Devil's Creek and back. As if time were no time, she became the bride's lady again. The sun on the western horizon had begun to dull. Vaguely, she hoped the guests had not eaten all of the chocolates.

The women said over and over how the company, enthralled by the events of what would long be talked of as "The Curse," had hung around chiseling away at the white goat cheese and such while making predictions on the results. "Better than fireworks," Azime said.

The crowd surged and murmured. The young lady, Adalet, stepped onto the stoop. With the sun paled, she could see clearly. Father, Grandfather, and Sabri stood with their shoulders back. Captain Prince Tevfik and his family fidgeted. Adalet did not hesitate to look them all in the face. She had ridden a mission among men who were not even her kin.

With his eyes yet simmering as if he held something hidden, Burhan stood near the front behind the prince. Adalet guessed what his secret could be, but she didn't care. Under her black skirts, the ride still quivered her buttocks and calves.

As she eased to the side, the guests crept closer. Nefise had stepped over the threshold. This time, Mother Zehra held her bride's elbow, ushering her out. Zehra's jaw was set. She glared at Prince Tevfik as if to say, "No glitter on the gown. No pearl sequins. The satin veil and cape are plain. Gone the rouge, the bows. A simple reward for a simple prince." Only Adalet could see the large sequined pink apple blossoms winking from the back of the cape.

Unabashed, the bridegroom's face broke into upturned wedges, no different than Sukru's when a serving of baklava passed his way. In the next moment, it would be said that the curious company crooned as melodious as a night wind kissing round the cir-cle on the top of a half-full barrel of summer rain.

With a sigh of relief, wide-eyed Adalet gazed beyond the people, past the quince and mandarin sunset. Tonight, fiddles and lutes and drums and feast would glow with the dancing away of the darkness, away in the moon glow, Thrace in the lull of a normal rite.

THREE

Lost

Istanbul, 1993

"Don't worry, I'll find Grandmother. She's somewhere in this conglomeration."

My nephew Orhan hangs one elbow out the window of the black Honda to help balance his cigarette while he holds us on course with his other arm. Filled with wavering hums and whines, a steady sound of staccato of air assaults my ears. As if we're in the midst of a psychedelic swarm of giant hornets, horseflies, wasps, cicadas and bumble bees, our horde of cars, trucks, buses, mini-buses and motorcycles vibrates forward at eighty kilometers an hour. We're straining to keep in sight up ahead an emerald rig that glints in the sun like the wings of a June bug. Behind sunglasses, my eyes skate back and forth across the road. This six-lane high-way runs from the Asian Marmara Sea side of Istanbul, across the lower Bosphorus Bridge and on west to the Ataturk International Airport on the European side, north of the Marmara. We're on the European side of the city headed west.

In the midst of all of this, there's hardly time to reflect on this day's concerns. We don't talk about it. To be heard, we'd have to yell anyway. On our right, an undulating moan emits from the bowels of a greasy red truck. Its bed is stacked to the hilt with wooden pens. Each cages two chickens. A billowing tarpaulin tied at four corners covers the tiers. Our Honda, the silver Mercedes behind us and a red Jeep alongside left, buzz an octave higher than the chicken truck. The sounds throw fits, jarring up and down as vehicles change lanes, pass and jet off to God knows where. A big barrel shaped truck in front sports the sign, "Dangerous Matter", across its rear.

A pickup and Jeep zoom off. The silver Mercedes zips around to our left. Pink and blue ribbons stream from its back. In the rear seat, young woman with thick dark wavy hair is wrapped in a white bridal gown. Groom in bright blue suit attached to her side. "Dangerous Matter" veers to the inside lane. Bridal car dives in front of us, accelerates and shears across beyond the chickens and follows a blue bus off a ramp at the exit sign.

We pass upended rectangles of multi storied concrete buildings wedged down into the hillside dirt, identical with those thrown up all across the landscape of Turkey to accommodate the swelling population. Often, there's little forethought to civil design. Some half-built and abandoned developments look like they've exploded from the inside out.

After we complete the span of the Golden Horn at the bridge, my nephew Orhan whips the Honda around and in front of the chickens. We slide over and off onto a utility road. There's a gas station and tourist bus stop. The station's "You are welcome" sign has toppled onto its side like a beetle baked in the sun. Orhan swerves around a hole and pulls over.

"What's wrong, Orhan?"

The cigarette bobs between his lips as he mumbles. He appears confused. Half-circle sweat lines sag under the arms of his long-sleeve white shirt. An hour ago, he tossed the jacket he wore at his grandmother's funeral into the back seat.

"Don't you know the way?"

"It's been a good while since I've come here, Aunt Lee. They keep changing the stupid exits." He peers up and down the road.

"The hearse – up there," I say, pointing a finger toward the glint of emerald in the distance.

Orhan checks the road again, and guns off. I keep my eye on the back of the funeral rig. The hearse is actually a pickup truck with its bed framed higher than the front. The back is partially decorated with green satin. It's half-open at the sides.

We catch up with the rig at a stop sign.

"This is not Adalet's hearse," I exclaim. We gape at the funeral truck as it bumps on out a road that meanders toward a mass of cemeteries. We have both seen the front of the now disappearing truck. The whole thing is emerald green. Its smoke dissipates. The front of Adalet's rig is high-gloss white.

These mazes of old and new graveyards spread for miles, with certain sections for Armenians, Greeks, Jews and all kinds of Turks and Ottomans. There are probably even some unclaimed Romans. Two years ago, when my husband and I went searching over in this area for his brother Vedat's grave, we got lost in the tangle of dirt lanes that wove through the jungle of weeds, trees and marble. Enough to build a new Ephesus. The communities of Istanbul's dead have few location signs. The living relies on memory – certain trees or rock banks. And hope the landmarks haven't been removed or altered since the last visit.

"You're right," Orhan answers. "Also, that was a black coffin inside. Grandmother's is brown. Sorry to report it, Aunt, but we've been following the wrong deceased." Orhan was schooled in British English. He speaks the language with a mixture of American slang and the Queen's English.

If Orhan is annoyed or embarrassed at our losing his grandmother, he's certainly handling it: just another enigma to unravel on any typical day. He lights another Maltepe unfiltered and blows the smoke over the wheel. Although he knows the smoking risk, Orhan prefers to join the majority of his countrymen who live on the edge. He doesn't seem particularly religious, but I've surmised that in matters like money or health, he adheres to the creed of Inshallah –"If Allah wills it"– to presume that fate is out of his hands anyway. His smoke inflates like a ghost of a small football and lodges between the dashboard and the windshield. I sigh and shake my head. Orhan grins back, wipes the sweat from his forehead with his right hand and smoothes it onto his black pants' leg.

"They'll have to wait for you before they start, Orhan. You're one of the pall bearers," I say to reassure him. I've been up now for two days. I know Orhan feels as heavy as I do, but actually this staying alive in the Istanbul traffic is a relief of sorts.

He spins the Honda off to the left. The change in air pressure boots the smoke across the dashboard. It flattens in my corner. He swings left into the congestion. Every hour is rush hour in this part of the city.

Across the lanes are the famous Byzantine walls. Each time I've come to Turkey, they've meticulously reconstructed more of the walls and gates. After several minutes, I spot the Mevlana Gate, a wide opening through the castle walls.

"It's a right turn about two blocks past Mevlana Gate, Orhan."

"I think you're correct, Aunt." Orhan appears surprised.

And, there on our right side stands a six-foot wall running along the highway. Obviously built to match the Byzantine Wall. I point again through the dusty window. Several blocks ahead, at a clump of trees, there's another funeral rig turning through an opening in the wall on our side of the road. Yes. There were old trees at the dirt lane out to our family's plots.

"Did you happen to spot a white hood?" Orhan asks loudly. He sucks breath through his teeth and puffs it out noisily.

"Yes, it had one." I see what vexes him – a traffic jam ahead. A taxi's stopped sideways in the middle of our lanes, maybe an accident, vehicles piled in all around. It will take some time to undo that knot. We are stalled. But this is Turkey. Tardiness is allowed. The others will wait patiently. Time is out of one's hands.

Back at the mosque, they told me to ride to the cemetery with Orhan so we could speak English. My son Kurt went with Orhan's sister, who also learned English in school. Nuri rode with the others. They always split the Americans among the relatives like pieces of a pie. I'm glad to have this time with Orhan. Over the months of my last summer here, he interpreted for his grandmother as she related to me the stories of her life. Adalet, Orhan and I had sat at the small table in her kitchen, where she kept a stream of tales going. The old woman wanted her life to be recorded and shared like a gift. *"Turkey is changing now too fast. All* the old faces are fading or gone. Young people have to remember. My generation gave them the identity they share," she told us.

"She says she sacrificed more for me than any of the other grandchildren," Orhan had translated. " I was the cause of the fourth time that she lost her security and future and the second time that her parents took away her birthright – the first being when she eloped with my grandfather."

The Honda is steadily creeping up closer to the traffic jam. Vehicles move around it one at a time. I sink into my seat, envisioning Adalet's face in that moment last summer: Soft as clay and framed by a white lace mantilla, all the wrinkles of emotion smoothed back into her mind. Mother Adalet looked beyond the table and through the panel of windows past miles of red slate roofs and off to the edge of the far horizon. I followed her gaze to the faint mountains in the distance. When I glanced back, I realized that with her cataracts, she couldn't see those mountains.

I glance over to Orhan. "This traffic is her last journey," I say.

Orhan silently rubs his nose with the back of his hand. "Well, from what we learned interviewing her two summers ago, she sure got to do a lot of traveling."

"To say the least," I answer. "Do you remember the first trip of her life?"

"Oh," he answers, "From that village, from Bedre, when she was a ten-year-old girl."

"When I asked her what was the best vacation she ever had, she said, 'The Balkan Wars.'" I remind him.

"Oh yeah," Orhan answers, remembering with me. "When she saw the shock on our faces, she politely explained how that was the first time she saw Istanbul."

We both sit in the dust and heat, lost in memory. I think of how Adalet's face would light up every time she would tell us the stories of her youth – all of it in detail, the beautiful, the humorous and the awful. It was amazing that she could recall it all. "I was born in an Ottoman harem," she had begun as Orhan translated. "Do you know? The women's quarters. We had rules, but we were Thracian women – educated. Our family celebrated all of the religious holidays with our Christian and Jewish neighbors." Her face had darkened. "And then," she went on, "suddenly it happened. You heard about the Balkan Wars, of course." She turned her nut-brown eyes to me and then to her grandson. She fingered the edge of her white muslin scarf, and then she sat forward with her smooth and delicate hands spread onto the glass table. "After that," she said nodding, "we lost all of our fruit orchards." She paused and let out a long sigh. "And the neighbors."

I lean my head back against the seat and close my eyes and think about how one would begin to write about what happened to Adalet during her youth in that time of great change. Perhaps I could write: *The Balkan Wars, they say, but it was really one long war breaking out in different places with the Greeks, Bulgarians, Serbs, Albanians and Ottoman Turks trading enemies and alliances back and forth. No one from the village in the center of Thrace could have imagined what was to come.*

Or maybe I should begin it a bit more dramatic: *It had already started, and still, there was time but no way to stop what they yet couldn't see. In a very short breath, the chaos would come and the village could never go back forever. The reluctant dawn over the plains and low hills of the place called Bedre rose up in a moody October chill. Emin Aga, who claimed the manor, ruled the peasants and collected taxes for the distant sultan was out surveying as he did every dawn. His grandson Sukru was dressing in white shirt and black pants as he did every day. Granddaughter Nefise was pinching her cheeks. Son-in-law Ahmet was combing his beard and listening for the lilt in his wife Zehra's voice. She supervised servants in the kitchen below. But, the bad news was riding, pounding toward them as hard as it could; not yet was it there, so it hadn't arrived. And so, they were waiting but none of them knew; and after, always they would hold the thought of this regular dawn, this space before.*

Or maybe not, maybe the effect of the prose should be simpler, more personal.

Tackling the whole Balkan Wars is just too much. I want to know why Adalet hung on for so long with Burhan and how she came to be the centered woman who came to America four times. She defied her family and ran away to marry at fifteen – but how could she have known much about love and life at that age?

One hour later

Our son Kurt and the other men of the family hoist the litter onto their shoulders and tote the coffin unsteadily through the crowded field of graves and markers that are topped with figures such as horned moons or turbans. Both Arabic and Latin are etched into the marble headstones. As we wade through the knee-high bramble, pallbearers and mourners alike are focused on finding footholds on swells of clay, broken rock and rotting branches. Arrogant weeds have laid claim to this territory, although there are signs of futile efforts to keep them pulled back off the mounds. Some names are scrawled on in black paint. Others, rusted beyond recognition, are bleeding down the slabs. Short walls of concrete end-to-end and back-to-back like scattered dominoes separate the sites.

The pallbearers stop, lower the casket and place it crosswise on the brim of the gravesite next to the opened ground. Fresh clods of soil are heaped at the sides of the hole. It gives up a dank copper smell of fungus and severed roots. The diggers have edged a neat rectangle inside a concrete border. Vedat's name is engraved on the headstone. Two shovels lie nearby.

When I take a step back and bend to swat at a bug that has taken a hit on my ankle, I see nieces Beliz and Filiz behind me holding arms. Another niece is off to the other side with her husband and some others. Near them stands the bachelor Ugur, who was Adalet's good neighbor. Nuri's two older sisters are home praying and preparing a grainy desert made of semolina, milk, sugar and almonds. The family's to eat this dish called "halva" all together later to symbolize taking in the sweetness and substance of Adalet's life. It vaguely reminds me of Holy Communion.

The pallbearers line up at the sides of the grave. The funeral attendants remove the green and white cloths. Nuri touches me with his glance and looks around at the others. Kurt has his back to me. The men lift the lid. I hold my breath.

A stocky little man with an unshaven face and rumpled shirt beneath a wrinkled jacket carries the coffin's lid back through the weeds toward the funeral rig. The other two attendants bend and reach into the coffin for the body, which is wrapped like a white cocoon from head to foot. They untie muslin strings at the base of her throat and under her chest. Filiz lays a hand on my shoulder as she balances on her toes. I lean back, whispering, "What are they doing?"

"They make an opening, Lee. Her spirit might enter again, if it gets lonesome, " Beliz answers.

The bundle is lowered onto two long leather straps on the ground and adjusted so that one thong is under the back and one under the legs.

The unshaven man returns and picks up one end of the straps, speaking sharply at his two helpers. The two grab strap ends and shuffle to the head of the pit. The stocky man grunts and orders. This little unshaven man seems to be as strong as the other two. The three position the bundled corpse up over the concrete pen that frames the grave.

The imam approaches the foot of the site and cries out words from the *Koran*. She is a fragile cargo going into the belly. Adalet, I think, wherever you are now, you won't come back to your worn out body. You're in another realm. I don't wipe my tears. I want to feel the uneven blotches that run down to the crevice of my breasts.

The men slip the straps from under the linen form, on the base of the pit. The unshaven one heaps the leather cords up in his arms and carries them away. The other two men diagonally place four planks across the body. Strident chant, thunks, and shuffling boots.

I edge over near the imam and take up a handful of dirt, step back and begin kneading it thoughtfully as I stare into the pit. Adalet's body, according to her wishes, is getting buried above Vedat's – the gentle stranger with whom I had little conversation. He was a heavy-framed man like the pictures of his father, Burhan. Adalet and Vedat were laughing with us in Virginia ten years ago. He was jolly, and got about town every day on his own.

I was taken with that big lonely man. He would buy up large fields for crops in southern Turkey and have the yield harvested and trucked to the markets of Istanbul. He owned two trucks by the time he took in the partner who scammed him and left him bankrupt. The lymphoma was found months after they went back to Turkey. Later, there was the phone call and my husband's race to get to Istanbul. When Nuri entered the hospital room, Vedat pulled upright in the bed and held out his arms. He had lain immobile for two days waiting for his brother, the doctor, to come with some miracle. Nuri held Vedat in his arms until he died before the morning broke.

The two men have the shovels, turning the heaps back into the pit, carefully allowing the dirt to fall gently. We are fixed on it. The white shroud dissolves scoop by scoop. Nuri has moved near the top of the grave. His face sags. With the weight of his thoughts, probably. Maybe this burial reminds him of that time in Marash and his little sister Oznur's dying when he was only a fourteen-year-old boy; and yet, he was the oldest son with the responsibility of the father. Nuri told me how his father could not be reached and notified of the child's illness and that Burhan returned home three days after her death.

The pallbearers spade the earth back into itself. Another niece moves up beside me. The family men take turns, heaving the load off the shovel, sealing the ground. One hands the tool on to Kurt, who has removed his jacket. His tanned hands take steady aim. He balances the scoop a second or two before taking a breath to heave it in. I step to the side of the imam and toss the soil from my hands after Kurt slings the dirt. His dark brown eyes catch mine and I nod.

"What did you toss into the grave?" Beliz asks me.

"Oil – a bit of myself rubbed into the dirt," I answer.

The other pallbearers take their turn. The diggers finish it off.

The gaping hole in the ground is gone. Mother Adalet 's body waits like a tulip bulb. Adalet's neighbor friend Ugur comes up to Kurt and says in English, "This is finished, no more to be said but, 'Peace to her.'"

As if he were finger painting or sculpting, with his hands, one of the diggers smoothes the top. He works the mound until the soil is fine.

I pick flowers out of the bunch my family bought. Kurt comes up behind and hugs against my back. I turn and we lean into one another.

"We'll ride back together, just the three of us," Nuri calls.

"Shame," Nuri's youngest sister says, staring at the flowers in my hand.

"Taking grave flowers – shame," she whispers. Her dark eyes are wide and sullen. Nuri takes my elbow. I press the bouquet onto my chest.

Kurt, Nuri and I turn to go, the last to leave the cemetery, feeling empty with what death takes away from the living, having no tasks to rush home to like the rest of the family. "We could use a good word from Grandmother right now," Kurt says.

As if on cue, the sound of a huge wave trough pulling back turns us around. We look up at once to the highest sprays of the stately evergreens. The muffled roar, come from a sudden uplifting, and seeming at first like a mirage, is a white mass spreading from the crests of the old Cyprus trees. We have seen such birds in Turkey nested in the top of a chimney or flapping awkwardly against the sky. We gape as the white flock gathers up like an epiphany into the cloudless blue, maybe twenty maybe fifty, each with their long stiff limbs folded onto their abdomens, phantoms that suddenly start uneven honks. They spread a brief shadow over us and leave.

"Look at that," Nuri whispers.

"My God. Storks!" Kurt says, gasping. "Awesome."

•   •   •

Tonight, I again pick up the book, *Ataturk,* by the British historian Lord Kinross. I open to 1919, when Adalet and Burhan started their marriage life in the same house. Their personal challenges would have been overwhelming even without all of the political turmoil – and the on-going conflicts and warfare throughout Anatolia and Thrace:

The country had been overrun with foreign powers ever since the end of the Great War in 1918. Some wanted the sultan to take control of the anarchy and occupation. The Allies had already decided to divide up the remaining and devastated Ottoman Empire, leaving the Turks some area in central Anatolia. Nuri emphasized to me that while it was true that Turks had little left, many patriots determined to die if necessary for the soil they had owned for six hundred years. From what Adalet told me two summers ago, there is no doubt that Burhan and Adalet were of an equal mind about this matter. General Mustafa Kemal, who came to be lovingly called, "Pasham – our General", who saved the Gallipoli Peninsula and the Dardanelles Strait from the British, French and Australian invasion at the beginning of WWI, some four years prior, was calling for an army of the people. Accomplished Ottoman Generals Kazim Karabekir and Ali Fuat and military leaders Rauf Bey and Refet Bele joined him in Anatolia, after he left Istanbul behind to start a resistance movement in the east. Once he landed at Samsun on the Black Sea in May 1919, what followed evolved into the Turkish Republic in 1923. The revolutionaries' resolve was that if Ottoman land were to be taken from underfoot, it would go with the last drops of blood, but with honor. Not understanding that conviction was the Allies great mistake. General Mustafa Kemal even wrote newspaper articles challenging the stance of the prime minister of the Ottoman Cabinet. And – the young woman Adalet kept up on what was transpiring and knew of many meetings of secret assemblies. The varied groups needed a leader capable of drawing them to a single idea. Mustafa Kemal was the one to do it.

I reach over the desk to my notes, fish out the time line that I made of Adalet's life two summers ago. In 1917, at age fifteen, she eloped with Burhan and was disowned by her family. By 1919, she and Burhan were located in Gebze on the Sea of Marmara. Today, that crowded industrial center with reams of towering apartment complexes is about forty minutes by car from Istanbul. When Adalet was seventeen, Gebze existed as only a step up from a village. Burhan and Adalet lived there in relative isolation. They were, as well, estranged from their families and friends.

FOUR

Orphans

Adalet pondered and waited by the light of fires she kept in the town of Gebze on the NE of the Sea of Marmara, wondering when Burhan would return. Many nights found him quite late. A good persuader, perhaps he whispered with others in some remote corner of the town.

When the fire began to pop and catch, Adalet laid the iron handle onto the stone hearth and stepped backwards until she felt the edge of the cushion against her calf; and then she sank into the chair. Of the four chairs the carpenter had made, she claimed this one by tying onto it the pillow embroidered with lavender buds and clover, a present Nefise gave Adalet when she and Burhan left Istanbul this past year.

Adalet pictured Sister, now married to a second prince with servants to tend her fires and serve her tea. Nefise was mistress of two beautiful wooden houses on the Bosphorus in Bebek and Ortakoy. Luck had been good to Nefise except for the death of her first husband Captain Prince Tevfik, killed in Gaza at the beginning of the Great War. Captain Tevfik's mother loved Nefise so much that after he died, she found her another husband in order to keep her close. Nefise's second Prince, Ali Fuat, a Circassian, was brother of one of the wives of Sultan Vahdettin, who had recently come to the throne. Prince Ali Fuat studied more than law in the palace school. Even with his royal attachments, Nefise whispered to Adalet's ears alone that Ali Fuat secretly supported the National Resistance that smuggled guns and bullets out of Istanbul to the National Liberal forces in central Anatolia.

On the eastern frontier in 1915, Adalet's brother Sabri had almost lost a leg in the war against the Russian and Armenian aggression come from the Northeast. Sabri believed that the Russian plan was to incite Ottoman Armenians to burn the Turks out of eastern Anatolia. Furthermore, the chilling tales of the marketplaces included not only the Ottomans' retaliation but also accounts of loyal Armenian countrymen who suffered and died at the hands of the invaders. There seemed to be no end to the constant grief that all of the innocent parties were suffering.

In old Smyrna now called Izmir, Greeks who had been Ottomans for centuries were joining the assault of Greek soldiers who had come from across the Aegean Sea. Turks were fleeing into the hillsides for their lives. The British, who at the end of the Great War announced that they were bringing order, were the very ones who encouraged the Greek invasion, permitting Greeks dressed in black with their heavy belts of cartridges and guns to take their guerrilla war inland.

From Iskender to Cilicia, occupying French and Armenians controlled the Mediterranean Anatolia. Even so, arms were smuggled to the Resistance Movement, sometimes even under vegetables and hay in the carts of peasant women who pretended to be daft – taking advantage of the fact that people commonly confused poverty and old age with simple-mindedness. Burhan said that Ottoman generals hid weapons in mountain caves before surrendering. Adalet made it her business to read decrees, speeches and newspapers and to pay a mind to the community water fountain chitchat. With so many factions, knowing who was supporting what required vigilance.

Gebze was not much of a place to be; but at least Burhan had been able to hold a position there as a teacher the past two years. He was now "acting" governor. Had Mother and Father blessed her marriage, Adalet could have joined him earlier. It was hard to be married for that first year and not to live as man and wife. But

Burhan had remained determined to be wed to her. She had waited to see what her fate would be, encouraged with his ambition to enroll in medical school while she continued to stay alternately with Burhan's cousin's mother Seniye and with Aunt Azime. Burhan came and went from Istanbul to Kirkkilise. Doctor Fuat thought medicine a good future for Burhan, who became dismayed when the universities were closed due to the war. At the same time, teachers were not drafted. And recently, he accepted the new post in Gebze.

Adalet studied the swaying flames on her heap of coals as if they were familiar companions. The gray corners of the room bloomed into amber and mandarin like the scarves of carefree Thracian maids dancing around campfires in meadows at harvest time. She imagined keeping step with drums and tambourines and the unyielding whines of the saz and flute while the air, thick with the scent of shish kebabs on open pits, wove the smoke around the tales of the old men and the laughter of wives.

The fire popped. She sat back and sighed. Her precious youth. It had been jerked away two years ago more quickly than she could comprehend.

From her Gebze door, Adalet could see neither green fields nor mountain trees. The land spread wide and lonely. The sun crept down behind shaved tan hills. Winds constantly worried the scruffy stubble of weed brush. If Mother Zehra could peek into her daily life, she would no doubt repeat: "My daughter has chosen the lot in life of those who redden their knees!"

"But Mother Dearest, I don't need a servant. There's only this sitting room with fireplace, one bedroom and tiny kitchen."

"When you had the chance you could have left him! And then, you could have had a proper marriage with a rich man – even a prince like Nefise did!"

"Oh, stop, Mother, it is not so bad with me. My Burhan is chief officer of Gebze."

· · ·

Taking the short hand-thatched broom from where it was propped against the wall next to the hearth, Adalet resolved that it would do no good to try to tell her mother these things. Zehra had a mind already determined as to what the future should be. Adalet bent over from the waist, sweeping, and began a song from the legend of the famous folk hero and bandit, Koroglu. She sang an improvised response of a beautiful lady named Telli to her suitor and abductor Hassan, the son of Koroglu. In the song, the lady sighs that her lover's words have set her on fire; and he replies to her that he will always do her bidding if she will come with him. When she ended the ballad, Adalet brushed her small heap into the fire, smiling at the embers blazing up. With the song, she began to think back, 1917 in Kirkkilise, more than two years before Gebze, when she had waited at the threshold of becoming a bride:

Seated around the samovar in a large room subdued by carpets, velvet and heavy oak, sharing folk tales and sipping lemon water with sugar and mint, Adalet had been in Doctor Fuat, Mediha and Seniye's home for several days. Reports continued to arrive from the marketplace, the hamams, the smithies and harems – through Seniye's maid or Aunt Azime – of what was being told of Adalet's abduction by the one called "Handsome," and of Mother Zehra's obstinate refusal – although all of the town knew that Adalet was safe in the hands of family friends. It was said that the respected holy man Hafiz Ahmet disowned his willful daughter.

Azime brought a livid report: The last eve on the rise of the moon, Zehra had the servants to make a heap in the road below her front yard. She presented a public show of retribution by setting the torch to Adalet's papers and books, dresses and scarves, bloomers and socks. The town folk went calling it a lover's bonfire that would never burn out. Others claimed that it made no ash at all, just flaming fingers reaching out into the night.

Adalet quite frankly found her parents' response confusing, for Zehra's abduction and even Zehra's sisters and their mother's abduction before them had always been a luscious bit of heritage. Adalet saw herself as merely joining the legacy of family tales.

"Ah, but my sister Zehra sees Burhan's father as a man of no great means," Azime explained. "A blacksmith."

"But Mehmet Nuri has made the pilgrimage to Mecca."

" My Dear, he doesn't have wealth or lands. Noble Zehra is Emin Aga's daughter and the granddaughter of a prince of ancient Harput."

"The same as you," Adalet replied.

"Ah, but my matchmaking heart is a troubadour."

As it had been, after her abduction, when Doctor Fuat had returned to find Adalet secluded in the harem of his house and with her expecting to become his cousin's bride, his alarm resounded in the stairwell. "Burhan's passions will be his downfall!" She had never seen the doctor upset, and worried that he would turn against her, too. Fifteen-year-old Adalet had no way to protect herself. If her father would not allow the marriage, perhaps she would be expected to kill herself to save her honor. Adalet thought such an idea rubbish and wrong. Life itself was a gift to open.

But, thank goodness, on the fifth day, Fuat relented and asked for Adalet and Burhan's presence with him. Their meeting with Fuat was the first time the couple had been together since the carriage ride from the town to Seniye's.

When Adalet came into the parlor, Fuat and Burhan stood. She felt apprehensive until Burhan placed the lute in her arms, saying, "Azime got it from the hands of Hanifey, who saved it from the fire."

"I imagined this was gone. Seems that Mother would destroy every trace of me," Adalet told him. She ran her palm over the smooth walnut edge of it. This lute is twice saved from fires, she thought. She glanced quickly into his flickering eyes. Her stomach quivered to her toes. Burhan surely could also be called romantic as well as handsome. This man lit a spark inside of her that longed to breathe, like nothing else had ever done. That he was her fate made her tremble. Love had cast a spell over her like the April sun does the dandelion.

"Your mother is a lioness," Burhan said. He turned to Fuat and raised his arms as he spoke. "Yes, Cousin. Zehra is said to have gone yelling, 'My daughter has thrown her life to the winds. She will be blown over the land like a weed fluff!'" Adalet was disturbed when he laughed. Her mother was highly esteemed, of course; and no one ever laughed at Zehra.

Fuat's lower lip tightened under his thick brown mustache, with no sign of displeasure. He looked at Burhan and nodded slightly. Fuat's glance met Adalet's. His eyes softened and crinkled at the edges. "Be peaceful, Adalet. I'll speak with Ahmet shortly," he said, stepping away to inspect papers on his desk. Doctor Fuat had just adopted her situation. All would be well.

"Your eyes are burnt almond; I'm counting each lash," Burhan whispered to the side of her face. He starred at her with such forwardness and heated gaze as if she were already his. Her hands could hardly hold onto the lute.

Adalet lowered her eyes and whispered back as she lifted the instrument, "I thank you for this."

"My Girl, when you sent me forsythia bloom in your handkerchief last month, I slept with it under my pillow, dreaming of what special present I could bring to you." Burhan raised his hand, tipped his fingers to his forehead and bowed with as much gentlemanly class as Nefise's prince.

Two days after that meeting in the drawing room, Fuat sent Mediha to fetch the willful bride. Mediha embraced Adalet, saying, "Congratulations Friend!" Her voice was joyful.

"Adalet," Fuat reported, "we have come from your home. Your father says, 'What has happened cannot un-happen. Let it go as it will, for there is already too much gossip.'"

"Are you going to tell her what Zehra said?" Mediha whispered.

Looking sharply at Mediha, the doctor knitted his brows. "In fact, I wasn't," he answered. "Now, I must. Adalet, your mother's still angry. Take this easily – she said that your reputation is lost unless you two are married, because now there is not another who will have you." Adalet drew her hand to her lips. Fuat reached out and touched her shoulder. "My Girl, time changes everything."

"Is there anything else?" Adalet whispered.

Mediha answered. "Zehra added that she should have known such a thing as this would happen back when you lost that engagement ring."

"Yeah," Fuat said. "Your mother told us of a betrothal you had several years ago." Adalet was taken by surprise, for she had almost forgotten the event of the Arab. It meant little to her. She had only been thirteen.

"That arrangement was certainly not in my cup," she said, folding her arms and glancing sideways to Burhan, who appeared more stunned than she. Adalet told them that the Arab was a rich sheik. The engagement fell apart when the sheik's father was found hanged after a revelation that he was a traitor to the sultan. Adalet had already misplaced the engagement ring several weeks before the news had broken; and when she couldn't find it, she took it as a bad omen for a marriage anyway. Aunt Azime seemed happy when Zehra canceled the engagement. Adalet had only met the sheik once. She knew right away that he was pretentious.

"Just dismiss any hurt and move on," Fuat continued. With a wide gesture of his hand, he asked Adalet to sit; and then, he stepped over to Burhan, taking him by the arm. "From this day on, misfortunes of the past are today's winnings." Fuat's voice sounded sure.

Burhan chuckled mildly and moved toward a chair, saying, "There's nothing now but to call the imam and judge and get the ceremony over with." To Adalet, he continued, "Come sit beside me on the divan, my dearest."

Adalet plopped down beside him in a sudden reality: For her, there would be no bridal gown. No food for a yard full of guests. No women painting henna on her hands at the hamam, no parade on a white horse through the town, no coins thrown to the children and no being Mother Zehra's Bride.

. . .

Ahmet arrived at Seniye's the next day and signed the marriage agreement with the judge without asking for Adalet. Fuat's brother Ridwan, a shop owner, found her a lacy dress from Istanbul. Seniye and Azime brought her flowers. Burhan and Adalet penned their names. The imam came, joined their hands, covered their hands with a cloth and said some prayers. That was it.

Seniye ordered a celebration dinner prepared, and when the meal was done with, the company relaxed in the parlor, singing old songs to the strum of Adalet's lute. Burhan strutted around in a new wool coat and vest, taking the floor and singing romance couplets in his rich baritone voice. Listening, and warmed by that way he looked at her, Adalet felt excited about beginning a life with Handsome. She would tell him soon of her plans for education. She could go past the tenth level. Perhaps even graduate from the girls' school in Istanbul and write novels like the Turkish woman she had heard about, that Halide Edib, who was a cabinet member of the Turkish Hearth organization, which promoted national pride and issues such as health, sports and the economy. Halide Edib also formed a new organization called, The Elevation of Women. Anything was possible.

During the week before the wedding ceremony, Mediha and Azime made hints to Adalet of what it was like to be alone with a man; but that marriage day had sneaked upon her all too sudden. Once the singing was done with, Adalet found herself awkwardly following Mediha and Seniye up to the guest quarters. She was ashamed and confused about what she should ask them. A large room had been given to the bride and groom for their special nights. After several days, Burhan would go from Kirkkilise, returning to teach in Gebze, where no quarters were yet prepared for her. She had before made no plans for herself, for where she would stay, naturally, thinking that she would be taken care of at her own home. Ahmet and Zehra always accommodated others. Certainly her parents would send for her soon.

The women fluttered around, helping Adalet turn down the bed. "The man will be anxious to make the union complete," Mediha said, cheerfully sprinkling some sachet of rose dust onto the sheets, lowering the oil lamp and lighting a small beeswax candle. Seniye had given Adalet a white cotton gown with a round neck of tiny eyelets. The long sleeves were full and gathered at the wrists by two silk ribbons that tied into butterfly bows. The two women unpinned her hair from the bun into which it was lifted and combed it over her shoulders and back. Mediha pinched Adalet's cheeks to make them pink. Then, they both kissed her. They told her to wait on the settee and to not be afraid.

But, Adalet felt truly afraid for the first time in her life. "You must be shy, yet willing to give yourself," Mediha added, holding her chin with her fingers.

"How should I act?" she asked.

"He will know. Let him guide you," Seniye answered. Of course, Adalet had seen the animals on the farm; that behavior seemed so rude and routine. A man and a woman's coming together would be tender, full of feeling; but she had not even discussed the details with Nefise, who behaved as if they were taboo. Now that the ordeal was upon her, she wished that she had protested getting abducted, at least until she should learn more about this trial of the marriage bed!

After the two friends left the bride, there was a soft knock on the door. The brass knob glinted with the candle's light as it turned. Adalet was alone with circumstance. Her head swam. Were she not sitting, she could faint. Her arms were weighted. She spread them stiffly at the sides of her hips.

The light from outside the doorway illuminated his figure for a second before he closed the door. "Dearest One, alone at last," he said in a controlled, breathy voice. Adalet nodded her head, searching for words a wife should say in this moment. He took a step and hesitated. "You don't answer," he offered. "I hope I didn't annoy you, keep you waiting." Adalet shook her head slowly. He moved to the settee, cupped her head in his big hands and kissed her hair. "Precious Girl," he said. When she raised her head he looked into her eyes for several seconds. "Oh my little one, you are anxious to be my wife. Your big eyes are inviting pools."

"Hello, my husband," she managed to say in a pinched voice. He grinned. "Sit and talk," she offered, hoping to hear of his day, his father, his dreams – anything.

He sat with vigor, so close that he was pressing her upper arm and thigh. His arm went around her shoulder and meshed them tighter. ...*Let him guide*, she remembered, and before she could finish her thought, he had, with his other hand, turned her face and kissed her full on the mouth. She had never been kissed so that she could not breathe and she gave a moan in her throat to let him know she needed air. He pulled back, jumping up, saying, "Oh my innocent bird, you've waited too long – same as me!"

In an instant and without a word, he was off to the side of the room behind her. "I'll only be a moment, my wife!" he called. There was a brief scuffle and rustling of clothing; then, he was hovering over her in a nightshirt, a stranger, and larger than she remembered him. He stood like a thick bull with his hairy legs almost touching her. She sat shielded by her thin gown. She closed her eyes so she would not see her body submitting to whatever was going to happen. His big hand touched her head. He was whispering sweet things to her but she could not reply. When she opened her eyes, she was peering into his nostrils. She stiffened her shoulders when he lowered himself so close beside her that she could hear his breathing as he leaned and positioned her the way he wanted and then maneuvered her hand into his, her cold and clammy hand, given away to the person pushing against her – who at that moment neither resembled the charmer of her fantasy nor the romantic of the stage. She met herself in a confusing scene of fumbled breath and blushing panic. When again, he slid his arm around her and tried to pull her to him, she shrieked.

Her legs took her up and away to the dressing table, where, panting, she stopped. He darted toward her. When she startled back, she knocked against the glass edge of the table and mirror, overturning a silver vase. It hit with a crackle, chipped the mirror, and bounced back onto the wooden floor. She stared in horror at her broken reflection. This was not a good sign.

Up, Burhan swept his bride in his strong arms just as he had done when he last week leapt from the closet in the tailor's shop to abduct her, the day Azime and Adalet's servant had left her to await a special package from "Handsome." He had stolen her from there, throwing a large cloth over her, carrying her out the back door and then cramming the two of them into a carriage bound for Fuat's house.

In her bridegroom's arms, what could she do but let her limbs give way? He laid her into the rose sachet. The scent for a second distracted her from the fact that her whole body was heavily covered by one of whom she actually knew nothing much except his name. She ultimately lost her fright, her pain, herself in the galloping rhythm of horses, in the smell of their sweat with their hard muscles determining to reach, straining to reach, gulping and snorting for breath to reach some place unknown to her. And when they did in time arrive, she was not the one she was before.

Later, he called her sweet names and inquired about the state of her health and being, as if it should now be better. Adalet could only nod, as she had no idea. He then tiptoed out the door. She curled up and wept for the disappointment of a matter held in such esteem as to be the honor of a woman's life. Was this really what all of the shame and secrets were about? Everyone betrayed virgins. It was an outright conspiracy.

No maid Hanifey came to help her make herself clean. She lay in the darkness for an hour, waiting to know what she should feel. When Burhan slipped back into the room, she pretended to be sleeping. Without moving, she listened to his breathing until it turned into soft snores.

With swollen eyes, she watched until the morning's light crept through the curtains. "So I am a wife," she whispered. Who could she trust with her ignorant confusion? Small wonder Nefise would not speak of it.

•　　•　　•

After Adalet's marriage, throughout that entire springtime and into June, she stayed with either Seniye or Azime. Since Burhan was working in Gebze, he could visit only on the weekend once a month. With the advice of her friends and aunt, Adalet managed to lose her fear of his huge hands all over her. With much more interest than duty, she began awaiting him. Simply put, her attachment to Burhan had been as much in the hands of that power beyond her as the lost engagement.

Shortly after, one week when she was staying with Azime, Adalet was summoned. The groom Hassan's girl, Zeyneb waited in the reception parlor on a low divan cradling a package wrapped in a large flowered scarf. The former childhood playmate wore a brown charshaf over her head and body. It was pulled up around her throat and mouth. The package was tied into a neat bow on the top – the same decoration that Adalet had seen her mother prepare many times. Adalet's heart leapt. Mother has sent her forgiveness, she thought.

Zeyneb turned as Adalet approached. "Hello, how are you?" Zeyneb asked as she stood. Adalet answered that she was well; and how was she, and Zeyneb answered that she was well also. On the palms of her hands, Zeyneb balanced the parcel. Her hands were the only parts of her body visible, besides her face. The old sparkle in her eyes was gone. Adalet had not seen her for some time.

Adalet rushed to her with arms outstretched. She responded shyly when Adalet kissed her on both cheeks.

"And so my mother sends me a present?" Adalet asked, relishing the package.

Zeyneb stepped back, awkwardly holding the bundle as if she was not sure why she had it. "Oh –I am not to say that– oh, the maid Hanifey packed some things for you, and gives this with her blessings." Adalet took the parcel, and deciding that she should open it later, laid it on a table.

"I send my thanks to Hanifey for thinking of me. And my love and constant respect to my mother and father." Adalet gave her a look so that Zeyneb would know that she understood who had sent the package. Mother had not forgiven her yet.

Adalet ushered Zeyneb back to the divan and sat beside her.

"Are your father and brother in good health?" she asked.

"Thank you, they are well and working, as Allah permits."

"Is my father's garden thriving after the planting? We've had such cold rains in this late spring."

"The rains beat the young stalks but they're thirsty. If the rains finish soon, we will not, if Allah permits, have the flooded Devil's Creek this year," she answered, glancing at the new bride with what seemed to be some admiration. Zeyneb lowered her face and became quiet, waiting for Adalet to continue the conversation.

"I have not seen you dress like this before, Zeyneb. I'm surprised."

Taking her hand to her head, Zeyneb allowed the end of the long brown sheet to fall back. Her shiny hair was pulled away from her face with a scarf. "My father" she answered, "is looking to find a suitable husband for me. With times so hard and yet getting worse, I should be careful to find such fortune." She glanced over to Adalet. "There have been many rough men come from the hills of distant places. Women must hide. An unblemished reputation is all one like me can offer," she said. Adalet pulled back and looked away. "Oh, Adalet, I did not mean to refer to your – situat ..."

"No, don't worry, don't think of it. But, tell me of you. Are you taking classes at school, the Mutasarrıf Ibrahim Sureyya?" Adalet had heard that Zeyneb was learning to read at the orphanage school that had been established in Kirkkilise after the Balkan Wars. Because her mother had been lost to the wars, Zeyneb had been a proper candidate.

"Yes, I have finished my class. May I say that I know that in times past your Burhan directed and acted the part of the hero in several plays at the orphanage; and although I could not go to see it, I saw him there once from a distance."

Adalet inched forward, bursting at the seams to narrate the tale to a friend her own age: In the beginning, she had several times sneaked behind the stage and briefly met "Handsome" with Aunt

Azime standing by. She had shortly thereafter gotten carried away with the romantic adventures of tokens and notes. And then, she was to play the center role in the exciting idea of elopement styled as abduction. Then came the high drama. Her parents discovered her interest in a suitor they scorned. She was locked up in the home. To which, Burhan let it be said that he had lost interest and was engaged to another. Adalet was set free. Finally, with Aunt Azime orchestrating everything from behind the scenes, the abduction and marriage, more quickly than she imagined, acted upon her and carried her forth into this day.

But, at the second that Adalet opened her mouth to speak, Azime came into the room with tea. The aunt moved Adalet's package to the floor to make a place for her tray.

"Ah – and so, my sister shows she loves her daughter still, huh? And so I said it would be. Everything in time."

"It is from Hanifey," Adalet said.

"I know the language of my sister – even when she is not speaking to me," Azime answered. She nodded to Zeyneb, whom she welcomed earlier, before Adalet was summoned down from her room. "Zeyneb my dear," Azime continued, lifting her nose and pressing her lips together, "let Hanifey know that any attempts to lure Adalet back home will be futile. The mind and heart of our sweet Adalet are attached to the union with a husband. Madame Zehra must embrace our Burhan or she will lose a daughter to me!"

In those first months of marriage, Burhan was a good one with witty words, his voice, sometimes like songs. Though he could be brash or moody in the little time they had alone. But if she sulked, he did not notice. She did not mind sleeping with him; but she could not bring herself to be as loving as he wanted. It was not her way to flirt and titter – especially to a man who smelled of smoke, and sometimes the liquor, raki. Late at night he'd sit at Azime's table eating half a watermelon with goat cheese, waving the knife in the air between bites.

But, the whole country back in 1917 was stuck in an anxious

state, waiting for something hopeful to happen. For most, goods were scarce, and sons disappeared under the boots of the Great War. All they could learn of Burhan's brother Ruhittin was that he was either dead or lost to the war in Yemen. Burhan feared that he might never see his brother again. Adalet searched for fortunes in teacups, for they could not get coffee. She saw birds flying over fire on mountains.

"The British hope to take the holy city in Gaza. As if to work a miracle, Sultan Vahdettin goes to plead with the Germans!" Burhan said one night, with his fist pounding Azime's table. He was sure that the Germans just wanted to use the Ottomans to get Arabian oil. "Those Germans! They are a rude lot who think they are superior to Turks! Same as the British, the tricky ones in London." Burhan stopped ranting and glanced over to Adalet and raised an eyebrow. "French are not bad, though. You could learn a little about intimacy from the French, my dear."

Three months after the marriage, Brother Sabri visited when Adalet was staying with Seniye. He took a small leave of his army duties to return to Kirkkilise. As he was wounded while fighting the war in eastern Anatolia, his crippled leg brought him an office duty post where he served as an intelligence officer in Istanbul. For several months, a worrisome growth on Adalet's throat had been getting larger. She had shown it to Zeyneb when she came again to Azime's bearing slippers and fruit. Sabri arrived at Seniye's door with a plan that included more than getting Adalet's throat healed.

"My Dear Girl, you are too lonely waiting for this Burhan to come and go! What of your schooling? Your life? This man has evaded the army!" Sabri exclaimed.

"He's a teacher!" she answered. Sabri's accusation stung. It was true that most of the able men had either enlisted or been taken to war; but, Burhan insisted that the Germans had tricked the Ottomans into their fight and had no advancement of Turkey in mind. "Burhan does not want to die for a cause in Europe!" she added. The government drafted every available young man.

"The coward has become a teacher in order to evade the army!"

"Our country will need honorable and educated men when the wars finish! Burhan's reading political science. He'll get a degree!"

Sabri regarded his sister for a moment. "The army provides me with a nice house on the upper Bosphorus in a desirable cove near Sariyer," he said sweetly.

Adalet was glad the subject changed. "The beautiful Istanbul," she said, sitting with Sabri on the divan. "But one hears distressing tales – that there are tents and soldiers along the shores of the Bosphorus Strait and the Sea of Marmara, that the city is crowded with Austrians and Germans."

"Together with other strange immigrants – but Inshallah, this war will soon be over. If you were with me in Istanbul you could visit Nefise at her two fine wooden Bosphorus homes."

The previous winter, Adalet had received a letter from Nefise full of news about going to dinner in the European quarters of Pera, to a fashionable restaurant where she dined on caviar and was serenaded by Gypsy violins – even with the war going on. Adalet wondered if her sister was exaggerating her life to please her, even though Nefise was living with royalty; for Adalet had heard that times were hard on all, even those of wealth.

"But, Sabri, they say goods are scarce throughout Stamboul, that there are long lines where the common people pay outrageous money for a small bread, that the trams are so crowded a woman or an old man can't get a seat."

"Yes, we sweeten our tea with raisins instead of sugar, but Istanbul is still the Center of the World. As an officer, I have ways, with a little nuisance, which enable me to survive fairly easily. My house has a view. There is a sweet breeze and friends – and there you'll be able to go with me to see a famous specialist about that growth on your throat."

"Perhaps there would even be time for studies while the doctor makes me well – so... "

"Of course, you can go to the Istanbul Girls' School for

Fortunate Young Women once the war is over," Sabri answered. "Our world is quickly changing. Can you believe – Muslim women in Istanbul can be seen working in shops? And of course you may know – a woman can even initiate a divorce."

"Unthinkable," she said.

"But true. And, do think of it: Why should a person –only because she is female– remain yoked –like one ox to the other– until she dies? One can make a mistake. One has a right to become unattached before complications develop." Sabri's words seemed sensible. Going to Istanbul again was a seduction so great, that to miss it was more than Adalet could bear. There, Burhan would not have so far to journey in order to see her. It would be a pleasant surprise for him. Her older brother always gave her guidance.

Doctor Fuat had been gone from the house the day that Sabri came to take her away. Seniye made no effort to stall Sabri from escorting her out the door and back to her parents' house and arms, where they would consider plans about her leaving for Istanbul at the end of the month. She struggled about the disloyalty to Burhan, but told herself that in their present housing situation, she and he had only been able to be together as husband and wife six times; and that the arrangement had proven to be an adventure that was a bit tedious. Surely he would concur that they could continue when things settled down a bit later on.

Adalet had been back in her parents' home less than a week when Burhan showed up. But, Ahmet sent him away saying that Adalet did not wish to be disturbed. She suffered about it and cried in her room, but Hanifey told her that time would take care of everything. "Adalet, for your own protection," Zehra said, leaning forward from her seat, "we must insist that you stay in our presence about the household, or be locked in your bedroom. Who knows what that crazy man may try? And, needless to say, you have proven yourself careless and weak."

Adalet accepted their requirements with understanding. Zehra was right. It was lovely to enjoy the comforts of home again

– while contemplating a travel adventure to The Center of the World. Things would work out once she got to Istanbul.

But then, there came the tapping one night outside her bed- room window. She had long since said good night to her mother, who had secured her door from the outside. Only five minutes before, Adalet turned back the covers on her bed and twisted down the wick on her lamp.

She stood in her bare feet in the dark, thinking: That pecking, it must be a night bird. Or the summer's wind brushing a branch against the house. Again, twice. Three even raps each time. It wasn't the wind, but it was one persistent bird. That measured sound was made on the iron grill that covered the window.

Adalet tiptoed to the edge of the heavy flaxen drapery and peeked outside. On a ladder, a person, a man, a shepherd. She could hardly breathe, for she knew the eyes by heart! Burhan. This lover of hers was certainly no coward, daring the stone fence that circled the stead, scaling the rock on the side of the house up to the second floor, sneaking onto the lower floor balcony, and then, the ladder – which he must have carried with him. He was startling in the moonlight, like Romeo for Juliet or Mejnun to Leyla. Yes, on that landing, with his back to the night sky, the crescent moon appeared to be balanced on his shoulder.

But then, her heart began to pound. Father Ahmet's man would not hesitate to shoot, would see him for a wild bandit. Burhan was daring to risk his life for her love! Adalet slipped into the drapery so that she could lift the window. She would raise it only enough to warn him of Father's guard. "You cannot be here," she whispered. She hoped that the man was dead asleep as usual down under the olive tree at the other side of the house.

"If you don't let me inside where I can talk with my wife, then I'll fall backwards and die – and you will be the cause of it." He reached through the bars, caught onto her wrist, and jerked it to his lips. A thrill like lightning scattered all the way down into her feet.

"I can't dare! You foolish man! What good is your dying?"

He gave no answer, but released her wrist and flipped up the metal safety lock that kept them apart. "I love you, my sweet, more than my lonely life!"

It occurred to Adalet that she should tell him immediately about her going to Istanbul, but the explanation would have been too complicated for that moment. As he was heaving himself through the window, his voice was breathless. "It will be a pleasure to die if I can't have you."

The second night he came, Adalet swore to him that she would not let him in. She would lift the window only enough for him to hear her voice. Out of a kindness on her part. "If you don't," he answered, "I'll be forced to go to the front door and demand justice from your father – telling how you let me in only a week ago."

"He won't believe you."

"Ah ha, but that night, to remind myself that I had been with you, I took one of your slippers." Adalet wondered where it had gotten itself. He drew the green velvet out of the drooping shepherd's vest. In those yellow pantaloons, he did look quite harmless – and exotic. She laughed to herself. They each had secrets.

Surely, a tricky jinni spirit concocted that scene in the bedroom and compelled her to deceive her parents, who thought they were saving her. At the same time, she deceived Burhan, who could not have guessed that she would be gone from that bed in a week's time. That jinni must have been mightily surprised; for, that situation, designed to vex Adalet – rather stirred her loins into a pleasurable trill.

The little house in Gebze had grown quite dark except for the room where Adalet mused alone in the chair by the fire, its patterns flashing on the wall, surrounding her in Thracian flowers. Thinking back two years before to those nights in Kirkkilise made her smile. Kismet has its own means of pushing and pulling us toward our destinies.

As for her behavior on that second time that Burhan came to her bedroom window, she had nothing to plead except that she simply could not cope with refusing such determination – as any honest wife might have been. After all, even Mother Zehra had pronounced her careless and weak when it came to matters of the heart. Yes, just such a one had she found herself to be on that night. She was not, no, not able at all, for the sake of sympathy and compassion, to refuse Burhan. As she was to leave for Istanbul in the next week, she had furthermore told herself that surely there was no harm in spending just that hour with one who was, after all, her own, "Handsome."

"My poor Mother Zehra," she said to Gebze's glowing coals. "She dreamed of me marrying into wealth, royalty or high position like Sister."

Ah, Nefise's wedding, now, that was something grand to always remember. Those forty evil thorns notwithstanding, it was, in fact, there, that Burhan first saw her to be a young woman. Yes, on Sister's very wedding day, when Adalet felt the burn of his gaze.

FIVE

The Plan

The sullen hills between Istanbul and Gebze were full of startling news from the World's Center. The tapestry of Istanbul's persimmon, olive and pomegranate streets contained a multitude of hidden thorns. Was there yet one true enough to pull them out?

Adalet stood, forcing her sluggish limbs. She replaced the broom at the hearth. At the divan, she propped up the pillow of embroidered violets, a remnant of a tablecloth stuffed with cotton from a worn out mattress. She straightened the stiff white doily under the paraffin lamp on the table and then wiped the dust from Burhan's water pipe in the corner, kept ready beside the huge wool cushion he sat upon when he smoked.

In the kitchen, she took four potatoes and two yellow onions from the basket by the door, laid them on top of the hutch beneath the window, stooped to open the doors, and took out a round tin bowl and set it onto the top of the hutch. Peeling absently, she dropped each into the bowl, thinly paring the potato skins as she stared out the window into the cold. Before she came here last year, Burhan bragged, "A garden comes with the nice house for the town governor." His garden yielded a bit last summer but not enough to string up any dried tomatoes or peppers. The eggplants didn't do well at all. Father would not have even called the plot a garden. In the spring, Adalet's plan was to work the ground herself and find some horse manure, like the peasants did back in Kirkkilise; but Burhan had hired a gardener and then didn't follow the man's negligent work. Today, the ground out-side consisted of patches of coarse weeds twisted with gray frost. Two trees were holding fast beside the ungated wooden fence. The winter had nearly dissolved the whitewash around the base of the trunks. The few leaves dangling from the thin oak branch-es were little brown fists that rattled as if they clutched faint spir-its from the summer past.

She sighed. She was alone but at least she was safe for the mo-ment. In Istanbul, enemies lurked behind closed shutters, and in strange uniforms at every corner. The city had been taken over by the victorious Allied foreigners, and there was nothing the Sultan could do about it. General Enver's failed committee government had fled the country in disgrace. The people were as angry with them as with the Allied Powers who won the Great War, the ones who now decided how things were to be handled and present-ed. Tales were rampant. Some rumors were a bit far-fetched – foreigners capturing stray Turkish children and roasting them for supper or Turkish women being pinched and bitten on the streets by the Sanglenese soldiers the British brought from India. Newspapers reported that whole families of Turks were simply thrown out onto the streets; their houses given to Christians and that there were ninety thousand Turkish orphans in the land. There were thousands of Christian orphans, too.

How life in the great capital city had changed. Any people but Turks could ride first class on the ferries; and yet, those in first class paid second-class prices. Turks could not ride first class at any price, and had to give up their seats to Christians or risk im-prisonment.

Adalet reminded herself not to dwell on dark images in which she had no power. She closed her eyes and saw herself on the day she had arrived in Stamboul from Kirkkilise with Brother Sabri two and a half years before now, in the first year of her marriage:

Then, in 1917 at Sirkeci Train Station, with the scattered noise all around, the wet-iron smell, and all sorts of people racing to-ward the howling trains, they had veered through a maze, her arm latched to Sabri. They wedged around vendors and wheels, through smoke from the jutting stacks of the ferries and near the sizzling grills. The square was alive with calls of *"Gazete! Newspaper is present!"* "Come buy a fish," "Come drink from the wooden barrel" that the water vendor had strapped to his back, offering sweet-spring water from his wooden cup. The Stamboul that had fascinated Adalet at age eleven during the Balkan Wars still pulsed. Across the wide boulevard, the ferryboats still bobbled and blared in the warm crosswinds. The square was yet full of foreigners and ragged heroes with missing arms or feet – only now they were back from fighting in the Great War. The foreign ladies, with their blond uncovered hair pulled up, ambled arm in arm, their faces bright as a painter's palette, their eyes aloft as if they owned the day. Adalet had thrown back her head as well and took in a whiff of the sea. She was on a new venture, with her parents' blessings. Burhan was living several hours on to the east in Gebze, not knowing that she had made this trip with her older brother. She squeezed Sabri's arm, proud that people could see by the medal on his chest that he also was a war hero and called a "gazi" – though the Bolsheviks had revolted, and the tzar whom Sabri had fought against, was dead. Many of the immigrants on the streets that day were aristocracy, Jewish peoples and Orthodox Christians who had since fled Russia to safety in Stamboul.

Sabri had spoken about his plans for Adalet on the train from Kirkkilise, and she had smiled to think of going to a school like the Turkish Lady Halide Edib who wrote about women of determination, passion and honor. Halide's father had been an official of Sultan Abdulhamid. Halide's father made it possible for her to become one of the American Missionary School's early Turkish Muslim female graduates of higher education. Halide became a journalist, and traveled in Europe; and she had become a heroine working for the Red Crescent and orphanages in these last years during the Great War. Her second husband was now a representative in the Ottoman Parliament. "I can do it!" Adalet had answered Sabri. Her words sputtered from her mouth without consideration. "I always wanted to be educated," she said softly. "But, I am now a wife."

"Everything is unstable now. Who knows the future? A woman like you needs her family's hand. Education means choices."

"Burhan is still planning on his education."

"Then you can give him a better chance, too. Let him seek his future and then come back to you. Perhaps, later, you both will have more to build on. In the meantime, place yourself in your brother's hands," he said, patting his chest. "Rest your mind on it now." Adalet was pleased to have this attention and concern from Sabri. It was a relief. Burhan was a good man; but, when he was around, she could not think what to do for her own best interests. It seemed possible that distance would be a safety for both. Who could know, perhaps Burhan might also be relieved.

As it came about, Burhan had not been relieved. From Aunt Azime, he learned her whereabouts and came to Istanbul. Sabri would not permit him to speak with Adalet. But one day, Sabri was gone and she answered the door and took a letter from a messenger. It was from Burhan, who was begging to see her. He was sure that she had come to Istanbul to be nearer to him.

Sabri found Adalet on the back terrace with her hands full of tears. She did not want Burhan hurting. She had conflicting obligations to people she loved. She missed Burhan's voice and touch.

"He is not about to leave you alone," Sabri had said finally. "I am going to take you up the Bosphorus to our friend, Saadet. He won't know where to look for you." Saadet was Nefise's sister-in-law, a spinster with a three-story wooden house. One could fish or dive right into the water from the whipped cream balconies. Nefise would come with Prince Ali Fuat. They could take their large dinghy toward the Black Sea on the northern edge of the strait. It would be elegant.

One afternoon a week later, recovered from the office procedure where the doctor had removed a large cyst from her neck, Adalet walked with Sister Nefise in a green area along the Bosphorus. They sat in a peaceful flower garden in a park. There

were no foreigners or soldiers. The fishermen glided quietly by
in colorful boats, along the dock, and bobbled side-to-side of the
strait. The constant sparkling waves clipped across the top like a
thousand hands applauding. Children ran in short pants, their
cheeks red. Girls in long dresses and hair tied back with ribbons
ventured toward a cart where a man sold nuts and sweets. A wagon sold lemonade and yogurt drink. Although the city was filled
with the maimed and the wretched, the people were going on
with their lives.

After a bit, Nefise spoke to change the mood. "What do you
think goes on in the mind of those two old men who sit stooped
over that game?" She chuckled. Adalet looked over to the two in
baggy brown pants, sitting on apple crates, hunched over an up-
turned cart onto which they had laid their backgammon board.
She watched the dice clicking across. One of the men reached a
thin-sunburned hand to take up two of the marble disks. "Allah,
Allah!" He laughed as he snapped the marble pieces down on the
outside of the game. "For him, everything in life becomes Allah's
game," Adalet replied. Near the water, several fishermen stood idly
casting into the strong current, as if the world had been stilled for
a hundred years. From a side street somewhere, music tumbled
out.

"Nefise Dearest, do you ever think about the year we spent
here during the Balkan Wars?"

"Of course. We would walk with the elders along the Golden
Horn listening to the bells of the churches. The prayers would call
from the mosques and the black birds would fly up all together,
mingling with the bells from the boats."

"Seems now a dream."

"Adalet, I met my dear late Prince Tevfik then, do you remember?"

Adalet glanced out to the water. Her sister had been made a
widow at age twenty. Here, Adalet, too, was a wife at sixteen, and
separated from her husband. Perhaps she shouldn't listen to her
family about Burhan. The sea had turned cobalt. A cloud floated aimlessly above.

"Adalet, Sister, tell me – are you truly married, you know, in the personal way?" Adalet couldn't meet her gaze. Her sight flooded.

"Whatever the marriage has become, Adalet, you always have a choice. Look at me. When my first prince was killed in Gaza in the Great War, I was devastated. But now I have a new life. One gets over loss. Life moves you on."

Adalet turned to her. She had not recently thought about her sister's grief, and had hardly been with her since it happened. Prince Tevfik had been such a gentleman. She had missed the company of her sister. "I will always love you," Adalet told her. "My spirit will never leave your spirit."

By the end of that summer of 1917, the family had made definite plans for Adalet to begin studying with a tutor in the next month. "Become a teacher!" Nefise exclaimed. "We'll travel to Paris once these awful wars finish and the foreign soldiers leave. You can study there, as well."

On a later afternoon of that same summer, Saadet accompanied Adalet out to the same area where Nefise and Adalet had gone. While they were sitting, feeding breadcrumbs to the pigeons, the large bush beside the bench made a breathy rattle. At once, they shrieked and jumped up. Someone stepped from behind the bush.

"Burhan!"

"You are hiding from me!" he said. His brows were furrowed and his eyes were dark circles. Saadet caught Adalet's arms and held her steady, for she had fallen back against the older woman. Burhan stepped toward his wife. "You belong with me, Adalet. I've come to take you as my wife!" he said.

"She has been healing," Saadet said. Her words came tightly placed and firm. She supported Adalet so that the young woman eased back onto the bench. She stood in front of Adalet and faced him.

"You can't keep my wife from me."

"She is under the protection of my house – and of the Royal

House. The trouble you could face is serious if you do not leave us alone. Now!"

"Adalet – come" Burhan reached his hands but Saadet backed up against Adalet's legs, prepared to strike him with her parasol. Adalet didn't want trouble.

"Speak with Sabri," Saadet told him. "Leave us be, or I shall order that policeman who now comes toward us to arrest you!"

Burhan's voice was as deep. Adalet thought of a bear. "I'll go; but only if you give me a definite time at which I can call on Adalet at your Bosphorus home tomorrow."

"Oh my goodness, what shall we do with such a man! We will see you at eleven – before noon tomorrow, then. Tea with Sabri, but do not expect Adalet!"

At length, when Saadet stepped from in front of Adalet, Burhan was nowhere to be seen. They took the carriage home. The afternoon had turned clammy. When they arrived at the house, Adalet took sick to her stomach and had to rest for several hours.

When she came down to supper, she learned that while she slept, the others had designed a plan: Burhan and she would be divorced when he came for his appointed time the next morning. As an Intelligence Officer, Sabri had little difficulty in finding out where Burhan was staying, and had already sent a message to him saying that the family would be pleased to receive him. Adalet was shocked, confused and a bit panicked. "But he won't divorce me."

"Do you remember that I told you about the law? A woman can bring about a divorce of her husband?" She remembered, her mind going in circles.

"Adalet, we are your protectors," Saadet said.

"Hear me," Sabri said.

"We have your answer," Nefise said.

"Burhan will no longer be a problem for your family," Ali Fuat added.

"But how can that be?"

"If you want to stay in Istanbul, get an education, have a worthy future, and if you want to please Mother and Father, you must do as we say," Sabri insisted. "You've thus far given us lots of stress and embarrassment with your willfulness." As they discussed the situation further, their reasoning overwhelmed Adalet. As for Burhan, yes, it was true that she was attached to him in a most curious way; but she should be free to choose her own life. All of her family, who, after all had her best interest at heart, who loved her, all could not be wrong. She should not let romantic feelings rule her. She was, after all, only sixteen. Burhan had shown no concern for her education. He only listened to himself, and the future of which he spoke was his. Perhaps, she had no choice. As for her next step, Fate would lead. Their ideas sounded right but they felt wrong – and hurried.

"I must obey my family," she agreed finally. But of course none of the plan had turned out the way they expected. So much is always made vaguely possible by the dream of Istanbul, so many dreams and plans launched from the Bosphorus shores. But, to be carried out, of course, all must be cast under the smiling eyes of fate.

In Gebze, young wife Adalet would often muse on the past few years and often recall Nefise's voice as she asked if Adalet remembered the first time they had come to Istanbul during the Balkan Wars. An unreal time, to be sure. Their life went along in relative ease in Emin Aga's friends' palace on the edge of the Golden Horn, while back home in Thrace, devastation ruled. But regardless, life did continue. In the midst of all the sorrow, Mother Zehra had not missed the opportunity to find a suitable match for Nefise.

The Balkan Wars

Living in the Palace with Poplar Tree Leaves that Shine like Mirrors – the Aynalikavak Palace

Everyone turned as Sukru shouted toward the familiar thunder of the war guns and cannons coming from Catalca, some twenty miles to the west. Sometimes, the ground and windows would vibrate from the stormy booms and clacks sounding from there.

"Let's leave Aynalikavak Palace to the men today, and not discuss the war in the Balkans, the refugees or things like cholera," Nuran, wife of General Husamettin announced at breakfast.

The family's friends had taken Mother Zehra, Nefise, Adalet, Sukru and the maid Hanife into their villa, which lay above the Golden Horn, amidst groves and gardens on a sloping hillside half a mile or so above the Galata Bridge. Husamettin's servants had come seeking them out in Sultanahmet Mosque after Zehra's messenger had managed a contact, following their flight from Bedre when the war broke out. General Husamettin was a special friend of Emin Aga.

The five refugees were given their own suite with a parlor and private entrance up the winding stairs in the back. General Husamettin had also found another place for their relatives who had come in on the train with them.

For three days at the compound in Sultanahmet Mosque, the five had been stranded like the rest of the mass and the many sick and dying from Thrace. Refugees piled onto the barren floor around the massive pillars of the great hall. All of the carpets had been taken away and the family slept on their cloaks. For Adalet and Sukru it was like camping out, such as they had done on Grandfather Emin Aga's farm in the summertime, only Father was not there with them to tell stories. Father and Emin Aga had stayed home to protect the manor.

Father Ahmet had gotten word to Mother Zehra. Grandfather and his life had been spared. She was told little more. There were disastrous reports one after another. General Husamettin, one of Sultan Reshad's military commanders, was an official of the Red Crescent, who took care of the sick and wounded. Each day, representatives or military men came to the villa to talk about how to care for the thousands of immigrants who poured into the city. Hundreds were in need of food and shelter. Even the deposed Sultan Abdulhamid had been brought back to Istanbul from his exile when the Greeks took Salonika. The hapless sultan, who had been at one time supreme for over thirty years, was to remain until his death locked in the Beylerbeyi Palace on the Asian shore. In the halls of the small wooden Aynalikavak Palace, it would have been easy to forget the refugees who were suffering in the nooks and crannies of Istanbul, had General Husamettin not been involved with their care. All of the side streets were crowded with their wagons and carts. Each day, when Hanifey took Sukru and Adalet to school in the section of Taxim, they would walk by the ones camped along the walls near roads and alleyways. Ragged soldiers, bloody bandages and amputated bodies were common sights. The Aya Sofia had been turned into a hospital. The enormous rooms of that great Byzantine church turned mosque teemed with dysentery and cholera. Zehra repeatedly said, "Every late afternoon, I can smell death in the air."

Nuran's announcement of their first excursion across the Bosphorus served to be a distraction for Zehra; but ever since last month when the family arrived at Sirkeci Train Station, getting onto that strait had been Adalet's unspoken desire.

•　　　•　　　•

The weather was balmy under the waxen blue November sky. White headscarves fell around necks and under chins. Nuran's servants brought the party on her private boat down the Golden Horn to the Galata Bridge. There, the five females in bright long cloaks, wide-eyed brother Sukru and one of Nuran's uncles prepared to climb aboard a ferryboat larger than a house.

At the ticket booth, a beggar in brown rags leaned on a stick she had shoved up under an arm like a crutch. Behind leathery cheeks and pleading eyes, the haggard woman drooped, her tattered black hair loosely bound with a faded purple cloth. Adalet couldn't tell what age she might be. The woman held out her brown palm, her eyes lowered. A dirty little boy clung to her rose-flowered garb. Uncle reached out as they passed and put a coin in her hand.

They waited with the crowd behind an iron gate inside the sea station. Adalet craned through elbows to see the broad white side nudge against the wharf. The boat was two stories high. There were wide wooden pews in the open air on the end of the second deck.

Adalet turned around, her eyes darting back toward the beggar. The woman raised her head, caught Adalet's eyes and held them for seconds. They lived in different worlds. Adalet smiled, the woman turned.

Nuran had her arm on Zehra, patting her gently. Zehra, hearing the distant explosions coming from Catalca, repeated, "Allah alone knows," and laid her gloved hand on Nuran's. "May Allah keep my men safe," she whispered. If those guns move east, Adalet thought, we will all share the same fate.

"Don't fret, Zehra," Nuran said quietly, stepping around to place both gloved hands on her. "Be praised to Allah that Emin Aga and Ahmet have not been killed by the enemies." Ahmet could speak Bulgarian. They kept him as a translator.

"Come, come now, we will miss the boat," Hanifey called, rushing back with two bags of roasted chestnuts. The iron gate opened and they made ready to escape the threat of beggars' eyes and enemies' guns for a while.

"Look at her, she is the finest passenger ferry in the world," Nuran said. The huge black and white paddle steamer jostled against the wharf. The stream of banners off its flagstaff whipped in the wind. Puffs of black smoke poured from the barreled chimney.

"It is German built, the Galata Bridge Haydarpasha Line," Uncle added. The name, "Halep" – Aleppo, was painted in big black letters across the side. They climbed the wooden stairs up to the second floor and found seats on the open deck. Foaming waters churned behind. Zehra's laments drowned in the croupy boat horns. Muffled voices floated up and around, so many different dialects that Adalet had never before heard.

"At the World's Center," Adalet said to Nefise as she offered over the warm and sweet-smelling bag of chestnuts. Nefise munched like a lady, holding the soft delicacy in her handkerchief with her gloved hand. With three fingers, Adalet pushed one between her lips and rolled the ball of it around on her tongue and then squashed it between her teeth.

"Adalet, don't be so greedy," Nefise said, handing her sister a handkerchief from the pouch she had tied onto her waist. Nuran bought glasses of tea from the waiter who balanced a tray of tumblers above his head. They sipped, gliding a buoyant avenue crowded with warships, embassy crafts, steamers, fishermen's rigs and rowboats. The bulky "Halep" veered past Karakoy and careened across the strait.

"We are going to Uskudar, to a wharf on another continent," Uncle shouted. "It connects with lands that reach Russia and the Central Asian Steppes." Nefise and Adalet widened their eyes and raised brows to show appreciation. "The steppes from where the Turks originated before they followed the gray wolf to Anadolu," he added. The plains of Asia stretched to the China Sea. Adalet imagined herself setting out in a few years on a pilgrimage. Were she a male, she could go alone like the blacksmith, Mehmet Nuri.

From the water, the skyline of the city looked clean and quiet, no garbage in the streets, no beggars or orphans. Adalet tried to count the tops of the rounded domes of the enormous Topkapi Palace on the hill of the point that pushed out toward the mouth of the Sea of Marmara. She had overheard it said that in olden times sultans behind those castle walls would at night conveniently rid themselves of disfavored concubines, or of wives with sons. The sultan's servants bound and gagged and stuffed them into canvas bags –a female's kismet– or unlucky Fate of having mothered a potential "Sun of the Earth." Sultans feared rivals to the sacred throne. It confused Adalet how a sultan-caliph, who was Allah's representative on earth and the highest seat in their Muslim world, could practice such evil. The pristine turquoise quietly covered all trace of those deeds.

Minarets projected from the ridges and shorelines like uplifted fingers of hands. "Look Adalet," Nefise said. She pointed to the hillside behind Topkapi Palace. "I pick out Sultanahmet Mosque easily."

"It is the only one with six minarets," Adalet answered, proud to show Sister what she knew. On the other side of the Golden Horn above the red tiled roofs, they could see the Galata Genovese Tower. At the edge of the strait, behind the tall iron fence, the white stone Dolmabahce Palace, the modern palace, stretched rigid and sure at Beshiktash on the European shore.

The ferryboat sidled up against the landing. Men wrapped thick ropes around the anvils and secured the massive vessel. They left the deck and filed down the steps with a crowd of others.

And then, all too quickly, Adalet stepped over the planks into Asia. Although she had the strange wafting sensation from the travel on the waves, she was interested to see that the ground beneath her feet did not feel any different than it did in Europe.

A Royal Prince, Alas Bedre

Istanbul, 1913

To have education and a bit of money in this world was an important thing.

One afternoon in the middle of the winter, Nefise and Adalet learned that the adults had agreed through mutual family friends that a young lieutenant prince named Tevfik should be allowed a visit to Aynalikavak Palace. He was scheduled to come for tea with Zehra and Nuran. Prince Tevfik was a nephew of the chief public official of the province of Kirkkilise, and a friend of Emin Aga, Zehra and Ahmet.

"No, Adalet, you may not join us," Zehra scolded. "This is a most important occasion. Lieutenant Tevfik is an Ottoman prince."

"If I am to serve the tea instead of the maid," Nefise said, "then Lieutenant Prince Tevfik is coming to assess me!"

"Of course!" Mother answered, "Last summer the prince noticed you when he visited his uncle in Kirkkilise and they came to Bedre. Surely you were aware of him as well?"

"From a distance, as I passed to and from the parlor. But, why should a prince be interested in me?"

"My eldest daughter is a treasure! Our family is much respected, and Nuran foresees an engagement."

"Marriage! I'm only fourteen and a half!"

"Engagement is the important thing, girl. You'll be at almost sixteen by the time of the marriage."

"But what if I do not like him? I don't know anything about strange men."

"What's there to know? He's handsome enough, a family of notable standing. Allah knows! Don't be daft, Girl – a prince wants your hand! Just make sure that you don't slop the tea on him and ruin your fortunes."

On the appointed day, Adalet stood sentinel at an upstairs window, yelling down the staircase when Tevfik's carriage approached the gates. When he stepped from the coach, she found him to be short, although he was dashing in his white jacket with its row of brass buttons. The stiff collar at his neck seemed to hold his head in place. Did he have a short neck as well? At least there was a strong, pointed chin beneath the twin crescents of his mustache. His curly black hair was trimmed neatly over his ears and crowned by a maroon fez with dancing tassel.

Adalet ran back to the circular banister above the stairwell. "He is bringing yellow roses tied with a big yellow bow!"

"Hush, Girl," Zehra snorted. "He'll think we have peasants in here!"

When they were seated in the parlor, Sukru and Adalet crept down the carpeted stairs and spied through the doors of the foyer, which had not been completely shut. Nefise wove delicately from the sideboard to the table in front of the divan and chairs. Like a royal butterfly, she hovered over the teapot and cups – for the tea was being served European style. Prince Tevfik smiled and nodded, while Nefise pretended to be unaware. The other two behaved as if all was normal, as if Nefise's entire future was not on trial. Adalet was glad it was not her hand that was extending the saucer and teacup over to one who had come to make a judgment of her worthiness. Definitely, she would slosh the tea under such pressure. Adalet listened closely to the tone in his voice as he answered questions and talked about the war. He was not the only one making a judgment in this hour. If his voice betrayed him to be a snake under a rock, she was prepared to get a letter off to Father Ahmet asking him to stop Mother's actions on this business at once. If necessary, she would contact Grandfather. An Aga would have the final say, even with a war going on.

The lieutenant sounded sincere. And he had a very sympathetic face. "Yes, I remember well your grand house in Bedre," he was saying. He paused and took a sip from the cup and set it down in the saucer on the table without even making a clink. He laid both of his hands on his white gloves, which he had earlier removed and placed on his black trousers just above his knee. He cleared his throat and looked at Zehra, who had asked a question of him.

"Lady Zehra, the news is that your house has been occupied by the Bulgarian forces." Zehra's cup jiggled in her hand, and the light that touched her ring sent sparks into the air. Her shoulders moved a bit but she didn't say a word. Sukru turned to Adalet with an open mouth. She brought a finger to her lips so that he would not betray their spying. "They use it as their hospital," the prince continued. "We must be grateful at that – that is, that Emin Aga and the Master Ahmet are allowed to remain on the grounds unharmed."

"How do these foreigners, these unbelievers, use our gentle friends?" Nuran asked.

"In truth," he said softly, "I imagine Emin Aga and Ahmet are little more than intelligent and useful servants." Father and Grandfather servants? Sukru and Adalet looked into each other's wide eyes. Father and Grandfather had never served anything but Allah and Mother Zehra in their lives. As serious and sad as it was, the thought made Adalet grin. Father was smart enough to act like he was serving the enemy while taking care of his own people. The girl had every faith that her father would manage well. However, she could not picture her bed with a dying soldier in it. With all of that rain, her linen sheets would be ruined. Soldiers would not remove their boots. They would vomit and bleed and stink.

"How could our territory be taken so quickly?" Nuran asked. Her voice was full of sorrow. "Is our military so weak?" She began to cry a little, dabbing her eyes with the lace napkin.

"The land has been lost by leaders. Not by soldiers," the lieutenant said. "Those who rule the Committee for Union and Progress control the Congress. They waste energies fighting each other for power. Our armies were not prepared."

"My husband complains of disorganization, lack of funds, lack of arms," Nuran said. "The devil will take the spoils."

"Unfortunately, these are desperate times," Lieutenant Tevfik answered.

Nefise sat down delicately. Sukru poked Adalet with his elbow when the prince smiled in Sister's direction, tweaking the pointed end of one side of his mustache and raising his little finger into the air. "Let me tell you this story," he said, glancing at each of them before he began. "Near the village of Bedre, a commander gave orders one night to begin fighting and his battalion searched for the enemy. It was cold, muddy, raining. When they came upon another battalion, they began fighting. The losing unit panicked and ran until they reached the village, yelling that the enemy was coming; but the villagers couldn't see any enemies. They awoke the corps commander of the area. When he saw the deserting soldiers, he drew his sword; but he could not stop them. It was later realized that the misguided units that had fought in the rain during the night were two of our own battalions. By the next morning, the Bulgars really did come; and there were no Ottoman troops in sight to defend the villagers; and, their homes were ravaged."

The four sat in silence – except for the women's sniffing. Adalet felt a tear. Sukru bowed his head. They knew all of those villagers. The girl brought her hand to her lips and bit on her finger. Had her friend Zeyneb escaped? Did she hide in the orchard? The tale was like a terrible lie, especially since what had been done was done and there was nothing to change it. Fate had protected her family. Adalet placed an arm around Sukru and brought his yellow head to her breast. Her back ached from where she had stood for so long, bending in order to peer through the crack; but they dared not move.

Under the flickering candles of the crystal chandelier, the gold-framed mirror on the far wall held the tea-drinkers like a painting until the lieutenant turned toward Nefise. Her wet cheeks blushed. She lowered her brown curls on which she wore no scarf to shade her trim profile, and it shadowed against the round globe of the oil lamp on the table next to her. The globe had a hand-painted branch with pink buds that matched the rose velvet draperies. A blue bird with pink breast and outstretched wings waited on the branch. The lamp's light flickered onto the bird. Adalet thought to take that flickering for an omen that things would get better. She had the urge to rush in and tell the family so, but her spying would be found out and she would be in disgrace. Perhaps Father and Grandfather would escape their captors and fly away. She remembered that there had been gold-enough to build a new house sewn into the middle of her parents' thick mattress. And the gold was now safe from the invaders, for she had overheard Mother speak of it to Nefise: "The significant stuffing between your parents' mattress was secured beneath the stables' dung and straw before we left the manor."

In the "Palace of Poplar Leaves that Shine like Mirrors," Adalet would awaken each morning throughout the winter to catch the glint of new light on the evil eye charm from friend Zeyneb. She had pinned it onto the drapery for good luck. She had brought little else from Bedre. However, Istanbul's winter was over and spring was almost at an end when the fighting stopped.

"Students, in the past eight months, the brave Ottoman forces have held the defense line at Catalca," the school's headmaster said. "Now we are into May, and you should know that there is an armistice in London; but we have suffered great loss." General Husamettin had at home in the palace already informed the family about the cease-fire. Of the losses, Adalet knew firsthand of the hundreds of thousands of refugees that had poured into Istanbul, and that thousands had gone on to Anatolia because they had nothing left in Thrace. "The loss of lives of both civilians and soldiers cannot be measured," Husamettin had said. The empire had lost Albania, Macedonia, Edirne and most of Thrace. Adalet sat listening in silence with the rest of the elementary schoolgirls of her class as the headmaster's voice hammered on. He spoke about atrocities and heroism.

When he had burst into the classroom, Adalet was sitting at the long table lost in her history book, reading about the tenth Ottoman Sultan, Suleyman the Magnificent, who lived in the sixteenth century and reigned for forty-six years, doubling the territories of the Ottoman Empire – expanding from Tabriz to Vienna. Of the six hundred years of the empire, Suleyman's were the most splendid. All of that glory now lay buried under a heap of pain and humiliation. It seemed that the present Sultan Reshad was weak. The adults often discussed the constant intervention by foreign powers into the empire's affairs. They said that the committee, the CUP, running the government had difficulty in making and sticking to decisions. These dark thoughts overwhelmed her; so, she absorbed all she could of her situation in Stamboul. Not only could she do nothing about the horrors of a war with losses as immense as a fantasy, but also she could not begin to comprehend the numbers.

The tassel on the headmaster's black and crimson fez swung like a pendulum. When he finished, he nodded toward Missus

Dilek, the teacher, who bowed her head to him in respect and he turned and swept out of the classroom. Stiffly, Missus Dilek walked to the front of her desk and stood facing the class. In her long black dress and scarf, teacher reminded Adalet of a Christian priest. Adalet hoped teacher would not scold them for some disrespect or inattention to the headmaster. Teacher pressed her thin lips together and turned her head only slightly as she inspected each in the class singly. Adalet did not dare try to see if their five rows looked neat, that all hands were folded onto the tables; but when Teacher tilted her head a bit and relaxed her lips, the girl knew they had satisfied her.

Missus Dilek put the class to work with slate boards and chalk markers in arithmetic – not Adalet's best subject. The girl thought it hard to make stories of numbers that had to equal definite answers. "Soon, this fifth year of school will pass into summer," she said to herself as she bent into it.

Few would have figured that the armistice would explode into a second Balkan War within a few weeks time – when the victorious infidels would begin fighting among themselves about who would get the most territory. Stranger yet, that by the end of the summer, Ottoman forces would have joined the Greeks, Montenegrins and Serbians to defeat the Bulgarians. Edirne, Kirkkilise and much of Thrace became Ottoman again.

Adalet and her family would spend a lovely summer in the palace and Imperial Park above the Golden Horn. Never did they miss an opportunity to be on the Bosphorus. There were always games and music and visitors at home. Sometimes, secretly, Sukru and Adalet would spy from the shuttered balconies of the palace onto the rowdy servants kissing in the rose garden. In the dark of the night, Adalet would peep at the old man who would come out onto his stoop at the servants' quarters on the narrow cobbled alley at the back of the villa to play his wooden flute. It had a nasal tone full of regrets. She loved to give herself into the sadness, something more complicated than she could explain. She mused on Gypsies rolling to far lands on many wheels.

On the streets in the section of Beshiktash, Adalet would see that camels make good substitutes when there were not enough horses for the cavalry. In Taksim, she would ride in a new invention called an "elevator," which could magically transport people to the top floors of the building. She would be taken to a lunch of little freshly-caught fish and sit among Europeans in Pera in the famous Flower Passage with its clock carved right into the middle of the marble arch of the entranceway.

After the Balkan Wars, neither Emin Aga nor Ahmet would ever again come to Istanbul to represent the serfs of Bedre. There being no serfs. There being no Bedre. That summer while his family dreamed out the palace windows, Emin Aga was just beginning his dying of a broken heart.

Albania and Macedonia would be lost to the Empire. Although Edirne would be regained, most of Thrace would be scourged with disease and blood, with tens of thousands dead. Many more would become refugees maimed and wounded in every way imaginable. Beneath the fallen leaves of the forests, and in the deserted villages, corpses would lie rotting with no one to bury them. The Ergene River and Devil's Creek would cough up swollen boots and tattered jackets bearing Ottoman and Bulgarian insignias alike.

In their June retreat from flattened Bedre, the Bulgars would take the time to loot Ahmet's cows, Adalet's ivory hairbrush and mirror, her lute, the brass door knocks and the glass from the windowpanes. The sheep, they had already eaten. The grandest house in Bedre, of no further use to them as a hospital, they would burn to the ground. Long since had they torched the peasants' bungalows, but they would not have time to destroy the caretaker's cottage where their commander had housed himself throughout their occupation. Father and Grandfather would not be killed because Ahmet had been a translator for the commander, who was from Shumnu, Bulgaria where Ahmet had grown up.

When the Bulgars left, Father and Grandfather would take shelter in the cottage. Blackened chars would fall in a heap where stallions had once been stalled. Then, when he was sure the Bulgars were truly gone for good, only the face on the moon would see him slip out to dig for treasure below the ashes in the barn.

A few days after that, Ahmet would look up from his workbench to see the groom, Hassan, walking up the slope from the road to Kirkkilise. As a soldier, Hassan would have acquired a limp and a scar on his cheek that healed to look like a curved swollen earthworm stretched from his ear to his lip. His daughter Zeyneb would come back down from the hills where it was said she and her little brother lived like vagrants in the forest. No one would ever know what else Zeyneb had to give away for her protection, but Adalet later suspected that she had to give up the gold locket. Of course, Adalet would never ask Zeyneb anything about that year.

One morning in Istanbul when the rains of October blew in from the Black Sea, Zehra called Sukru, Nefise and Adalet from the bedrooms out into the parlor of the suite. Zehra was perched on the lemon and fuchsia-striped divan with satin pillows at her back. Sukru went to her feet and sat with his knees pulled up to his chest. "Come girls, sit with your brother," Zehra told them.

With her feet on the low stool that matched the divan, Zehra looked commanding in her Bosphorus-blue cotton caftan. Her hands were clasped at her chin. Her sleeves fell in a triangle at the cave of her breasts. Her wide moon-mystery eyes revealed that she had recently come from a trance.

Nefise and Adalet scooted to her like barn kittens, apprehensive at what she may have seen. Hearing of horrors had become a daily encounter. Mother Zehra opened her hands and lifted them above the three, keeping them fixed to her as she held her breath. Then, she exhaled with a gust, smacked her hands together and laughed. "Ha!" The three seated at her feet darted glances at each other but did not move back.

She tucked her hands together again and spoke in her husky voice. "I had been sitting to take in the fragrance of the dawn," she said. "A blue space moved about me. In a circle." Zehra raised her hand. The long sleeves sailed above the three heads. "Wrapped like arms around me. Comforting," she said, bringing her hands back to opposite shoulders. "Then, it opened my sight so that I looked down from the sky." She lifted her palms toward the ceiling where she gazed. Nefise and Adalet pulled back into each other. Sukru hugged his knees tighter and looked at his toes. Zehra took another breath, quietly this time; and then, she whispered. "I looked down. What did I see? – My darling husband and your Father Ahmet surrounded in black."

The three gasped at the same time. Was their father was in a coffin? In a well?

"Ha!" Zehra said, opening her arms again. Her mouth was a red cave. "Not a bad thing," she said, realizing the extent of their fright. "The black thing he was in – it was the train from Thrace to Stamboul!" Adalet sat forward touching the hem of her caftan. When Mother Zehra spoke again, she clapped in unison with Nefise and Sukru jumping and shouting.

"Father is coming to get us and take us home to Kirkkilise!"

"We must get dressed right away," Nefise said, with sparkles in her voice that had almost vanished. She pulled the red tassel that called for Hanifey. With her help, they would make ready.

"Hanifey must inquire about the arrival of the train," Zehra said. "Then, my beautiful girls – she will accompany you to Sirkeci Train Station – where your father will most surely step forth. Sukru will attend to me as we wait."

Soon, Nefise, Adalet and Hanifey were riding in a carriage with their father, Ahmet. When they began to call him a war hero – because after all he had managed to survive the two wars, he held up his hand for quiet.

He spoke softly, "The fires were squelched with the blood and tears of heroes now dead to our world."

Neither Nefise nor Adalet ever again troubled their father's mind with talk of that past year and a half.

SEVEN

The Hero

Often, he would talk as if he were giving a lecture.

The cold February evening gathered around the house in Gebze. Adalet cooked, adding a dollop of butter and some salt and pepper to the turnips cubed with onions and minced lamb in the tin pan's water. Taking the iron handle, she lifted the lid and poked at the fire, then replaced it and watched the pan until she heard the spit and sizzle on its bottom. From a wooded bowl on top of the hutch, she took carrots and began to scrape them for a salad with lemon juice and raisins. There was no way to know when Burhan would return; but she preferred to have food prepared for his coming.

In the months they had lived here, Adalet had little opportunity to make friends. Loneliness was a new experience. Burhan could block her presence with a sullen mood. His work as local governor would usually keep him out all afternoon; and often, he would go to the coffeehouse and talk politics with the men until around nine o'clock in the evening. Sometimes, later than that.

When he came home this day at noon, he ate the brown beans and rice with the bread from last night. Adalet sat with him at the wooden table in the main room and listened to the news that he brought. As he spoke in between bites, he furled his brow and eyed her sincerely. Her husband was a gifted speaker who could have been equally successful as a province chief, politician or carpet dealer. A reply to his talking was hardly required of her. Sometimes she wished that Burhan would ask her opinions more often, for she studied events as they happened and developed her own conclusions. However, she had learned to listen.

"The situation of what might be left of the sultan's government sits on the edge of disaster," he told her. "Listen to what I say: the sultan might be hoping that the Resistance –it's on everybody's lips– somehow will save the country."

"If Sultan has no courage, the people will show him how," she answered. "Our country's going through terrible times."

"Izmir! Terrible, yes!" He sighed, and then spoke softly again. "The virgins spoiled. Houses, property taken."

"Our people there have run into the hills this winter –Allah give them shelter," she added. Her habit was to glean every newspaper or report that Burhan left in the house, as well as any news she might pick up from the shops. The six months that she had stayed on in Istanbul before joining Burhan in Gebze had been a time when she learned to read the news and think for herself.

Burhan pushed back his chair and began pacing the room. She watched him go deeply into his mind. Finally, he regarded her, giving emphasis to his words with his fisted hand. "The moment is now, Adalet. You and I will join the Nationalists' Movement! We've got to get ideas of submission or American mandate off our heads – for this soil! And our future children!"

Adalet had been thinking just that. Burhan was as quick as a fox, as blacksmith Mehmet Nuri liked to say. "And for our children's children," she added.

Burhan went to the window and looked out at the mid-day gray. "Until these last few months," he said, speaking to the window, "we have not known how we can do it – only that with our life we have believed we could." She did not move until he came back and approached her. Then, he sat and leaned across the table. She could smell the sweet sweat of his neck.

"Adalet, listen. I am not foolish." She took his hand. "There is more talk lately of the leadership of General Mustafa Kemal,"

Burhan continued. "He inspires the Movement. He's in league with the loyal Nationalists Generals Kazim Karabekir, Rauf Bey and Ali – "

"Even Halide Edib has joined them," she said, interrupting. She felt such excitement. Something was going to happen besides the waiting. She knew it.

"And many others who can lead," he said. "They have already gathered forces in the plains around Erzurum, Sivas, and they're moving toward the center to Ankara."

"There are societies for the defense – " she added.

"We will resist!" Burhan said firmly, but not so loudly that it could be heard outside. There were so many spies. "The government in Istanbul calls Mustafa Kemal a rebel," Burhan said, taking her hand in his. "But we will call him Pasha, our own hero. Why should we wait to be crushed to bits?" Burhan stood, beginning to pace back and forth in thought. "Never!" he whispered, pounding his fist into his hand again.

And so, at least our course of action is decided, Adalet thought.

"Be careful, don't dare speak of this to anyone," Burhan said, turning and bending down to her. "Fuat says the Stamboul Central Government is furious. Being known as Nationalists could be dangerous."

She knew better than to tell it. Mustafa Kemal may well become an elected president of a National Grand Assembly. But that was over in Ankara in the middle of Anatolia. Istanbul was another matter. There was a price on the Pasha's head. And a lot of the people were simply waiting to see what the sultan would do.

Adalet took a rag and wiped her eyes and then pulled her stew away from the heated part of the stove's top. Such times. Grandfather Emin Aga had been laid in the ground to rest forever. And, last year, her mother and father to save their lives from invading Greek troops had again fled to Stamboul. Allah bless, Kirkkilise had survived a series of wars and occupations ever since 1878.

Her supper was ready. She stood in the quiet, feeling the stillness that comes just before dawn or dusk. Perhaps Burhan would be early. Perhaps he would bring fresh bread and some aged cheese. They would have a nice meal tonight. Adalet had also made a pot of yogurt from goat's milk. She glanced up through the window past the garden gate at the back of the house and caught her hands to her chest. A male in a white outfit had just vaulted over the garden fence! He was bounding toward the door. A bandit?

"What should I do?" she repeated aloud, her voice raking the walls of the kitchen. She picked up the paring knife and stepped back from the hutch, poised, knife clutched and ready. She would stab him – or herself. By all means she must do it quickly and certain. It was an honor to kill an enemy. An honor as well for a woman to kill herself rather than be shamed.

The bandit landed with a hard thump against the kitchen door and began pounding! She squeezed the trembling knife in one hand and took up a small bowl of ground red pepper with the other. If he broke through the door, she would blind him with the pepper, and then plunge the knife into his bowels and escape. She listened, and then – stepped back, shocked.

"Adalet, for the sake of Allah, let me in!" She waited several seconds, listening to the ragged voice.

"Burhan?"

"Yes, Woman, open the damned door!"

She crept to the door with the knife and pepper still held ready. "Burhan?" she asked again. It could be a trick.

"Wearisome wife, I order you to open!" It was he.

She laid down her weapons and pulled the bolt. Burhan lunged into the room and landed on the floor. Leaning back, she eyed him suspiciously. He caught his breath in gasps, grimacing up at her. She shut the door and let her weight fall against it. He remained hunched against his bottom with his knees bent and his legs spread brazenly.

"You are looking at a successful venture. Bring me my raki, if you will," he said catching his breath. Venture? He was stripped to his underwear with his bony feet sticking out of the legs of it. The wad of his private parts underneath presented itself excessively. His breath calmed down and his face took on a smug look of pride.

"You doubt do you?" he asked, sitting forward and slicking back his hair. "Wife of mine – the man you regard with such a wary eye has just barely managed to escape the gang aroused by none other than a dangerous ruffian. And, I have accomplished the escape by the wit of my mind."

He was either crazy, trying to make up a story for his bizarre behavior and attire, or he was telling the truth. In either case, he did need his raki. As Adalet went toward the shelf to get it, she heard him lug his body to a chair at the table and fall into it. She poured his drink into one glass and sloshed water into a second.

When she plopped the tumblers on the table in front of him, he mixed the liquor and water. Together, they turned milky; but raki was not in any way like milk – by taste or effect. This anisette liquor made men sing, then curse.

He gulped it half down and then blurted out his tale. "I have been tracking this gang for days." She quietly sat in the chair and leaned over toward him. "I have looked everywhere; but they hide well," he continued. Burhan was relishing his dragging out this tale, widening his hazel eyes and pausing to pull the mane of brown hair back from his forehead. "All this time I have been too smart to let anyone suspect that I know they're somewhere about here. Can't trust whether anyone is friend or foe these days."

He swallowed the rest of his drink in a gulp and wiped his mouth on the sleeve of his underwear. The thin woolen garment was dirty. He must have splashed through mud. She noted that the underwear didn't look as white sprawled on the kitchen chair as it had appeared through the window. Some scrubbing with lye would be called for.

"What are you gawking at? Wife, I am trying to instruct you out of your ignorance! What do you think I do all day? Assistant governor is a serious job! Citizens would be in a shabby shape without those of us who keep a sharp mind."

As he made such a strong protest, for only the barest second or two, she got a clear picture. But, it was a shameful image from some old village fable she had heard. What flashed through her mind bore the result of a man caught in the wrong bed when a husband came home unexpectedly. The man was diving out of a window in his underwear. Adalet dutifully rebuked herself. How could she have allowed such a suspicious and impure thought? To hide her fluster, she reached around and pulled the shawl from the chair behind her. "I'm sorry, Burhan. Here, put this over yourself. Are you hurt?"

"Will you not listen?" he said, craning forward and slurring his speech a bit. She wondered if he had been drinking before he came to the door. He said he'd been working. "Do you not want to hear how an hour ago your husband followed what could be none other than the infamous Anzavur's gang, that butchers our people in the dark?"

"Burhan! You could have been killed!"

"Exactly! But I was more resourceful than any member of those cutthroats! I came in through an attic of a storehouse where I saw them go –"

"I thought that wily Circassian worked for our sultan," she said.

"You thought so. Oh yes, they destroy in the name of sultan and empire, but they are wanted criminals who hate Nationalists."

"They are brutal and clever –"

"No, they are not clever. Today, I survived by my wits. And so –I stripped off my clothes down to this– and well," He rubbed his hands down his broad torso and held them out and laughed. Adalet looked confused. "So that I would be able to climb out the window onto the roof!" he explained. "From there, I let myself fall into a wagon of hay."

"Why half-nude?" she asked.

"Well, it's obvious. To escape the building without them seeing my dress clothes – which would have shown them that I am someone important! You see, I had been spying on their talking. Who would bother about a poor man in his underclothes? Any day now, I'll get some men together with me and ambush them in the middle of their nest."

"Burhan!" Now, she was more concerned than ever; but still perplexed. Why didn't he just stay hidden up there until they left? Wouldn't a half-nude man draw more attention than a man in dress clothes?

"A woman can't understand a man's war," he said. "More raki. And food. I need strength. Tomorrow, I'll begin to gather more national guard to help me." Well, at least she was glad that an assistant governor had access to the local police guard unit. "Adalet, your husband will become a bit famous in this war to keep the soil under our feet as our own!" He reached out and pulled her onto his lap.

She laid her hand to his cheek and her head on his shoulder. She was so relieved not to have to kill anyone. He rocked her gently for a moment and then pushed her up, giving the back of her skirt a grasp as she started off to fetch his meal.

Adalet turned back over her shoulder, looking at her man. He did love her. "I hope someone doesn't steal your pretty clothes back there in the meantime!" she said, laughing as she shoved another log into the stove's belly. She stepped back from the orange fizz and pop of the aroused embers.

Governor Burhan and Adalet stayed only four more months in Gebze. And, true to his word, Burhan did make himself a small celebrity when he took men to the house where bandits had been gathering. When Burhan and his deputies knocked at that house, an old woman received them, saying that there was no one else there with her. But Burhan heard a noise under the carpet. After yanking it back, he discovered a trap door. Brandishing his pistol, he quietly opened the hatch. "My men and I leveled our guns on ten very surprised ruffians, all seated around a table gambling as if they were safe rabbits in a hole," Burhan told the men at the baker's shop. Burhan's captured renegades turned out to be local Greeks, and not the infamous Circassian, Anzavur. Still, the arrest raised Burhan's rank from assistant to that of a first-degree governor.

• • •

For the next three months, Adalet and Burhan continued their concealed life as best they could, isolated from family and too suspicious of political and secret alliances to trust making friends. Adalet made her daily trek to the village fountain for water and another to the community's clay oven to bake her bread. There, she heard stories coming from various parts of the country. Burhan brought new ideas and news every day. Adalet wearied of waiting for something to happen. It was as if she walked a dark tunnel day and night alert for the sight of any dull light ahead to signal that her direction was right if she just kept going forward. Neither of them slept well at night for there was no peace to settle down into. Burhan often drank ra-ki until he would fall asleep where he sat and not even come to bed. They shared daily life more like brother and sister than man and wife. Stress cut their passion sure as a knife separates a loaf of bread.

It was too dangerous for Adalet to even think of going from Gebze to visit her family in Istanbul. *She had managed to spend one afternoon with Nefise before she and Burhan had left Istanbul to come to Gebze. Strolling by the Bosphorus together, first they heard its horn blare. It came down from the Black Sea with its Union Jack flying high. It eased around the point of Tarabya, huge and slow as it tore apart the turquoise waters. As it passed, a shadow invaded the sisters' peace. In stillness, for what seemed a long while after it had gone, they sat listening to the hard slap of the waves against the European shore, not hearing the waves hit Anatolia, but knowing they did. They both thought the same thing: Now, it was the outsiders who owned the Center of the World.*

And now, there were so many hoodlum factions around – besides the various soldiers from other countries. The British had raided the Istanbul Parliament, arrested the deputies and imprisoned them on the island of Malta with no explanation. The world was gone to hanging upside-down, for the British had hauled their warships up the Marmara into the strait of Istanbul and let loose militia who ran in the streets. They broke down doors, shot Ottoman soldiers in their beds and dug in the sacred tombs looking for hidden guns. It could certainly be said that for the past few years, the whole world had been insane. Uprisings, insurgencies, invasions. At least the Bolshevik's Revolution brought an end to the Russian-Armenian pact to overrun eastern Anatolia. But now, the fear loomed everywhere since the occupation of Izmir that Greeks would move to the Marmara coast, cross the water and go inland to overtake Thrace. Here it was May with another summer at the brink and the war with the Greek invasion raging western Anatolia – another wildfire catching up and destroying everywhere all at once. She would stand motionless sometimes and just stare through her windows onto the patchy-green yard for a sign. She'd wonder if Nefise watched the British warships on the Bosphorus from behind her shutters in Bebek and Ortakoy. It was said that the barrels on the guns of their vessels were capable of exploding the side of a house.

With each dawn recently Adalet felt a need that had grown urgent like a festering boil ready to burst. Burhan and she had to get out of their situation. Sooner or later, one of the warring factions would seek them out and cut their throats. She let Burhan have his dinner before she faced him with what she had pondered all day long. "Burhan, we can't stay in Gebze. We're only fifty kilometers from Stamboul."

From across the table, Burhan startled up from his plate and held his eyes on hers. "Yes," he answered in a steady voice, "Strange that you would say that because I was going to discuss the matter with you this evening." Adalet moved her plate aside and let her weight drop toward his fixed gaze as he continued. "Cousin Fuat got word to me this afternoon by a messenger. He wants us to move to Ankara as soon as possible. He thinks it's taking too much of a chance for us to stay here any longer."

She nodded her head, glad that he was not going to protest leaving. She had been afraid that he would not want to give up his post. "Consider the more than a hundred of the Istanbul Parliament in Malta," she said, knowing that he already knew that. She wanted to emphasize their case for getting out. "The women were talking about it at the oven this morning."

"Ha," he said in his low and measured tone, "The man at the telegraph office was telling me how the gutters are full of blood in Stamboul, and the stones of the walls are pasted over with posters offering rewards for those who find a Nationalist." He sat back and fingered his mustache, adding, "Even the Red Crescent building has been raided."

"Burhan, the danger! The sick and wounded left in the hospital to die, and, oh, my family there –Allah safeguard us– we'll take the train to Ankara tomorrow!"

"No. Foreigners, spies – remember, Ottoman agents; and the British police, they watch even the ferryboats." Burhan brought his fist to his forehead and leaned his thoughts onto it. After a few seconds, he placed both hands on the table as if he were bracing himself. "We take horses around the outskirts of Izmit," he told her, "and then, we'll edge through the woods and hills to Adapazari." When she raised a brow, he explained. "Father Mehmet Nuri's first wife's family lives there." She nodded solemnly. "And then, we'll go east toward the center to the Nationalists headquarters with Mustafa Kemal Pasha. We'll go to Ankara."

"I'm a good rider," Adalet added.

Burhan considered her for another long moment. "So you are, lokumum – my own sweet," he said. His voice and eyes held the weight of tenderness. "I first knew the fates would put you in my arms on the day I saw you ride to Devil's Creek."

A warm wave rolled over her and she dropped her eyes and focused on the shoulder of bread left from their meal. Nefise's wedding seemed like a hundred years ago. Through a wet blur, she lifted her eyes that he called, "my burnt almonds" to meet his brownish-greens. Her husband did not often call her sweet names any more; but she knew that he cared for her. She wanted to move to his soft arms and bury her head in the smell of his rose-scented neck and say. "Burhan, you are my own Handsome." But they were both too heavy with the weight of what they had to do and of how they would make their escape.

At length, he spoke into the silent air of the small kitchen. "It's a shame how our marriage has been bound by so much endless conflict." She answered only with a nod. It was a thinly voiced fact, said as if he were talking about the country's common lack of sugar or grapes.

When they scooted back the wooden chairs and got up, she rather absently bothered with washing up the dishes. Whoever came to check on why Governor Burhan had not shown up at his office tomorrow would contend with their house and its meager belongings as they wished. She packed some food while he got the horses ready at the backside of the house. After that, she made personal packs for each of them for their saddlebags.

When Adalet stepped out into the glare of the early summer evening sun setting wide across the horizon, she studied a crimson ebb tide streaked with orange into which they would ride on golden flecks. A good omen. She would hold that vision in her mind to steady her against fear. So, now I become a wife of a revolution, she thought.

They rode forward, slipping into the shadows of the trees and keeping a careful avoidance of dogs and humans. Adalet did not look back at their first little house together, nor did she give any thoughts of regret for the ashes left to die in the dark.

That tide sucked the two of them into the night. She had stuck a kitchen knife in her boot. Burhan had tucked into his belt under his coat the silver revolver that had been his reward for the capture of the bandits. They left nothing behind, for what they owned fit the saddlebags. Like outlaws, they slipped slyly off the known paths, as silent as wolves in the dark on the edge of a sheep farm. They stayed on the footpaths, on alert for common hooligans and enemy soldiers – which now included the Ottoman Army. Adalet was moving on the glint of stars into the heart of Anatolia, "Anadolu – Land of Many Mothers." Swinging farther away from her mother, her family and way of life, she had no plan for what they would do other than survive.

In her earlier vision of the burning tide across the sky, Adalet remembered the old Swedish song that the revolutionary Nationalists had taken as their theme:

Friends, we will march!
Our songs will be heard on earth and sky and water.
Every place will groan under the heavy thump of our feet!

She well knew what it meant to flee from danger. This was the second time she had set out suddenly with nothing but the clothes on her back in order to save her life.

EIGHT

The Day Her World Changed

All at once, out of nowhere.

In her room on the second floor, ten-year-old Adalet watched out the window while tying a red bow to the neck of her school dress. In the distance, a storm began to spread south across the pale sky, dimming the wavering dawn like a wick turned back on an oil lamp. Heavy clouds rolled onto the northern peaks of the gray Istiranca Mountains. Sunrays like jeweled swords speared through the clouds and quivered in the gleaned fields beyond the manor house where she stood. Grandfather Emin Aga's village of Bedre, for which he paid the taxes to the sultan, spread out around the house and its wide yard that led to the orchards.

Under the cool green and shadow of the peach, cherry and apple leaves in the spring and summer, Adalet had spent many hours playing with her friend, Zeyneb the stable groom's girl. Only yesterday, the two of them heaped the tarnished autumn leaves into the black iron pot and pretended to concoct pumpkin sherbet, the same as in, "The Stepdaughter and Forty Thieves." They played out the tale that ended with a happy marriage to a Padishah, the fancy name for the sultan.

Beyond the wide yard, the oak trees hung heavy and golden. Maroon elm leaves wet with dew shimmered like ripples on Devil's Creek. The colors split onto the rolling plains beyond the village. Adalet couldn't see the creek from her window. It edged the village beyond the rocks. In August, it shrunk to a stream, but in the spring, it changed into a monster that slurped up everything in its path. Adalet pushed back her straight black hair to braid it into pigtails when a gust of northwest wind seemed to swoop up out of nowhere. It scattered the colors as horses came galloping toward the manor. Adalet stretched her neck to the window. Four Ottoman soldiers riding hard tore around the bend of the road from Bulgaria. The horses' mouths slung slobber as they cut up toward the house, ripping apart Emin Aga's flowers.

Adalet slipped her white headband over her hair and pushed through the door onto her balcony. Something important must be happening. A proclamation. A festivity. Sometimes Grandfather Emin Aga would call his hundreds of tenants to a feast in the orchard. Adalet peered over, stretching her stomach across the railing.

Older Brother Sabri rode among these men. Adalet squealed down to him. He was the family's pride and her big brother, so handsome in his mustache and officer uniform. Sabri was a graduate from the military school, Harbiye, in Istanbul and a captain in Sultan Reshat, Mehmet the Fifth's army.

Sabri didn't notice her waving to him or hear her voice as he called instructions to his men. Adalet strained to understand but couldn't hear. He was not wearing his new black drum hat. His eyebrows and mouth were gathered and hard. Sabri yanked at the reigns. The horses kicked air.

Father Ahmet pushed out onto his balcony across from Adalet's. He stood with his arms open in the usual welcome for his oldest son.

Sabri called up. "The Bulgarians have crossed the Balkans and overrun lands to the North!" Ahmet's gesture froze mid-air. Sabri kept shouting. "Edirne may have fallen! Cutthroats! All in their path – burnt!" Shocking words. Impossible. "Serbs, Albanians! The Greeks rampage!"

Terrible words! Adalet had watched the old Bulgarian neighbor and his two grandsons in their black woolen pantaloons and red and blue vests. They herded Grandfather's sheep. Was the smile beneath that handlebar mustache traitorous? The old man's wife made feta cheese for Mother's kitchen. Emin Aga brewed wine especially for the Gentiles' holiday celebrations. These people had been Ottomans for hundreds of years.

Ahmet replied loud and rough, his right hand slapping against his left fist, and then jutting out. "Curses! The sons of donkeys!"

Sabri retorted in his officer's voice, pointing to the North, shouting orders to his men. The three soldiers spurred their chargers around and galloped back toward the hills.

Sabri went on yelling. "Fighting in the villages. Our men unprepared, ambushed! Deserters already! I must go back!"

Ahmet swept around and called into the sky, "We are crushed!" With his arms uplifted, he headed into the house, crying, "Merciful Allah – the sultan's a fool!"

Sabri took off beyond the left side of the porch. Adalet froze, her heart thumping. Raspy voices in the wind swept back and forth. Rumbling rolled nearer from the distant skies. She'd heard tales of what an autumn storm meant. A long harsh winter would step on the skirt of the fallen leaves. Henna and saffron shoved through the clouds. Screams and shuffling sprung up from the kitchen. Doors banged and popped open.

Ahmet pushed out the porch gate below without pausing to latch it, calling, "Emin Aga! To the house at once!" Sabri rode from the right, halting before Ahmet, sliding his long black boots over the side of the horse and taking his father's hand to his forehead as he bowed. The chestnut stomped in the dirt. Their voices were muffled.

Mother Zehra, stirred from the kitchen, pushed through the gate, lifting her long beige skirt split over pantaloons. She waddled down the three steps like a goose after corn, and then, halted, hands on her candy-soft hips, straining forward to catch the men's words.

After hearing, Zehra's barn cat scream leapt from within her. "Like a wildfire?" she gasped.

Ahmet turned, laid his hand on her shoulder. "Sabri took leave to warn us." For a moment he looked at her as if he was waiting to see if she understood. Zehra jerked around, cutting her gaze off to the right, and then, to the left. Adalet, too, searched into both directions, but saw only space.

"Zehra, Dearest," Father said hoarsely, touching her long brown hair. It tumbled over her shoulder unlike the ordered style she usually wore. "Gather the children. There's little time – war's upon us."

Never had Adalet seen Mother move as fast as her flight back into the house, her voice echoing strange and ragged through the rooms below and up the staircase. "Nefise! Adalet! Sukru! We fly! Quick, be quick. We are to Stamboul short away!"

A bit later, midway on the stairs, Adalet pulled Nefise's hand so hard that she tripped. Nefise shook her head and glanced wide-eyed. The maid Hanifey came running out of the great room through the foyer. She paused to exchange secret nods with Zehra. "It's all safe in the barn," Hanifey said. "Emin Aga's out there finishing it with Ahmet." Zehra clasped her hands to her mouth. Hanifey bounded on up the stairs, sputtering, "Fetch your essentials!"

Zehra disappeared back toward the kitchen, calling for Sukru. The four-year-old was in the barn getting his warm cup of milk from the cow.

The girls came back down the stairs again. Emin Aga charged in through the back door, giving orders to himself. "Take down the guns! Find the sword! Load the guns!" Nefise and Adalet lingered in the foyer listening to his side-to-side steps. His cane resounded across the kitchen into the back room with a hollow, "thwack."

"Nefise! Adalet!" Hanifey yelled. "Come to the pantry! Help pack food!"

Ten minutes later, Hanifey shoved the three children out the front door. "Move!" she ordered. "They are less than two hours away!"

Ready in the driveway, the groom Hassan waited with two black horses harnessed to the buggy. Adalet hugged her heavy coat around her chest and felt for the gold heart on her neck, a present from her red-haired Jewish tutor. On Fridays, the Russian Lady Molotov came to teach her the lute. The smooth heart locket contained a photo of her self-alone. She rarely let anyone see it.

Adalet could not imagine anyone wanting to kill her family. What the adults said this morning seemed unreal. But, she knew about wars from books. Father had told of his Tartaric Giray Tribe, of his father, a wealthy farmer who lost his home in the Crimea to Russians, of their flight to Catalca near Istanbul, and then to Shumnu in Bulgaristan where Father was born. For thirty-eight years, his family had lived on the Danube. Finally, Father was safe in Bedre. Adalet's Aunt Azime said, "In the present, the future rides on winds that blow past." Kismet. Fate. Adalet's mother believed in spirits and she could foretell events in coffee dregs.

"Don't pull away," Nefise screamed, her dark blond curls a mess. "We have to stay together. If the Bulgars overtake us, we are ruined." Adalet reached to her older sister. Nefise's fingernails pinched her wrist. "Sweetie," she said to Nefise, embracing her, "Allah will protect us." Weeping was a waste of time when one had to flee. It almost seemed as if they were performing a play. This could be a false alarm – with a chance to see Stamboul, the Center of the World. Nothing bad could happen to Bedre. It was forever. Perhaps it was the strange gray smell in the air. That was it; everyone would come to discover nothing but rumors; and then, village women would gather in the parlor around Mother Zehra reviewing this day, quibbling as if they were bargaining on an item in the Saturday bazaar.

Hanifey helped Ahmet hoist Zehra into the phaeton. Sukru climbed onto the front seat with Hassan and Alijan son of Hassan.

"Wait!" someone yelled. Adalet wheeled around to see Zeyneb running across the lawn. Adalet's face flushed with dismay. Zeyneb would be staying behind. Adalet's hands hung like stones. She could not raise them toward her friend as she always did. Who would care for Zeyneb and her mother? A numb tingling like a hoard of spiders crept over her back and skull. Mother Zehra snapped in a strident tone, "Adalet, hurry, no time for talk!" Pretending not to hear, Adalet watched Zeyneb bounding to her with unbraided hair frizzed about her neck, her eyes and mouth wide.

"Take this!" Zeyneb said, pressing something tiny into Adalet's palm, a blue glass disk, and a black dot in the middle of white. An evil eye charm. "Protection," Zeyneb said.

Zehra called again. Adalet slid the disk into her pocket. She brought her hand to the back of her neck, unhooked her locket and shoved the fistful of gold into Zeyneb's hands. "Inshallah, the trouble will pass around us!" she said, turning away. She didn't know how to say good-bye.

Zeyneb didn't wait. As Adalet pulled up onto the phaeton, she heard the scurry of Zeyneb's slippers across the lawn.

Hanifey squeezed in between Nefise and Adalet with a basket of food. Adalet stared across at Mother Zehra's face. Zehra sat stiff and flushed, clutching lace. And then, as if a silent gong was struck in her chest, the girl suddenly knew what Mother knew. Fifty-year-old Father and eighty-year-old Grandfather Emin Aga would stay behind.

We will save what we can," Ahmet said. He leaned into the carriage and touched his wife's cheek. His slender fingers fell to her arm. "Zehra Dearest, I know this land means everything to Emin Aga. I'll look after him. Together, we'll manage."

Zehra laid a heavy hand decked with sapphire and ruby rings onto his. "Save yourself first, Dearest. Possessions are nothing to the dead."

"Where's Grandfather?" Nefise asked.

"He's loading the guns," Hanifey answered.

Mother spoke to Father in that mysterious voice. Leaves rattled across the yard. A damp wind brushed her forehead. The air seemed to stiffen. The storm was gearing up to hit Bedre. Adalet shivered and pulled her blue scarf across her ears. The alarm in her chest was now a dull throb. How could she have even thought of the chance to see Stamboul as an adventure? She was not a child. She was almost eleven years old. Thracian village girls could be married by the age of nine. This situation was making her parents afraid. Her lips went dry with the thought of that.

"If the evacuation train has left Alpiya, run to Stamboul," Ahmet told Zehra, who grabbed the side of the seat and stood.

"Why not catch the train in Kirkkilise?" she asked.

Ahmet stepped up onto the side of the rig, placed his hands on her shoulders and firmly pressed her back down on the seat. "No time to explain!" he answered.

At the harsh tone of his voice, Zehra raised her eyelids. He took a deep breath. "– Train wreck south of Kirkkilise last night. Sabri told me. Many dead."

Hanifey stifled a gasp. Zehra brought her hands to the moan in her throat.

"– loaded with people, panicked, with guns. Forced the engineer to go."

"And what?" Zehra and Hanifey said at once.

"They'd seen the Bulgar soldiers near the border. Engineer told them the ammunition train was coming but they wouldn't hear."

Adalet sat stilled. "While they were sleeping, two trains crashed," Father said, his face drawn and pale.

"The wreck's only part of destruction to come," Ahmet added. His voice was ragged. "Alijan will return with the rig from Alpiya to help his mother and sister. Hassan will go with you on the train and see you safely to Stamboul. Find Sultanahmet Mosque. From there, you can contact Emin Aga's friends. "

Zehra opened her mouth but Ahmet swept his hand with such sharpness that she shut her lips tight. Their secret language flashed between them.

Ahmet called to Hassan. The wind seemed to take his voice away. Hassan cracked the whip. The black horses split through the dry red leaves. Adalet twisted around. Father's mouth was a thin line above his beard, his face noble as any prince. Her darkened bedroom window gaped from beneath the delicate latticework of their home. Beside the mirror on her dresser, lay her ivory comb, her horsehair brush. The set had belonged to her Mother's Mother. I should have hidden them, she thought. Perhaps the maid Leyla would do that. But Leyla had not come in this morning. Her father stood as straight as a cypress tree against a tomb, and then he turned. Just before the buggy swung around the bend toward the east, she caught a glance of Zeyneb and her mother running out past the field. In the next second the stateliest house in the village of Bedre sucked back out of sight.

The Awful Flood

Who would tend the three hundred sheep? Who would get hay for the cows if the tenants all fled?

"Aiiye! We'll be thrown in a ditch!" Hanifey wailed as she rocked back and forth in the buggy. Blurred surroundings jolted past as if they were unreal. Cutting through razor-thin rain, they met the road to Kirkkilise. Winds wrestled the scraggly pines that jutted from the occasional low bank. Adalet remained silent as Hanifey's hip jostled against her. Strangely, it made her feel safer. Adalet strained to hear scraps of conversation between Nefise and Hanifey: The train lines stretched from Istanbul to Edirne. Would the train be waiting? Would there be room on board? Were friends in that train crash? Who had taken care of them? The rain made a steady sting on her face.

The mass of people poured from the forests, low hills and scruffy earth. A fluid caravan of people ran from their whitewashed homes of dirt, stones and wood. Some, caked in mud, thrashed through dead stalks in the fields. A white-bearded man on a stumbling donkey held his fez with one hand rather than have it blown from his head while cradling a red-faced child in a crocheted coat in the other. A girl about Adalet's age in blue pantaloons and long pink blouse splashed through a trench. When she fell, no one stopped. Adalet choked back the hard lump in her throat and forgot it when the phaeton barely missed sideswiping a black billowing shroud, a woman as a sail overriding a wooden cart with three small kids. Their sobs floated up from the wide well of the downpour into which all of these bodies had fallen.

"Do you think these children had a breakfast?" Hanifey asked. Her voice was as vacant as her face was hushed. Through the wet horde of colors, horses and other transports, Adalet could no longer see the dirt road path that ran through the fields.

Faces bobbed before and beside their rig, some in headscarves and turbans, ruddy, deeply lined, some toothless, all slick as persimmons. They were only a tiny part of a flood of people. Nefise pulled her scarf across her nose and scrunched into Hanifey. The dank smell of this deluge was spoiled fish, onions and smoldering coals. In the next hour, the rain would not only drive into their faces and hands, but soak onto their chests and thighs. Like everybody else, they had no choice but to push into it.

Every soul on these fields hoped to make it to Stamboul. People always spoke of Stamboul with a glint in their eyes, Stamboul – ornate as a land of picture book tales, the ancient and cosmopolitan gem, where from a single point the sultan oversaw both Europe and Asia, Islambul, Istanbul, Constantinople with its bell towers, minarets and cobbled streets, its dinghies, palaces and the Bosphorus Strait that could soak up the sky. It was the city of protection and shelter. It coped with terror, held the empire's grief.

Adalet pulled her chin to her chest and thought about how Mother Zehra had said, "Butchers." She saw images of red mouths foaming, the slaughtered sheep at holiday time. She remembered Father and Grandfather left behind. In the path of rapiers. What now of the vineyards? Last summer, the trellises hung heavy with grapes, the orchards with peaches, apples, pears and plums plucked, dried and cooked in cakes that were topped with a sourcherry jam called, "Balkan sun on a spoon." This month, Adalet had walked to the garden where the corn stalks were cut. The jade and white pumpkins lay over the ground. The Greek servants helped with the harvest, joined the food festival, the dancing and drums. Tomorrow, she thought, it would surely be told that the quarrels were done with. "Inshallah," she whispered, If Allah wills it, so will it be. Perhaps Father, our guardian, who has memorized the whole *Koran*; and so, is called, "Hafiz", will convince the invaders to sit down and have tea. Maybe he stayed behind to make peace. Father's family took refuge in the Bulgars' land.

With her head bowed, Zehra was a clump. Adalet watched her mother grimace when the phaeton jolted. Last summer, Mother hadn't even come to Igneada on the Black Sea shore when Father took the girls on a holiday, renting a big boat for three days' sailing. Resisting travel's pains, Mother sought the harem room where she received those come to petition her powers, her visions beyond the present and into dreams. Like a queen, Mother gave counsel regardless of faith. But, even Mother Zehra did not foretell the storm of this day.

Impact

In the confusion, the unexpected closeness to this young man made her more confused.

Almost two hours later, the crowd had fanned out by the time they came to Kirkkilise. The buggy jostled back and forth from the clack and clatter on the cobblestones. The rain had subsided but the main street was soaked. Drops as big as February hailstones dripped from the drooping ash and elm. The gutters streamed muddy. Shops were dark; boards nailed across the doors. Adalet stared at people coming and going but no one paused. Fog drenched the market near the mosque. With the center usually half filled with shoppers, Adalet loved to accompany her father here, when old men with cheeks like chestnuts rolled dice for backgammon on wooden tables and smoked in the coffeehouse on crude benches and chairs. Women sipped tea and swapped stories while children wrestled and played in the streets. But this day, there were no men, not even ones bent on the low stone benches at the fountain making ablutions before prayers.

There were no farmers with pushcarts of pumpkins, potatoes, apples and bread.

Groom Hassan flicked the whip and the buggy glided past the town center. The tawny mosque, the closed bazaar and the hamam were left behind. The horses took the length of the broad curve. As the phaeton swung round, it slipped on the street. The back end of the rig skidded and crashed. Adalet grabbed onto the side of the seat and bent into Hanifey. She was stunned only for a second or two. When she looked up, they had stopped.

"Crazy Hassan –" Zehra yelled, "will you get us killed?" She was half standing. The groom, his son and Sukru scrambled down from their seats. Sukru ran behind Hassan, who was headed toward the back of the buggy.

Alijan was trying to steady the horse. "Easy girl, slowly, slowly," he repeated. Hanifey nudged Adalet and she stiffly crawled out on her side of the buggy. Hanifey followed. The phaeton had back-ended a wagon with a buckboard and a team of excited red stallions. From the buckboard a boy attempted calming them down.

Hassan pleaded in a high-pitched voice, "Blacksmith, sorry, of course my fault. Slick stones!" Mehmet Nuri the blacksmith of Kirkkilise reached out a big hand and dropped it on the steward's shoulder. "Don't worry," Mehmet Nuri said, "my women in the wagon's bed are unhurt."

Nefise and Hanifey ran to the wagon where the others piled out over the side. Before them stood Mother Zehra's sister Azime and her husband along with the blacksmith's third wife and her daughter, Hayriye. Mehmet's daughter Sabiha, from his first wife long dead, hugged Nefise and Hanifey. Adalet grabbed Azime and held on tight, grateful that no one was hurt by the frightening crash. The shrill voices of the women roused the horses again. They began to speak all at once about the impending disaster.

Zehra called out. Adalet went to help her down from the phaeton. When Zehra positioned her bulky frame to clamber over the side, Azime cried, "No, Big Sister. Stay seated." The women rushed over to the buggy, laying hands on Zehra, squeezing her arms and touching her cheeks and crying, "You poor woman!" "Allah is merciful!" "Are you all right?" Adalet imagined how odd they must think it to see the lady Zehra out in public in the middle of the street in a phaeton.

The men rushed back around the phaeton toward the black horses. "Let's check their legs," the blacksmith said. As they moved in front, one of them paused. Adalet looked up into the eyes of the one called, Handsome, the eldest son of the blacksmith. This Burhan stood at arm's length and stared at them with a crooked smile. Burhan had performed on the stage. At once, Adalet realized that this young man was not looking at her, but past her shoulder to Nefise, more nearly his age. She flushed with foolishness. Nefise would blush, but she was used to young men staring at her.

Azime slipped up to Adalet's side, taking her elbow. "You know my Burhan," she whispered. Adalet nodded. She had seen him and his brother Ruhittin at Azime's house. He always took the hero's role in the community plays given by the province. Burhan was well known. It was said that his voice was full of value. One certainly noticed.

Ruhittin had quieted the stallions, but the black ones were uneasy and causing concern. As Mehmet Nuri examined their legs, Burhan ambled over to watch him. Adalet looked in their direction. Burhan had a fine lock of brown hair. She had first been aware of that when she saw him just last month at the school performance with Doctor Fuat's Welfare Society, raising funds for widows and orphans. That twist in his lip gave his smile a devilish charm. But, what was she thinking – this was no time to be silly, no time to remember a play. She slipped quickly back into the alarm of the present.

"Tall, isn't he?" Azime said, holding her elbow a bit too tight.

Zehra called sharply from the phaeton. "Sister Azime! We must be out of here!"

"To be sure," Azime called back. "Pray, how do you go?"

"We rush for the train at the Alpiya center. And you?" Zehra asked.

Sabiha answered, "With the wagon to Izmit."

"Why not Stamboul?" Hanifey asked.

"Blacksmith Mehmet Nuri has friends in Izmit where my mother died," Sabiha said.

Adalet knew by heart the story of how nineteen-year old Mehmet Nuri from Tashkent near Samarkand beyond the Caspian Sea had left his family for a pilgrimage to Mecca. When his second wife died in Kirkkilise, Aunt Azime, whose own baby had just died, became a nursemaid for the baby Ruhittin and two-year-old, Burhan. She suckled Burhan for half a year and Ruhittin for two. When Mehmet Nuri married the third time, Sabiha became more like a mother than a stepsister to the boys. Mehmet's third wife was good enough, but had no particular fondness for them. When Adalet would accompany her father into Kirkkilise, he would always stop by the blacksmith shop to hear travelers' news and travelers' tales, of which Adalet could not get enough. Blacksmith Mehmet Nuri was special. He had come from so far. And he had made the pilgrimage. She pictured the hot forge. Her heavy coat held the wet and cold.

The men finished with checking the horses' legs and declared them safe. The two parties hurriedly kissed and left each other to Allah's care. Fifteen minutes lost. Could mean missing the train.

The Train

The people were packed like wet sheep in a stall.

By the time they got to Alpiya Station, it was almost midnight. The evacuation train boiled glistening wet into the mist. It sat heavily, shrilling its whistle, huffing steam and reflecting gaslights. Guards held back a crowd on the platform in front of the building. Panic gripped the four in the phaeton. They began yelling for the groom to hurry the horses. Hassan drove up to the side of the stand, around it, down the grass incline and then, in as far as he could, forcing the horses through the crowd. There was only the thought of getting through. But, the horses balked at the wall of bodies.

Hassan jumped down, leaving Alijan to manage. He helped Hanifey down, and then pulled the others out.

The two of them led, prying elbows and thighs apart as they pushed through for Zehra. As if she held reins, Zehra grabbed Sukru's coat from the back, commanding "Go! Go!" His slim frame slivered between the fig-shaped hips and bundles that tumbled toward the train.

The engine screamed urgently over and over. Hassan forged ahead, using the luggage as a wedge. Hanifey followed close, creating a space behind by extending her arms back as she plowed between the hard bodies, ushering Nefise and Adalet forward. The groom shouted, "Make way, ho!" through the din, with an air of importance, though no one yielded.

There was noise, noise like the worst nightmare from which one couldn't retreat. The old or crippled couldn't get to the doors. Those who fell were knocked aside or stepped on and left. Adalet felt only shock and the absolute urgency to force her way.

Hassan disappeared inside the black car. Hanifey hung on the rail at the steps. The train lurched. Metal collided and screeched. A roar went up from the mass. Hanifey squalled, "Come my girls! Push your mother!" Shoved forward, Zehra was swallowed into the opening. Brother Sukru went next. Adalet locked her hand around Nefise's wrist and pulled. The engine hissed, the train paused and groaned. Other bodies bent on saving themselves tried to pry the two sisters away. Adalet stepped from the frenzy up over the hiss of steam, grabbed the rail, and lunged, digging her fingers into Nefise's flesh as she went. Nefise hesitated, then stumbled frontward. Like the debris of a flood, the two girls washed into the car as much because of the tide behind as the thrust forward.

The whistle began sounding again and again as the cars jerked and the wheels turned. Hundreds who didn't make it through the doors were running down the sides trying to grab on. Many who did climbed the sides of the cars and held onto the tops. Some were slung off and fell in between where the units locked. Those who were left at the platform were told more trains would come, and not to riot. Later, it was known that no train came.

Adalet stood lodged somewhere near the middle of the car, stacked body-to-body upright in the aisle. She wiggled around then pressed her ribcage into the wrought iron side of the seat. She leaned onto it; turned, hearing Hassan's voice a few feet beyond. "Ho, shame, do you not know this is the daughter of Emin Aga of Bedre? Will you see her stand? Out, out!" Four boys in two of the seats facing each other obeyed the groom's voice of authority, giving up their side of a booth to Zehra and Sukru. "Adalet, Nefise!" Hassan called.

Suddenly, Hanifey tugged Nefise from behind Adalet, to settle her down by Sukru. Adalet did not budge. She knew that her mother required two spaces. She placed her hands on the top of the iron, laid her forehead onto it and closed her eyes, wondering what would become of her warm featherbed. Hanifey's sagging bosoms warmed her back. At least, the rain was no longer coming down on her head. And the panic of missing the train was past.

NINE

Anykara, Ankura
Angora, Ankara

September 1993, Ankara,
two weeks following Adalet's funeral

But seriously, how much of the Earth mother was inside a woman like Adalet...

After Kurt flew south to the Aegean Sea a couple of days ago, Nuri and I decided we should get out of the confusion of Istanbul and make a trip into the center of Anatolia to continue my research into the life and times of Adalet while the two of us also could take a short vacation.

I've been here to visit the Museum of Anatolian Civilizations before. This time, I am trying to put this land of Turkey into perspective. Anatolia is the cradle of civilization. So many different cultures have lived here. Actually, the Turks were the last to come. Think of all of that mixing of religions, mores and bloods.

When I glance back toward the front alcove I see that Nuri still basks in the sunlight spearing through the small rectangular windows. He's reading the chapbook on Ankara that he bought prior to our lunch in the garden restaurant.

I take the marble steps to the central hall, telling myself that we were right to grab this vacation from the stress of the last week. *We learned that we not only had to deal with the death of our mother but possible disruption of family relationships over property rights. Apparently, Adalet as matriarch held the children and grandchildren together all these years. She was no sooner in the earth than I felt a stranger in their eyes. That reality was harder to believe than Adalet's death. Adalet spent her whole life dealing with her primary family over the idea of home and inheritance. Strange that the material concerns should divide her children at her demise.*

My shoes produce augmented clips through the domed central hall that runs the length of the building. Assembled in a chronological order, the surrounding corridor presents relics and data on all of the civilizations that have inhabited Ankara from the Paleolithic age to the Roman.

Pausing at the Phrygian display, I read the inscription. Legend is that "Anykara" was home to the Phrygian King Midas. Oh yes, the guy with the golden touch. Anykara meant "anchor' in Phrygian. Maybe they were longing for the sea? A far stretch. I'd think "Anchor" is where you settle down.

Upended glass cases on streamline design bases and glass cubicles spreading out across the stone floor at irregular intervals are filled with statues and artifacts from the Hittite Empire. Shelves in the cases hold wide-hip urns and pitchers, boat-shaped oil lamps, ancient goddesses, stone works, and earth works brought from digs such as Bogazkoy, Catalhoyuk and Alacahoyuk. As I move along, there are explanations in English and several other languages: The digs uncovered the handiwork of the Hatti from before 2500 up to 1700 BCE, a people who lived by a fair and humane code of law, recording details about their conquests stretching from the Black Sea to Palestine, recording in hieroglyphic and cuneiform script learned from the Mesopotamians. Their city of Hattusas was just east of modern Ankara. I recall what I learned about the Hittites as a girl in Vacation Bible School: The prophet Abraham bought a field from a Hittite to bury his wife Sarah. Isaac's son Esau married two Hittite wives. King David had his General Uriah the Hittite killed so that he could marry the man's wife Bathsheba, who became the mother of King Solomon. And here are the ruins suspended in the air on glass shelves, reclaimed from the earth: Cleaned, bronze disks forged to aid in the worship and glory of the rising sun, a square of swastikas whirling like frozen fans, four in a row. The airy disk is cut so that the rays of the sun pour through the blades. Bronze and copper deer and bulls lift long antlers to salute the dawn. The twisted circle overhead is the rim of the rising sun.

There are dancing horned-hair gods in coned hats. Can there be some legacy from these to the Whirling Dervishes – the Mevlevi in cone hats who turn in the rhythms of the heavens until they lose themselves in the spin of the universe –blades that no longer separate but become a part of the moving whole? Rumi and swastikas– hmmm. Makes sense. For some three thousand years before the Nazis took the symbol, it was a positive sign of the sun power and good luck.

Here's my favorite display: the hand-size obese, earthen mother goddess giving birth while sitting on a throne. Way to go girl! With big baggy boobies hanging to her sagged triangular abdomen, her arms have rested on these leopards' heads since the Paleolithic (Old Stone) Age. She lived in a cave. Her mate carved spearheads and axes out of material he picked up from around him. I remember once when Nuri and I climbed up to the famous cave near the Mediterranean city of Antalya – the Karain, named for the eons of black soot still covering its high and massive ceilings and walls, soot accumulated from fires, continually kept burning from the Old Stone Age until the Roman garrisons. Some tall tales were spun into that soot. Like a goddess, the cave delivered its relics but kept its secrets.

A later goddess looks like one of those modern emasculated runway models: Thin and hairless, almost hermaphroditic, a bald bronze head, eyes closed in meditation, hands folded across the stomach, breasts high and firm. Her all-important life-giving triangle stands out prominent between the hips. The female can bleed and not die, give birth at random and feed her young from her body. "The goddess was held in highest sacred honor along with the bull." The bull's triangular-horned head resembles the sacred triangle.

Nearby in the reconstructed Neolithic room, I note how the goddess icons eventually emerged as hardly more than feminine-principle circles and triangles. To my back, on the other side of this circular hall, are the Greek and Roman, full-body goddesses again. Christians did away with Venus and Diana and took the Virgin Mary. The bull in the fresco in the Neolithic room was removed from a wall in the dig of Catalhoyuk. The thick-horned head side-glances at the tiny humans engaged in movement all around it. Similar to a painting taken from a palace in ancient Crete. The bull has a crescent moon set above its head. Interesting to parallel Islam's sign.

Asia Minor. Anatolia means "to the East" in Greek. Anadolu translates from Turkish as, "filled with mothers." The mother-goddess had various names throughout the thousands of years of her reign in Anatolia: Gaia, Demeter, Cybele, Ishtar, Isis, Ma —and among the oldest of all— Inanna, Ana, Mother. Anatolian Turks still say, "Ana" for "Mother," although the modern usage is coined, "Anne – pronounced An-neh."

The earthen goddess reminds me of Adalet bent over work, two sagging mounts beneath her blouse tumbling onto her abdomen, her deft fingers trimming an apple, or an eggplant, one of her plump legs tucked under her, a pearl of sweat on the side of her nose, the scarf's knot like a signet on her crown. I'm also reminded of my grandmother who had twelve children and loads of grandchildren. Granny was warm and nurturing. After my grandmother died, I always wished that I could nestle into my mother's breasts in the same way I did with Granny. Interesting that I should make that connection in this place before this statue. Maybe Adalet filled a spot that had been empty ever since my time with Granny.

I step over to scan a map and read its plaque with all of the data: Anykara sat along the center of the trade route known as King's Road, built by Darius I in 400 BCE. Alexander the Great spent springtime here before the Galatians came in from Europe and made it their capital. Huh. "Galatians" is a book in the Bible, Saint Paul's letter to one of the first churches. I never realized that the place lay near Ankara. I read on and find out that with the blade of his sword, Alexander, whom the Turks call Iskender, un- tied the famous Gordian knot that gave him the key to Asia. The Romans began to invade, and renamed the city Sebaste, the Greek word for Emperor Augustus. The Galatians built a temple here to honor Augustus and the goddess Roma. I recall that in 320, there were also forty soldiers who became early Christian martyrs, dying for their faith. Remembrance of them is still widely celebrated throughout the world

The Roman Empire split and the Byzantines came. Peace lasted until the seventh century, when the Arabs brought war. Then, again under the Byzantines, Anykara had two hundred years of peace, until the Seljouk Sultan Alpaslan defeated the Byzantines at Malazgirt in AD 1071. Anykara was grand in the golden age of Aladdin Keykubat. But the Mongols destroyed it in 1237 and changed Anykara to Angora. The Ahi Beys traded East with West until the Ottoman Sultan Murad I claimed it for the Ottomans, who kept it until the War of Independence, when Mustafa Kemal chose Ankara as the capital of the Turkish Republic. Wow.

I study the map again. In this juncture of four bowl-shaped mountains on a high and barren Anatolian plateau, differing tribes converged across this steppe, one wave overriding the other with rules, religions, crafts and intermarriages. The ancient description of Ankara is that of a town between the mountains, with three rivers. I look closely. Those rivers join to form the Ankara Stream.

I dig in my purse and pull out a map of Anatolia and find the Ankara Stream. I follow with my finger how it continues west to the Sakarya River. That's where the Turkish Nationalist forces first began to resist the Greeks in 1921. I read about the Turkish Resistance Movement after Adalet told me the story of how she and Burhan had early on joined the Nationalists.

All of this history compels me to respond to my mystic muse. Did Mustafa Kemal choose to come here to the heartland to begin the Resistance? Or did this historically rich soil called Ankura,

Anykara, Angora, Ankara pull him with a magnetic power? Did the Anadolu "many mothers" draw him –and then a whole nation– with a seductive raw force of survival? Was it fortune and destiny – what Adalet called kismet? Did this plateau that has claimed so many and integrated so much beckon to him? Mustafa Kemal Ataturk – was he a tool in the hands of a higher power once upon a time called the Storm God and Cybele, alias Inanna? Was that why he was far ahead of his peers to champion women's rights? What power actually placed the alem – the brass crescent horns – on top of mosques? The curved bullhorns were a symbol of the mother goddess culture. Lots of connections. Sometimes my wondering gets eerie.

How much of the Earth Mother was inside a woman like Adalet, who gave nine years to the nursing of seven children, who patiently moved whichever way the wind blew across Anatolia, making a hearth fire, honoring her bullish husband in her various houses, starting over and over again with hope, always open to new ideas and loving all kinds and classes of people? These depictions of mystical birds and leopards were a symbol of invisible strength.

I'm so taken with a huge copper map of Asia Minor that I hardly hear the muted voices and intermittent swishing of feet in the halls.

"Hey –Green-eyed Lady– where've you been?"

I jump up out of my speculations. Nuri.

"Sorry. Did I take too long?" I ask, folding up my map and sticking it into my purse. "I'm just trying to piece together all of this history."

"OK, Lee," Nuri says fondly, placing an arm around my waist and giving me a squeeze. "And what did you discover?"

"That the Turks of today are only the top level of layers."

"Yes," he says, squinting at me amiably. "And?"

"Baklava," I say, chuckling. "The centuries of Anatolia's history are like a baklava. One civilization on top of the other like the forty dough leaves. The nuts and sugar are the relics – coated with butter and syrup."

"Turkey would be honored to be called a baklava. What do you mean?"

I point back to the burnished pottery figure in the glass case. "That goddess, she is your mother."

"What?"

"Look at her, large enough for many to hug, earthy, mystical–"

"Mother was never that heavy. And she wasn't a pagan." He stares at the figure, protruding his lips. "That's not a joke. My mother was a woman of substance." He turns to me.

I see the shadow of loss on his face. He presses his lips together as he pulls back from me. I can't have him think I've insulted his mother. Stepping to him, I touch his shoulder.

"What I mean is this: That piece of clay is of the very soil of Anatolia. The earth, the womb, see?" Nuri moves around to consider it again and tightens his brows.

"Your mother was smart, embracing," I continue. "But she was also common at the same time, and she could read people. She was given stuff in dreams –look how she dreamed about me and knew our marriage was right before she ever got our letter– she had visions…"

"How do you know she really dreamed about you?" he asks with a grin. "She could have made that up just to make you feel good." Nuri folds his arms across his abdomen.

I take a step back, hike up my shoulder bag and fold my arms. "I don't believe she made it up. She accepted me from the git-go. Believed that our marriage was meant to be – and she never questioned that. The proof for me was the way she never failed to treat me."

"She didn't have a mother-in-law to treat her badly; so, she didn't have the urge to dominate a daughter-in-law in the traditional custom. Besides, she just liked you. She loved America, and you were America. You were good to her, and you were my wife." He shrugs his shoulders. "But why are we discussing my mother? We came on this trip to forget sadness."

Nuri checks his watch, and then raises the Ankara guidebook he's got rolled up in his hand and points toward the entrance.

"We'd better get moving," he tells me, walking away a few steps. He pauses to regard me with a softer face. I nod and lift my hand, indicating that I will follow in a moment.

I take a last glimpse at the goddess. Eons ago she sat in some high and honored place. Inanna, Nana, Anahita, Anat, and more. For thousands and thousands of years before God or Allah: Mother Earth. It wasn't the figurine they worshiped; it was the cycle of life in the earth and the air, the spirit of nourishing and being perceptive. It was to honor the fact that life comes from the soil in many forms. People like Adalet and me are believers in the power of the spirit, signs and protection. Adalet once wrote in a letter to Nuri that I have a heart like hers. There was understanding between the two of us. That link with her nurturing spirit is what's missing now that she's gone. Her daughters are different. I wonder how growing up with the influence of their father, all of the moving to various sites in their early years and the focus on the secular republic affected them? Certainly, none of them had the chance to have Adalet's social background.

I watch my husband amble off into the rays of sunlight coming through the entrance windows. It dawns on me that the calm realism in Nuri's nature has always been surrounded by his mother's intuitive spirit – whether he believed in it or not. Her spirit embraced his skepticism.

Nuri was raised under Ataturk's creed of nationalism, where the idea of being led by a Higher Spirit was overwhelmed by the civil spirit of progress, where the old customs were deemed inferior. Adopting the ways of the West would bring Turkey into the modern world.

When I went with Nuri to visit the town of Kargi, in central Anatolia where he first practiced medicine, a man who remembered him said, "We called this young doctor 'cowboy' because he loved America and said he would go there someday – and he did."

At the end of World War I, and then during the National Resistance, and in the early years of the republic, the millions like Burhan and Adalet couldn't possibly have imagined how the

Western would flood their country. They would be so occupied with the struggle for survival that they wouldn't be able to evaluate the effect of events until much later. Their marriage was both a victor and victim of those turbulent times.

TEN

The Sharpshooter

The graveyard in Gumushacikoy bore both Muslim and Christian inscriptions – crosses and crescents sharing the same headstones. Those symbols could be found together on fountains as well.

Young wife Adalet threw the log into the belly of the iron stove, jabbed at the coals with the metal rod and then closed the door and turned up the latch. The thick hollow clank seemed to prod the wide silence surrounding her. The night had fallen down over the mud and stone bungalow. She scooted the tea-pot onto the front of the stove where the fire would be hottest. At late morning, Burhan had come in with a fresh pouch of the famous Rize tea from the Black Sea. This afternoon at their heavy oak door, she called the "Good-bye!" as he rode through the yard and on out the metal gate on their horse. Adalet had named the horse Lightning. He could gallop like a flash from the sky; his name also bore the memory of Lightning Girl that Adalet owned in Kirkkilise. As he left, Burhan had turned and leaned down over the roan stallion to fasten the bar back across the gate. It was only a gesture. They both knew there was no real safety in the gate or in the five-foot stonewall that he had the peasant boys build all around the house. The shoulder-high barrier stood fit as could be expected. Most of the able men were either crippled, in the army or dead. Down the dirt road of the village plateau, there were quite a few Greeks with chattering wives and children, family people who seemed to want no part of rebellion and hate.

Non-Muslims had no desire to serve in the military. Adalet knew a few Armenian families still living quietly nearby. It was people like this that Burhan was sent to protect. The area governor before Burhan was Armenian. In the past, high Armenian positions were common, especially in these parts. One day there would be unity again. At present, different sects had little to trust in each other.

The whole country was tired and bitter with killings – retaliations, while children went hungry and sick. People whispered that Kurds would be fierce if crossed. The independent Kurds didn't like orders. The guerrilla bandits still rode in and out from the east, although last month National Forces recaptured the town of Kars. The Circassian, self-governing Caucasian tribes from the Black Sea, could side with either Nationalists or Ottoman loyalists.

The jagged orange that pierced through the cracks in the door of the stove scattered all around the dark kitchen. Adalet jerked her hand to her mouth. There was a noise. Something had brushed by the side of the house. Hands trembling, she picked up the rifle from where it was propped beneath the window, steadied her breath, pulled back the drape and peeped out. The moon gave the fig tree in the yard an uncanny glow. She could see no one. Bandits could be hiding under the high window. No one could easily leap inside. Burhan had taught her well. She could shoot a rock off a fence thirty yards away.

Adalet slid back the lock and cracked the window. Sticking the tip of the barrel through, she pointed to the top of the tree and pulled the trigger. The blast ripped open the darkness. She held her breath. And listened. In the distance, only a dog's bark.

With the kitchen window shoved back and secured and the rifle there re-shelled, she slipped into the front room as quietly as one of the shadows flickering from the oil lamp on the table. Careful not to let her nerves cloud her mind, she looked through the side of the curtains. The wind was up. It was only that, which went rattling the bush. All that she could see between the iron bars across the window were patches of green and red earth. Adalet squatted and squinted up. There were no stars, but the sky was filled with translucence. She opened the window and fired into the full moon's glare, but she could not see the moon.

At the room's other window, she discharged the rifle that was laid against the wall. After, she went to the bedroom and did the same with another rifle. Burhan had seen to it that there was no lack of shells for her firing the four rounds into the night every several hours, even when he was home. Some nights, it would be toward daybreak and he would not yet have made it back. Since Adalet could not sleep, she said her prayers through the night as though it were day. She was sure that the village people of Gumushacikoy knew by now that she was often left alone. Adalet hoped strangers and bandits would think that armed men sat at the windows. Burhan sent dispatches begging for a regiment, but no reply had come in the month they had been there.

In the kitchen, the water boiled. Adalet pinched several fingers of tea into the small pot. After she poured the hot water from the bottom pot over the tealeaves, she breathed in the stiff and friendly aroma. One pot settled onto the other, the way some said a marriage was supposed to be. The secret to not losing her wits was to keep busy. Something had always protected her and would do so now. But there was no peace for anyone in these times – what with that Sevres Treaty signed back in August yet attempting to divide up the country into various pieces for other nations to have, leaving Turks only a wedge from Ankara to Samsun. After loading another two limbs into the fire, she pushed the pots to the back burner so the tea would steep. She fixed herself a tumbler, thinking of how often in Kirkkilise she had poured tea come from the Black Sea region, never guessing that one night she would be this close.

The Allies as well as the Ottomans now declared Mustafa Kemal Pasha an outlaw. But the Nationalists had a vision that did not include what the rest of the world thought should be done with the Motherland. Across the heaps of blue-gray mountains surrounding this plain laid the port city of Samsun, where that small ship had come quietly from Istanbul bearing the Pasha. Mustafa Kemal stepped onto that shore of Anatolia with a resolve to be the mind, soul and shadow of his people. Pasha's pictures in the papers showed him thoughtful and lean. They said his eyes were blue and clear, and that when one looked into them he or she could believe in the future.

Adalet's mind kept thinking of Kirkkilise, now overrun by the Greeks. Only Allah could know if the fate of Kirkkilise would be the same as Bedre's. Her mother and father were with her brothers and sister in Istanbul. Their safety was unknown. Nefise's husband Prince Ali Fuat had to be careful. If he was still helping to smuggle arms out of the capital city to Nationalist forces in Anatolia, his life was in danger from many factions. Adalet still couldn't let go of the wish that the sultan couldn't help but privately hope success for the Nationalists.

Adalet took her drink to the front room and sat at the long wooden table that served as their eating-place, as well as county Governor Burhan's reception desk. The life that she knew in Kirkkilise was a distant dream. More change was to come, according to her tealeaves. Tea was not as accurate as coffee dregs, but coffee was as impossible to get as sugar.

She reflected on the vision of the crimson sunset when Burhan and she had ridden from Gebze last June, when darkness stopped being a time for restful sleep for her: Burhan and she had bedded down in a barn beyond Sapanca when the first sun broke on the journey toward Ankara. The next night, they slept beneath vines on a bank by a river. The lucky sighting of the sultan's soldiers on the bridge made them thankful to see that threat passed by. In Adapazari, they found Mehmet Nuri's first wife's relatives and stayed through the day; and then they continued their 12-day journey after dark. They passed Bolu's mountain and made their way on to the outside of Ankara where Doctor Fuat and Mediha received them before the early hours of dawn. Fuat had been sent from Kirkkilise to Bolu a year and half before, after the new party took over when the failed CUP government fell. The politicians got Doctor Fuat out of Kirkkilise, although he had faithfully served the area as the public health officer during the wars.

In Bolu, Fuat served for a year as public health officer and founder of a new branch of the Society for the Children's Protection, as he had done in Kirkkilise; for there were so many orphans everywhere. He established a Society of Music in the town and also wrote a newspaper column under the heading of "The Man from Trakya." At the first Grand National Assembly in Ankara, he became recognized as congressman from the Bolu province and was appointed the chief office of the National Defense and Justice of Bolu.

Adalet leaned her arms on the table, remembering a conversation last June at breakfast, the morning after Burhan and she had first arrived at Fuat's village home. She and Burhan had known that Fuat's election to the congress placed him in a dangerous position, but they were shocked to hear his story. They had already heard that there had been an uprising in Bolu against the Nationalists. Fuat had barely escaped being hanged.

"President Mustafa Kemal sent five of us congressmen from Ankara before our first congress opened on April 23rd," Fuat told them. "A Nationalist advisory committee. We were on our way to Bolu to organize stronger support from the mountain people."

"So, you missed the opening session?" Burhan asked.

"Yes. Mustafa Kemal had us leave Ankara days earlier. At the beginning, when we stopped in a village close to the town of Gerede, we were well received by the neighbors of one of the men in our group. The success of our mission looked promising. But afterwards, we had continued only several kilometers toward Gerede when a crowd put us on guard. As we approached, they began to shoot at us."

"Oh, Doctor," Adalet said, bringing her hand to her chest. "Did they kill anyone in your party?"

Fuat reached across the table and touched Mediha's hand.

"Not one of us was hit, as luck would have it." Adalet sighed and sat back. Fuat continued. "They came, surrounding, with their guns on us. Shouting praise to the sultan, they dragged one of our officials from his horse and beat him in the dirt."

"What happened?" Adalet whispered.

"They took us into custody and hauled us off to the town of Gerede, where they held us in a small room and informed us that they were contacting the leaders in the town of Duzce."

"A nest of sultan power!" Mediha said.

"Exactly. After some time, others arrived and placed chains about our necks and took us in a cart toward nearby Duzce."

"I was out of my mind when I heard of it," Mediha said, her voice breaking. Fuat waited several seconds before going on with his story, pulling back the top of his collar to show a scar.

"In prison in Duzce, we learned that a small battalion of Mustafa Kemal's forces – ones that had been sent to precede the five of us – had been ambushed by unfriendly Circassian bandits. The commander had been killed, and some of the squad was captured."

"Were they of the same group that seized you?" Burhan asked.

"Exactly," he answered. "They held us, waiting for their leader, Servet, to return."

"It was awful for you, dearest," Mediha added.

"It became worse," Fuat said, getting up and moving to her side.

"They received a telegram saying that we were ordered by the sultan's government to be brought to the port of Izmit, where we would be shipped to Istanbul to be hanged." He paused. "But you know that did not happen. Their leader, Servet, came and spoke with me. He and his family had been patients of mine."

"Did you plead with him?" Adalet asked.

"We talked for a long time. I wanted to convince him to join the National Defense. He thought it would be difficult, that Mustafa Kemal might not accept him. Finally, after some days of conversation, I made a plan with him to send someone to the telegraph office in the next town – which was supporting Nationalists. The telegraph would say that Servet wanted Mustafa Kemal Pasha's permission to join the National Forces."

"And Kemal Pasha must have said yes – and that is why you are here with us now," Burhan said.

"Not quite." Fuat answered. "The next thing we heard was that Circassians friendly to Nationalists and led by a fellow named Cherkes Ethem were on their way to Duzce. So, I also had a telegram sent to Cherkes Ethem telling him not to come – because Servet had been won over to our side. The thing is, Ethem has been known to be too independent in his decisions. In time, Ethem wired back that he did wish to come, that he would have to see surrender; and then after considering the conditions, he would do the correct thing."

"Was that acceptable to the various parties involved?" Burhan asked.

"No," Fuat answered. "The next morning, I learned that Cherkes Ethem arrived in the middle of the night. He conducted a summary court immediately. Twenty of those who held us, including Servet, were taken out after the midnight trial and hanged."

"Didn't they bring you out as a witness?" Adalet asked.

"No. Unfortunately, there are so many zealots. The Circassian Ethem must be watched. Such a shame. Servet could have served our cause. We need every good man."

"Fuat," Adalet asked, "How long were you in captivity?"

"Thirty-five long days." Mediha and Adalet stared at each other without speaking. Fuat shook his bowed head. "Mustafa Kemal Pasha's answer by telegraph did come," he said. "Pasha accepted our plea for Servet a few hours too late."

Several days after the breakfast, Mediha insisted that Adalet should remain with her and the children while Burhan accompanied Fuat into Ankara. Burhan could more easily secure himself a place in the Nationalist's work force. Once he found lodgings, he would send for Adalet.

In the meantime, Adalet was glad to be left in the company of Mediha. Enthusiastically, they discussed the workings of the new congress, Fuat's position as a member of the Parliament of the Grand National Assembly and of a rising Turkish state. Adalet still hoped that Sultan Vahdettin would now not remain so aloof. But, in Adalet's coffee cups, she could no longer find the crescent of the sultan-caliph; and she wondered about the sultan's role in the future. "There are so many who have their spirits with the Nationalists, but hearts with the sultan," Mediha reminded her. "They can't be trusted."

"The Sultan is known as 'Allah's Shadow on Earth,'" Adalet replied.

"From the beginning of his term, Fuat's been convincing the leaders in Bolu to cut communications with the sultan's government in Istanbul," Mediha informed her.

Mediha and Adalet had waited together for a month. Burhan apparently was working hard as a competent civil secretary in Ankara, tending to many details. He had published two articles in the *Hakimiyeti Milliye* newspaper –with his name– explaining the National Cause. On his own, he was also trying to study political science. There was no university. Burhan was not a dignitary like Fuat, but he was helping the Cause. When Adalet received the news that Burhan had found them a small place to stay, she immediately set off to join him.

The oil lamp on the wooden table in Gumushacikoy had grown dim. Adalet adjusted the wick, got up from the table, went to the window, and watched again out into the shadows. There was only the wind blowing a piece of paper across the dry November ground. With the stove's burning, the closed house felt too warm. Wishing for fresh air, she tottered to the back and sat on the bed and pulled her brown dress above her thighs. She slipped her feet from the wooden slippers. The lumpy cotton mattress was cool. She had earlier folded the duvet to the foot of the bed and laid two of Nefise's throws over the pillows. She often studied each stitch made by Nefise's hands. Sister didn't need to draw the flowers and leaves onto the material before she got her needle and yarn. The yellows and blues and reds made a cheerful splash in her bedroom. She wondered if her sister was with child by now. Burhan's hints about Adalet's giving him a son had lately turned to teasing when he drank a bit too much. "I can have a second wife, you know," he said with a wicked grin. "You are not a very productive one."

"A little company while you are off who-knows-where at nights would not be such a bad idea," she answered.

"We are orphans," he said. "Let's have a child."

"It would be difficult now – to fret over the safety of a child's life as well as my own," she told him.

The week before, nevertheless, her shame tossed aside, she had gone from Gumushacikoy to the American doctor at the Christian Missionary School in the bigger town of Merzifon, accompanying Burhan on the twenty-five kilometers across a flat dirt road, four hours each way by cart and horse. A sister of the mayor, unbeknown to Burhan, accompanied Adalet to the doctor. That Doctor Martin had been famous for taking care of women's problems.

Adalet's thighs now against the sheet of her bed looked red and fleshy. Maybe the blush came from being on the table in the doctor's office when he did the small operation. He had reached deep inside her and opened up the door to her womb. She had closed her eyes and thought of herself as being far away in her father's garden. It had not taken long at all, though it was painful. "Go have a baby now," the doctor told her.

Adalet had not told Burhan what she had done. To pay for it, she sold a gold earring to a neighbor who dealt in such things. No need to risk Burhan's reaction to something that was her private matter. If the operation would work – who could say? Adalet lay with her secret against the duvet and closed her eyes.

Jerking awake, she sat up, her toes searching for the slippers. Seconds later, Adalet's hand was on the rifle by the bedroom window. She was still as ice. Her ears were trained to know what was outside. A big horse clopped down past the house. OK, now, here boy." It was Burhan.

While he bedded down Lightning, Adalet ran a comb through her hair and twisted it up again into a knot. She splashed her face and arms with lemon scent before rushing to the kitchen. Her face was flushed with welcome as she opened the back door.

She stood up on her toes to receive his kiss on the cheeks; but he reached the hand that held his riding crop around her back and lifted her to his chest and held her tight against him. There was no smell of raki. "You're hurting my back," she said. He let her feet go gently onto the floor.

"It's good to enter the warmth of this house on such a weary night," he said, shoving the door closed behind him.

"What happened? Are you hungry?"

After draping his crop and leather coat on the nail at the wall, he sank onto the stool. She stooped to help him off with his boots. His woolen socks were wet with sweating. When she brought his slippers to him, he stretched each leg before he stuck his feet into them, giving out groans. She stood back up and over him. "Your tea is made," she told him.

"Any problems tonight?" he asked.

"No, none. You?"

Sitting on the stool and leaning against the wall, he stirred the honey into the tea. There had been no sugar to buy. "Had to take the health officer to the village by the foot of the stone mountain pass. Influenza outbreak. The doctor didn't want to be left to travel back alone. Two women were gunned down this morning in the field while they hoed up the last of their turnips."

"Who?" Adalet turned from the counter, the knife in her hand where she had been slicing beets for his bread and sausage meal. "Why such a thing!" The red juice ran down from her wrist to elbow.

"You don't know – peasants. In the field, those skirts they wear over their bloomer pants matted in the earth. Shot, each of them, twice in the back."

"Pray they died quickly," she whispered.

"When I turned them over, the blood and red earth stuck on their faces," he continued. The juice began to drip onto the floor. Adalet didn't move. "The form of their breasts was there in the soil where they had worked the morning away. I never saw such a bad thing." He looked up at her. "Don't fix me food. I can't eat." Adalet stood with her mouth open, the paring knife in her hand still up in the air. She put down the knife and went to him, wiping her hands on a rag.

"You must eat. Come; let's go in at the table. Bring your tea." She led him to the other room and he slunk into the chair. "Two simple peasant women. What do they know about boundaries?" he said.

"They were an easy prey in the sight of those who mean to keep the disturbance going," she answered.

He placed his elbows on the table. "Another stick in the fire, another blaze. Tomorrow, those not sick with flu will be out with guns. And no one to stop it," he said, and hung his head into his hands. "I can't," he whispered.

She watched him a minute, and then went back to the kitchen. Tomorrow would be another day. She would make his food and he would eat. She bent to wipe up the juice from the floor.

"Adalet!" She heard him call. At the same time, his chair slammed back against the bare floor. Galloping sounds came from the dirt road outside. At once, she darted into the front room.

They grabbed each other by the arms and listened. The iron squeaked on the gate. Hooves cuffed onto the yard. The heavy clops resounded against walls of the still night.

Burhan looked his wife hard in the eyes. "It could be the bandits who killed the women. We can't be taken by them."

The air froze between them, for they knew it was time to do what they had decided. There was no other choice. Bandits would torture the man and then make him watch his wife's being raped. Or they would torture them, rape them in front of each other and burn them both alive. Adalet brought her hand to her mouth and turned. She ran to one window and Burhan ran to another.

They carried loaded rifles back to the center of the room, watching each other's movements through welling eyes.

"Steady!" Burhan's voice was hoarse. "Not until I say, then together. Only then!"

At arm's length, they raised the guns, resting the barrels at each other's mouths.

The low voices talked altogether outside. Torches flickered through the thin blue curtains. Their arms shook with the terror that either might pull the trigger too soon. Boots stomped up onto the porch. Sweat ran down Adalet's nose.

"Governor! Burhan Sir. We are the National Guard sent from Merzifon!"

Balancing only on the glint in each other's eyes, and numbed with suspicion, they eased their fingers on the triggers, and slowly turned the guns toward the door.

ELEVEN

New Life

She was fairly stunned by it. The blood, after all, continued as it had done since she was twelve-years old.

Only last moon did her monthly blood cease. No wonder eight months ago, Adalet thought her nausea had come from the regret of parting with Lightning after over a year in Gumushacikoy. Burhan sold the horse to a neighbor for no profit. They bundled up their few things, broke down the portable furniture and set forth in last December's winds from Gumushacikoy to Merzifon when Burhan was appointed first assistant to the province director in Merzifon.

In February, she realized that she was pregnant when the new life shuddered in her womb. That was less than two months after the settling down in Merzifon. And then, again, Burhan and Adalet set out, this time in a two-wheel covered wagon pulled by oxen with barely room for Adalet to wedge herself inside for the journey. They began a six-day journey two hundred kilometers southeast where Burhan was appointed by the new congress as Governor of the town of Ulash.

Five of those days meant winding along the skirt of the dark Chanik Mountains. Burhan crouched on the buckboard under a large sheepskin contending with snow and sleet while two national guards rode ahead of them on horses. On the third and fourth days, the road was so covered in blinding snow that there were times it would have been impossible to keep going, had not

Burhan gotten out and led oxen by the bridle, talking courage into their ears while one of the guards held the reigns. Beyond the settlement of Tokat on the fourth day, the snow turned to mush.

They rode against icy rain from Yildizeli village into the bustling town of Sivas where they bedded down in a warm travelers' inn. Adalet was pleased to be in Sivas, for it had been there back in 1919 that Mustafa Kemal Pasha had held an extensive congress for independence.

Burhan and Adalet had stocked the wagon with supplies in Sivas before heading out toward the wide Kizilirmak River, Inshallah, and toward whatever the morrow placed in the path of Governor Burhan and his plump-red-apple wife once they could finally settle in Ulash. They sat together on the buckboard, rumbling over the cobble streets on the way out of town. New guards rode discretely ahead of them. Adalet looked up at the two colorful porcelain glazed minarets sparkling back a pale sun. Those minarets had endured since the thirteenth century. It was a good sign. In Ulash, Burhan and she would stand in the sun together. Her babe was quietly growing inside of her. Adalet was anxious that the new one should have a space in which it could survive and flourish. Inside her womb, all was well. Outside was confusion and insecurity.

"You know who first told me about those minarets?" Adalet asked, touching Burhan on the arm. He glanced up and dipped his head playfully toward her. Burhan wasn't very interested in old mosques.

"Your father, Blacksmith Mehmet Nuri," she said. Burhan raised a brow and looked back at the road while she continued. "As a girl, when I used to go with family into Kirkkilise, I would wander to his shop; and if he wasn't busy shoeing a horse or giving men directions, he would offer me a treat and we would talk."

"He had seen Sivas?"

"When he was a young man making his journey westward from Mecca." she smiled, remembering how she had lingered in fascination at the words of Mehmet Nuri's story: Led by kismet and wonder from the bowels of Uzbekistan, on a pilgrimage from which he could not turn.

Burhan shifted his hips and flipped the reigns. The mules trotted a few seconds and then slowed to their own pace again. "Well – those times have little meaning now," Burhan said flatly.

Adalet realized that she had made a mistake in bringing up a sad subject. Mehmet Nuri now remained trapped in Izmit on the far eastern inlet of the Sea of Marmara where the Greek troops had seized everything. Adalet and Burhan did not know if Mehmet Nuri and his wife still retained comforts of a home, or even if they were yet alive. At least, Adalet had word that her own family in Istanbul was still safe.

And, the will of Allah had allowed Burhan's brother, Ruhittin, to return from the war after three years in Yemen and then three more in Egypt as a British prisoner of war. It was told that when Ruhittin got off the ship with the other prisoners of war, none recognized him. He was like a yellow skeleton. Still trying to make himself a fit man again, Ruhittin, a year and half ago, taking no chance of facing another enemy, stole away with his wife and child. Burhan and Adalet heard they were hidden somewhere.

Back in January of 1921, the Nationalist Army had won at Inonu, some ninety kilometers south of Izmit. The Greeks had been stopped at the second battle at Inonu two months later in March, but they had advanced and still held Eskishehir – a little more than two hundred kilometers from Ankara. Those who could, fled ahead of the invaders; but what of women in the act of birth? Or those in labor – bumping along the hard earth in a wagon, straining against new life, knowing two throats cut almost as quickly as one?

All was in the hands of Allah, but keeping faith was not easy with so much to fear. Mustafa Kemal Pasha remained calm and sure – or so it was said. Let the sultan stay fixed to the old ways. Adalet was done with pondering and caring what happened to the sultan and his inefficient court. Pasha told the people they would find the strength within themselves because they must. There was nothing left to lose. Will and heart for the future must be greater than the single need. Yet, here was she, far from her kin and restrained in her dreadful ordeal. Brave, one must be brave. The newspapers had in 1921 described the strong peasant women, who had gone with the men to the Black Sea. They brought handcarts from the Black Sea port of Zonguldak to Ankara, loaded with cannons and shells from Russia. Some of the women carried heavy weapons on their backs. The new supplies from the Bolsheviks had to make it to the front in time to stop the Greek's progress. The Nationalists situation in the country was much like Adalet's predicament. Desertion was not an option. The National Defense Army would soon start the Greeks running. But, Burhan said that Fuat held great worries even though pacts, constitution and celebrations went forth in Ankara. Doctor's friends were afraid the British would join the Greeks in their war and invasion. The Greeks already had more men and better guns than Turks. They also had motorized transportation.

"But nothing's ever lost, Dear," Adalet said, finally answering his retort. "If Mehmet Nuri hadn't felt his fate pull him to Thrace, he could have settled in this place; and then you might have never been born."

Burhan raised his brow again and threw his smirk across at her. "And then Dearest, your life might have been in Paris."

How long had he known that she had once dreamed of Paris?

"Missus, see what I have brought you!" Adalet had not heard Fatma come through the open door of the kitchen because she was intent on carefully lifting the lid on the wooden box. "See! I have the special green apples of Ulash – picked today." Adalet did not answer because there could be no disturbance to the boiled sheep's milk into which she had stirred the starter for the cheese the morning before. As she eased the lid off slowly, then lifted the corner of the cloth, she could hear her servant girl spilling the apples from her apron into the big basket on the floor. If Adalet had been in the kitchen, she would have made Fatma unload the apples one by one. Now, some of those eagerly awaited treats would be bruised. There was so much to teach the blue-eyed Fatma. She was fifteen, but had not yet been engaged nor even promised. Her strawberry ringlets should have made her a prize; but her Circassian men, the same as Turks, were occupied with being lost or waging war.

The water underneath the cloth was yellow on top. That was good. Adalet carried the box out of the pantry, resting it on the round top of her bulging stomach. The babe kicked at her ribs.

Fatma lifted the basket and presented it to her. "You have been craving these, Lady. Shall we boil some for Governor's supper?

"Ah, wonderful, Fatma. Of course, we shall, but I'll make pastry of them. Governor brings guests to dinner tonight. Set three extra plates." It was amusing to Adalet that the maid had taken to finding special treats for her husband, Burhan. He had, of late, begun to tease the young girl – to distract the heavy mood of the war, no doubt – for they were always looking for ways to forget it.

Fatma took the apples over by the window, set them on the counter, and picked up a knife. "There is no need to wash them," she chirped. "There was a hard rain at noon, and I let none of them fall to the ground."

Adalet had gone to the other side for the rest of her task – to her cooking stove, which even had an oven for baking. Good kismet placed Burhan and her in this house with its kitchen, wide and long enough to have a large table. There was even a separate room for Fatma. With the oven, Adalet could make fresh stuffed vegetables and sweet cakes every day without going outside to a clay oven. The two parlors at the front gave them the privilege of entertaining the men in one and the women in the other. Of course, they were liberal; and if there were singers after the meal tonight, men and women would be together on one side or the other.

Fatma had a lovely voice. "Like a violin," Burhan said. After Adalet and he spoke together of the singing bouts one day, Burhan had returned that evening with another lute for Adalet – to replace the one she was forced to leave orphaned in Kirkkilise when they went to Gebze. Everyone said a third event was a charm.

She hoped that her second lute's walnut frame was in good hands again.

"Now, in the Thracian spirit, we can make a trio." Burhan said. "There's nothing but mourning all the time. Let's sing and make ourselves light whenever we have a chance." He gave her a peck on the forehead and smiled at her repeating, "We really do need to make ourselves happy. Life is short."

To forget in the evenings, Burhan often favored his raki; and that would have worried Adalet more had she not heard that Mustafa Kemal Pasha also leveled his sorrows at night with raki and song; and many were insisting that Pasha was a brilliant hero. Adalet thought it was understandable that a man of exceptional responsibility would require some small consolation.

Allah Knows, they had enough sorrows. Burhan and she combed through newspapers come from Ankara. The Greek king himself had landed in Izmir. The Allies encouraged him by referring to the might of his people's armies of ancient lore. Fate held them all. Adalet often pondered the vision that she had at leaving Gebze, and wondered when the crimson ebb tide they had been sucked into would ever unleash to crush the Greek invasion that had gone on now for three years. For, as it was, the Greeks now occupied and held the western portion of Anatolia, although the signs were that Allied support of those Greeks had grown cold. In fact, the Italians were angry that Izmir had been given to the Greeks instead of themselves.

Adalet set a pan of water on the brick stove and added wood to the fire. When it boiled and cooled, she would salt the water and pour it onto the cheese in the box. In a day and a night, the cheese would be ready to serve.

"Fatma," she said, turning around, "wash them anyway."

Fatma had begun to peel the apples. "Lady Adalet, you are too full of rules that take time." Her voice was a bit of a whine. Adalet knew Fatma did not want to take the wooden bucket to the fountain at the corner of the mosque. A little vocal harmony with Burhan might be enough to win his praise; but for Adalet,

this young girl must learn to cook and take a bit of instruction –
and they would keep everything clean.

"When the supper is prepared for tonight, Fatma, girl, you
may take time off to visit your mother."

"But Lady, I don't mind staying, what of –Gov…"

"Girl, I insist. Go show your face to your father. Would that I
could to mine."

"But Lady, tonight – I"

"Enough. When the guests leave, the Governor will no doubt
wish to be alone with me.

"Kezban! Come to me – Kezban!"

Adalet could hear the new maid running from her bedroom
straight across the stone floor of the kitchen. The clack of the
woman's wooden slippers seemed to drive into Adalet's head.

"Adalet, Lady, I thought you were asleep," she said. Kezban
coughed, catching her breath. She coughed again.

Adalet was not about to start supposing that this peasant woman could have consumption. Perhaps Kezban was not as clever as
Fatma had been; but her appearance was not so distracting to a
husband, either. Adalet squeezed her eyes, then put her hands on
the bed and raised her shoulders forward.

"Are you in pain?" Kezban was pulling the pillows down behind her back.

"I have been in pain for three days now. Is the midwife not
yet here?"

Kezban poured water from the pitcher and handed it to her
mistress, who motioned it away. "Send the midwife to me." With
the fluid, Adalet's legs were tight as eggplants. Her lower back felt
as if a battle-ax were lodged into it. The babe's readiness brought
her great anxiety. Would it not be done with? Her tangled bed
sheets were damp with sweat.

"She was here all morning, Lady; and when you fell asleep, she
went to visit her daughter."

"Daughter! I could be dying –my baby's at the brink– and the
midwife can't wait with me?"

"Her daughter is only down the street, and I can fetch her back quickly. Governor looked in on you after she left. He is at his office. What shall I do?"

Adalet wiped her hands over her face, for she was weeping; though she wished that she could be brave. She recently turned twenty-years old, after all. A woman should have her mother and sister by her side at such a time. All she had was this peasant girl and a midwife who was occupied with the wants of neighbors. The heaviness in her heart spilled into her eyes, and she rolled onto her side so that the peasant woman would not see.

"Adalet, Lady – the midwife says there is no labor yet. She told me make hot towels, lay them under you, and tell you that, 'Only patience will ease the misery.'"

Even in that heat, with no breeze to speak of, the hot towels did help. Adalet sipped at the sherbet drink that she finally took from Kezban. The woman had left the bedroom door open so that every now and then, a small draft of cool air floated like a balm across Adalet's body. Her hair was damp at the neck. Why had she wanted a baby in the midst of this unending war?

"Lady, the mutton stew is finished. Can you take a bit of bread and some broth?"

"Yes, Kezban. When you come, bring pillows for my legs. I can't move."

After the broth, Adalet let Kezban heat the towels again and tuck them under her; and then, she had her to set the baskets for the army at the front of the house, where the dispatch would pick them up. Following that, she instructed Kezban to fetch the midwife to examine her again before Burhan returned. What if the baby's heart stopped beating?

Adalet listened to Kezban humming as she came and went through the front door. Supplies from every household had been requisitioned. Burhan had loaded three baskets and two apple cartons with the necessary soap, candles, boots, underclothes, cloth, flour and leather goods. Today, Burhan was going to the houses for the surrender of all civilian weapons as well as any horses, carts and carriages he could take. All were vital provisions for the movement. Peasants on all sides had so little left, and now they had to give that, too. How would civilians defend their homes without weapons? But, if the Greeks overtook the Nationalists here in the center also, no one would be foolish enough to try to defend a piece of land. Kemal Pasha stated that people are more important than territory. Yesterday morning, in Adalet's tea-cup, there was a figure of a slingshot pulled back, waiting to discharge.

When her water broke three days later, Adalet learned that she had only been practicing for the real pain. The midwife proved to be like an angel hovering over her; and her daughter, whom she brought with her, continually washed Adalet's body with cool water, though the contractions lasted half the night. Twice Adalet prayed to die; but she did not die; and then came the last agony. It was like a burning sword that pierced into her groin – and then, at long last, she heard the squealing; and she knew her most major role with this new life was done. The baby came screaming, angry at getting pushed and pulled into such a scene; but Adalet laughed with joy. Finally, she had some real kin in her arms again.

"Is my son well? Adalet, Dearest, I'm here." The babe was sucking at Adalet's breast. When she opened her swollen eyes, it seemed that she was looking up out of a dark hole. The curtain was almost closed, but the brightness of the morning stung.

"You have a fine daughter," the midwife said. "A demanding one," she cackled.

"A daughter – are you sure?"

The midwife pulled back the blanket.

"No matter," Burhan said softly, laying his hand on his wife's head. "We will call her Elif, 'First.' Anyway, she will have the mind of a man."

Burhan bent to whisper into the baby's ear. When he did, she began to cry. Adalet did as well, for she wished that Grandfather

Emin Aga or one of the fathers or Mother Zehra could have been there to carry on the tradition of a senior family member's whispering the child's name into it's ear. Elif should hear her identity spoken for the first time by an esteemed elder. It is said that way a child would always remember the breath of her or his ancestors.

"And so!" Burhan said. "She recognizes her name! Let it be Elif!"

Governor Burhan went to the front door calling for drinks. "This babe is a symbol of what we dream!" he yelled into the stifling summer heat. "A new baby for us, and soon a new country for our people!"

The infant at Adalet's breast had struggled hard at that door of her womb that she had secretly unlocked in a different time and place. The republic would take another year to develop.

TWELVE

The Reunion

*Central Anatolia, Ankara
and Aegean Coast, Izmir, 1922*

*In the tradition of the ancient heroes and early sultans, Mustafa
Kemal Pasha was at the front, leading his men, Lieutenant Burhan
one of them.*

In August 1921, when the Greeks advanced on Turkish forces pulled back to the Sakarya River, they met with the bloodiest
battle since their invasion of Izmir, with Mustafa Kemal Pasha as
Commander-in-Chief of the National Forces. Halide Edib was at
the battlefront with the troops to lend her support as a national heroine and to record this vital period of her country's history. Earlier that year, Doctor Fuat had asked for leave of his duties as congressman to serve the fighting soldiers as a physician. If
Sakarya fell, the Greeks would advance on to Ankara in short time.
After twenty-two bloody days, and many thousands killed on both
sides, the Greeks were pushed back. Mustafa Kemal became Gazi
Mustafa Kemal, the one who had literally saved central Anatolia
for the Turks. Adalet remembered at the outbreak of the Great
War when he held fast at the Dardanelles Strait at Gallipoli and
saved Istanbul from Allied capture. The Turks, who felt they had
nothing to lose but their lives, were more than ready to gamble all
on the only real hero they had known for such a long, long time.

During the summer of 1922, Burhan and Adalet had left Ulash
and headed for Ankara to become a working part of the active

movement. Nationalists were convinced that winning this war was going to take the sacrifice of every Turkish man, woman and child in terms of manpower, weapons, goods and service. The copper plateau of Ankara ran amuck with rumor, debate and im- patience. The streets remained clustered with factions from many areas of the country and wrestled within itself for a single definition out of so many creeds. Mustafa Kemal made successful negotiations with Lenin and the Russian Communist Revolution. Communist sympathizers with red patches on their suits were among those speaking heatedly in the halls and streets. At length, after his service as a staff secretary to the National Congress for several months, Burhan, like every other able-bodied man, was drafted to the ranks at the battlefront.

When Burhan left for the Afyonkarahisar battlefront, Adalet and Elif moved into Fuat and Mediha's home. This house of Fuat's was originally built to be a summer place outside of the city but it now served a convenient full-time purpose. From there, a carriage took both young mothers to lectures, hospitals and army service areas in Ankara two or three times a week. Wives, mothers, and daughters had taken over field and farm chores with the able men of every age and station away at war or dead. Women joined occupation protest organizations, helped to organize meetings, volunteered to nurse the sick and wounded and provided food and shelter for widows, homeless wives, and children. Others sewed clothing and mended boots and other equipment, collected supplies and packed them off to the front. Some served as interpreters between the nationalities and tribes involved in the diverse effort. Adalet and Mediha were essential in many of these areas because of their education and social upbringing. They were a team, enthusiastically appearing wherever they were needed most.

Because of Fuat's position, the house sat on a street at the base of the exclusive hills of Chankaya along with a congregation of other Nationalist leaders. There were orchards all around, a pleasant view of green, healthy air and a guard in the area twenty-four hours around the clock. Adalet felt safe. Peasant women attended their children when the two women had to be away.

The Victorian house on top of the hill east of Fuat's belonged to Gazi Mustafa Kemal Pasha. Adalet had several times seen the Pasha riding in the back seat of his big black roadster. Lamps lit that spot on the hill from dark to early morning. Often, music floated down from someone playing a piano or violin. It was said that Pasha even had a billiard table to take his mind off the constant stream of generals and dignitaries with whom he had to deal. Allah Knows, the Greeks remained encamped at Afyonkarahisar, Kutahya and Eskishehir, all of them two hundred kilometers west of Ankara.

No wonder Pasha needed his distant relative, the lovely young Fikriye, to ease his mind. "Some call her his private secretary, some his housekeeper," Mediha whispered. "And some just use the word 'companion;' but I dare say that providing her services so easily, she will never be called 'wife.'" Why must the women always give? Adalet remembered her Kirkkilise friend, Zeyneb, who relinquished her right to be uncovered in order to find a husband.

Adalet remained comfortable enough in Ankara, but her mother and father were still in Istanbul with Nefise; and the Greeks were poised to march there. The British had sent troops to Catalca to hold them back – so as to protect their own interests on the strait. She often thought of her older brother, Sabri. Retired from the sultan's army to a desk job in Istanbul because of his war injuries. The times were additionally disturbing for him. Although he was an Ottoman soldier with trained loyalty to the sultan, Sabri joined the Nationalists when the Allies led by British Prime Minister Lloyd George and the Allied Powers laid out the Treaty of Sevres, meant to cut Turkey to pieces. Who could have expected that the sultan would ever be spending his days playing parlor games with the enemy at the expense of the country? Sabri held his position as intelligence officer, and secretly fed the ears of the Nationalists in the Istanbul government. Sabri's soldier's heart wanted to be a part of the Kemalists' forces. He kept waiting for the right moment to join the defense, even as another desk job. He determined to do so when he thought his services to the cause had come to an end in Istanbul. However, even though the country had been waiting in misery for so long, the retaliation to the great offence on the country seemed to erupt out of nowhere, and suddenly. The assault swept forth as surprise to all involved except the cunning Gazi Kemal Pasha and his closest generals like Ismet Pasha, the hero of the two previous battles of Inonu. August 26, 1922 became the epic beginning of a two-week counter-attack labeled the, "Great Offensive." For three years, the Gazi had prepared. On the day before his attack, Gazi Kemal spread the word that he was having a party in his house on the hill. In fact, without insignias and medals, and like a trickster jinni already envisioning the various maneuvers the enemy could make in their dance of retreat, he was steeling toward a surprise at Afyonkarahisar in southwestern Anatolia's early sunrise – when the Greeks would be sleeping off an all-night celebration. The enemy troops were shocked, and didn't comprehend what had happened to them until the victory was accomplished by mid-morning.

News from the battlefront descended onto Ankara in disturbing patches of hearsay, fear and hope. It was critical to Mustafa Kemal Pasha that his attack be sudden and without warning. The three towns where the Greek troops held their positions stood as a wall of ammunition and manpower that the Nationalists did not possess. After Turkish forces surprised the Greeks at Afyonkarahisar, the news came that the Pasha had been driven back in defeat. In reality, having sent the Greek forces there running, he circled the Nationalist Forces around to attack Kutahya, the middle town of defense, from behind their lines, so that they could not retreat. Those to the north and Eskishehir soon scattered into the chaos of Greek Forces.

On the sixth fretful day of the Great Offensive, a servant ran into the room where Adalet and Mediha and the babies were having a brunch of creamy wedding soup and hearth bread with shepherd's cheese and tomatoes. Even Doctor Fuat had left for congress that morning not knowing the fate of the Nationalists Army.

"They've taken flight – five days ago," the servant girl yelled. "News came in by telegraph!"

"Who?" Adalet squalled back, standing and knocking over a glass of water. Elif began wailing, but Adalet held transfixed on the face of the maid, afraid to hear the answer. If the Turks were fleeing toward Ankara, all was lost.

"The Greek army! Yes, Lady! It's been announced," she said, bouncing on her toes and clasping her hands to her mouth.

"Allah be merciful," Adalet said, looking over to Mediha who was slowly standing as the news took shape in her mind.

Mediha jumped up and dashed to the balcony, straining toward the distance as if she could see the battlefront. "And the Turkish Cavalry will be on their heels," she yelled. "With swords to cut off their tails!" Guns fired in the air and rang across the high plain.

Adalet picked up Elif and began to kiss her on the face and hair. "Your father's driving out the enemy to the west to the west," she told the child, who had stopped her wailing to watch her mother's strange behavior. Adalet handed Elif to the maid and immediately ran out the door to hear the news for her own self. She could already hear the people coming down into the streets. Someone played a flute. A firecracker went off. She had been waiting three years to hear this news and now it seemed unbelievable.

When the Greeks were ambushed that morning, they fled, leaving everything behind, fires still burning, teapots in the dirt and boots beside the tents. Took off, grabbing only that with which they could run. The overwhelmed invading army succumbed to such defeat on that high ground in central Anatolia that they did not attempt unit combat again. Rather, they stampeded raggedly toward the sea and to their homeland. Only fourteen days later, the survivors of the invading army were clamoring onto the decks of Greek and Allied ships anchored at Izmir.

It was a swift victory. But, in the scattered fields that had been villages and towns, the National troops waded blood and ash left by the retreating Greeks. The entire countryside of western Anatolia was ruined, three hundred miles of the ravaged, the torn and the burned. Some villages remained as nothing but heaps of black char and shells. Villagers, huts and field crops lay trampled, looted, destroyed, raped and wasted. Reports said the stench of human and animal bodies hung over the meadows and plains. The dry earth was scarred with hooves and wagon wheels. You couldn't divide the tracks between retreat and pursuit. It was said that everything looked and smelled like rotting and smoking Hell. Trapped in helplessness, the peasants again suffered more than anybody else. It was like the aftermath of the Balkans again.

Once it was over, Burhan remained in the military as a staff secretary for a few weeks. He told his own particular story of the Great Offensive: Lieutenant Handsome made use of his finesse and talking ability to pull his slapdash self out of that mess. Well, this new country will require those with the gift of speech and charm, she thought. In the midst of the push to the sea, Burhan had occasion to have talked himself out of a court martial – after he led his unit into a swamp. In darkness, the soldiers bedded down. They awoke in the early light sick and disoriented. Like so many drafted, Burhan lacked training for the field.

Adalet stayed on with Fuat and Mediha in Ankara until Burhan's appointment as Governor of Kushadasi, near Izmir. He sent for her. Adalet had no desire to travel that distance on the roads with an infant, with such devastation fresh at hand. One of the essential reconstructions had been on the railroad tracks that the Greeks had ripped up in the western Anatolia areas between Aydin to Izmir. Once that was completed, she was able to bring herself and the baby all the way from Ankara to Izmir on the train. Luckily, Elif was still on the breast and Adalet had an ample supply for a hungry mouth. From Izmir, she rode down to

Seljuk. Two hours more from Izmir, and she met Burhan at the station. He was waiting with a rig to take her and the baby out the sandy gravel lane toward the sea and Kushadasi.

Burhan stood back on the platform a bit; as if he feared they would not be on the train. When Adalet, with Elif in her arms, appeared at the car's doorway, he ran to them like a schoolboy, calling their names. There had been so much death and ruin. Somehow, his life was still his own, and love had come back into that life.

She saw him coming, almost running into the baggage cart, his eyes searching for hers. When he caught them, she bobbed her head and shoulders up and down. At his approach, she could barely whisper, "Husband." She paused in the opening of the train to let him help her down. He stepped up onto the wooden box and took her by the shoulders. His face was drawn from his ordeal but his eyes were wet and clear with excitement. She placed the baby into his arm and took his hand. They moved away from the other passengers and smiled into each other's face for a long moment.

When Elif began to kick and squirm, Burhan gave her back to Adalet. "I'll get my man for the luggage," he called, turning toward the station where the steward waited.

Their life together took on a new preciousness and direction. It was so good to be together again. Still, Adalet could see no reason why the baby and she should stay alone in that cabin in Kushadasi while Burhan would be gone much of the time day and night. Izmir was close enough for him to come each week from Wednesday night through Saturday morning, the first day of the week. The isolation in Kushadasi would be worse than Gebze, and the living conditions poor. Adalet was determined to have her way about the matter this time. With an eight-month-old baby, she insisted that she could not stay in that little mosquito-swarmed mud house, although it was understandable that Burhan wanted the baby and her with him. After all, they had been separated for four months. The road from the railway station in Seljuk to the town was little more than ruts.

"You want your baby should have malaria?" she said, after two days in the assigned accommodations.

"We placed this netting on the crib."

"Passing through Izmir, I saw there were still nice homes left standing. I saved your gambling winnings that you sent me these past six months. We can use it."

"I'll take the two of you this next week-end. I have some influence in these matters now; and, if we find a suitable house in Izmir, you'll stay. Otherwise, my wife will share my quarters here. We'll have the place fixed up. Easy enough."

Adalet prayed for three days to find a house; for even though many had fled the city, there was still a shortage of living space.

Three-fourths of Izmir once called "The Pearl of the Aegean" had been burned to gray. Nobody ever knew who started the great fire that spread when the Greeks were clamoring aboard the harbor's boats and ships. The city now had many charred single walls of what were once gallant dwelling places. Other relics stood vacant in the air like skeletons. There were fences around nothing but foundations dividing spaces where families had eaten and slept – reminding Adalet of the ancient ruin sites all over Anatolia. The gaping window holes whistled as the wind blew without restraint from the sea to the hillsides.

Kismet led them in the late afternoon of that next Thursday to a house that stood intact, on a street just off Kordon Boulevard, vacated by a Greek businessman whose family had for three generations been famous for the export of olive oil. This Greek was only one of the several hundred thousand Christians to move out of the country. Burhan would be able to come and go every few days. Turkish Izmir very slowly began the crawl out from under the ruins of Turkish-Greek Smyrna.

Old Smyrna and the surrounding provinces, famous for the independent efe, a swashbuckler famous for his heavy regalia: plum-shaped headgear rimmed with goddess-like tassels, short bloomer pants and leather leg guards, boots of hand-stitched ornamental designs, blouse and embellished vest, mound of tapestry wound around his belly to hold his knife, sword and moneybag. Gone from the boardwalk his long dangling beads, sagging mustache and smoking pouch swaying as he swaggered in the confidence of his domain.

From the hills to the coffeehouses, Smyrna, a harbor for the world, would never be the same. As for Anatolia and Thrace, the entire landscape was a ghost of tens of thousands of Christian merchants and craftsmen. The British Navy had protected and secretly moved out of the country the ineffective Vahdettin, Sultan-Caliph and the "Sun of the Earth," to where he would die in exile five years later. There were those Christians who had wanted nothing but to continue living as they always had –in peace with the Muslims– but the majority of those had no private choice. They had to leave. Scattered remnants of the Ottoman Greeks and Armenians managed to stay in place and lived on in the new country with the Jews, the Laz, the Circassians, the Kurds and other ethnic groups.

Those Ottomans, who resisted leaving the Motherland, but who were forced to go, would certainly live and die with the memory of Anatolia or Thrace in their hearts. In their eyes and words, people would no doubt know them as persons with something of focus lost, as vanished as yesterday's meaningful glance.

THIRTEEN

Izmir

Women were now able to do such things if they wished.

The Aegean Gulf of Izmir and its surrounding bountiful plains and rising hills and mountains were no stranger to change. The name, "Smyrna," grew from the Anatolian Ionian dialect and dated back thousands of years to the Trojans and Hittites of Homer's *Iliad*. The Persian Empire took the site; and then, Alexander the Great. Exalted by the Romans, the Byzantines, the Crusaders and the Ottomans, it now would again be the "Gate to Asia," but that of the Turkish Republic.

Though green parks, avenues and the sweeping curve along the bay remained, Izmir sighed and complained with the weight it had carried those last few years. There were still a few scattered white bungalows nestling among their groves as if nothing important had happened at all. Intermittently, the palm trees produced a weary rattling and hiss as people passed; but few had time for reflection.

The first weekend that Burhan brought Elif and Adalet into Izmir from the village of Kushadasi, they stayed in one of the hotels left standing on the quay, and the three went strolling along the broad promenade within the nips and curling caresses of the evening breeze. "The trolley is coming, Elif, baby. Hear the bell?"

Adalet asked. They waved at the horse drawn carriage cutting through the placid air come off the shore, its curtains tied back tight against the tops of the vertical railings in order to give the seated passengers a panoramic view.

"Tomorrow, once we're settled in, I'll take you to Konak," Burhan said. "The German Kaiser Wilhelm Clock Tower still stands." Pulling her round cheeks up into a smile, Adalet beamed back at him with the glowing belief that her marriage was at last on solid ground. Up until the present, they'd hardly had a chance to relax into it. The army had made her husband a bit leaner, but he seemed not so nervous. He was so obviously pleased that they were with him.

"One day, if you dare to visit me in Kushadasi again," he added with his distinctive grin, "perhaps I'll show you something you won't believe." She smiled across to him. "The locals took me out on horses to see the province and we rode into an ancient marble city." Adalet raised her brows in question. "In ruins, of course. Ephesus." He nodded his head. "There's much in Turkey to see. Nearby, is the spot where Mother Mary herself lived." He shrugged as if he didn't want her to think that he would believe what he was going to tell her. "Some believe that if you drink the water at Mary's place, you can be healed of whatever ails you." Burhan placed his hands together in reflection. "They tell me that there's still a huge amphitheater where they used to perform," he said, pursing his lips. The wind blew his hair playfully across his forehead.

Adalet thought of how she'd first been entranced by Burhan on the small stage of her middle school back in Kirkkilise. If they had lived in different times, Burhan could have been an actor. "I can see how a large theater would interest you," she answered.

Adalet had read the life of Mother Mary in the *Koran*. "It's finally safe for my Mother to go back to Kirkkilise," she added. Burhan only acknowledged politely. She knew that he still had disturbing and distant feelings about her parents.

"What do you think the history of the ancients have to show us?" he asked, nudging slightly her arm that helped balance the toddler on her shoulder. "We had better become philosophers if we're going to build a modern nation."

She was taken aback and flattered that her man had asked her such a thoughtful question. Maybe he was beginning to see her as more than a girl. She shifted Elif in her arms so that the curly brown head lay on her breast, for the child had fallen asleep in the warm air. "That everything you can imagine can be made to come to pass," she began slowly. "That miracles do happen when there is a great leader and when the will of the people is strong," she proceeded. "But, achievement comes with some tragedy and defeat in its wake." He regarded her seriously. As they walked on, she continued. "The Ottoman Sultans are now history. Once we were Ottomans, you and I. What can we say to ourselves? One must tend to the daily home fires." She had concluded in a definite tone.

Burhan stopped and gently removed the child from her arms, careful not to wake Elif. The three had come to a stone bench that faced the open harbor. They sat in the silence for a few minutes until the belching horn of a small ship stirred up Elif's thin whine that threatened to burst into bawling. Burhan transferred Elif to Adalet, who knew how to calm her back into quiet. After a bit, he scooted to the end of the bench and took out his tobacco pouch and papers and picked back up on the conversation they were having before. "Who are we now to be, we Turks," Burhan said, spilling the brown bits in a line along the edge of the paper, "the spirit of the Gray-Wolf tribes who came from the Asian Steppes?" He slid the bag into his inner coat pocket and then delicately rolled the smoke while he talked. "Or, is our future to be so many well-trained puppets like our last sultan –" He licked along the end of the paper and sealed the cigarette and stuck it between his lips. Patting for a match, he finished his question, "Dancing wildly for Western audiences?"

A phaeton rushed past behind them. Adalet turned and watched it jog on around the wide boulevard, listening to the hollow clops of the heavy hooves as they busily faded into the distance. She wondered if Burhan pondered much about his father, Mehmet Nuri. Burhan usually didn't share his inner feelings. The two of them had heard that the blacksmith had died under the legs of run-away horses that dragged an empty buggy. It happened during the chaos when the Greeks retreated from Izmit. Who would have thought such a fate? No one seemed to know if he was buried, or where. Burhan did not want to speak

more about it; and naturally, neither of them had seen Burhan's brother Ruhittin for several years. She turned back toward the sea and watched the undulation and changing colors of the water. The sun had all but set. This day would move on toward tomorrow. Mehmet Nuri had lived a decent life. Allah keep him. Perhaps there was not much more to say about it.

Mustafa Kemal Pasha would later tell the new nation that all must respect the tradesmen who were vital to keep society going. So many artisans had been lost with the Christian deaths and evacuations. "The true owner," the Gazi would say, "is the peasant who is the real producer." For Adalet, this would include shoemakers, tailors, carpenters and blacksmiths. The memory of Mehmet Nuri's life and journey would always provoke Adalet's heart and mind to wonder. Was all of life a planned journey toward a certain death?

In January of 1923, Mustafa Kemal Pasha's mother died in Izmir. Since Muslim burial took place within twenty-four hours, he was not able to make the funeral. He was busy pulling the country back together, inspiring them to study, naming equality as the key, especially for women. Furthermore, he proclaimed that the future meant engaging in the invention of art and science. Turks should not continue the ways of the conservative, submissive past. Education was the first duty, ignorance the curse. Pasha soon arrived in Izmir to give an elegy at his mother's gravesite. Gazi Mustafa Kemal said that women such as his mother had been victims of the sultans, and that society had restrained women like prisoners. Pasha stated that although she was blind and her body broken, his mother's spirit had remained strong until the end. He emphasized that he most honored her zest for life and her spirit of survival.

Adalet treasured those words. She had heard the report of his passionate words when she visited the cinema near her home, where she went often to see silent movies and to hear the news. She wore a headscarf – or not, at her pleasure. In the afternoons, she was free. Elif had a nursemaid, a young woman who had been left all alone in the world when her entire family had been killed. The young woman had run to the blue hills above the gulf where she hid with a band of other refugees until Izmir was liberated.

Izmir's parks, public places, mosques and theaters held lectures on political and social life. Curious Adalet went as much as she was able. Burhan continued to engage his wife in intelligent discussions. Adalet studied the new choices for women and the poor. Gazi Kemal had the gift of vision, explaining the rights of people in a common language they could understand, and outlining programs that would enable progress. Empire and supreme Islamic law were scattered in the trenches of war. Now, nationalism and democratic idealism held sway.

In her own cups, Adalet saw that Pasha was to be the master-artist who could create something out of little, and the master-teacher who was going to show Turks how to perform such miracles themselves. Adalet conceived creative spirit to be like the genie from Aladdin's lamp in *The Arabian Nights*. What a kismet they held in their hands – to be living at the time of a rebirth. Adalet woke up every day wondering what new thing was written on her own forehead as a part of it.

One day not long after, they heard that Pasha was taking a wife. Fikriye, his amorous cousin through his stepfather, had become sickly and was sent to receive treatments for tuberculosis in a sanatorium in Europe. Poor thing. But, apparently, Pasha had found an educated, suitable woman to share his visions.

Burhan received a telegram from Fuat. Mediha and the Congressman were coming to spend the night with them in Izmir following one of Pasha's wedding receptions.

For that important event, Adalet had a Jewish tailor create a white jacket for her black gown. After its bodice seams were taken in, Adalet polished her gold and gem-studded brooch. And then, she had her hair trimmed. Burhan would need a new black suit and tie for the formal affair. Governor Burhan and Adalet would accompany Congressman Doctor Fuat and Mediha as well as Adalet's courtly neighbors, the Italian Consulate and his silver-haired wife. Adalet sent a letter to her mother and father, now settled back in Kirkkilise, highlighting the exciting details. She also sent the progressive news to Nefise and Ali Fuat.

FOURTEEN

After the Flood

Izmir, early winter to summer, 1923-24

*"Yes," Adalet answered. "The lady Latife asked him twice for an
audience before he received her; and when he did, she showed him
her gold locket with his picture, which she had kept around her neck
for the past two years, praying for his safety night and day."*

Burhan and Adalet at once scooted toward the heavy oak front
door when they heard the carriage wheels on the cobblestones
outside their home. The nursemaid, instructed to take the curly
hair toddler upstairs once she had been presented, followed slowly behind them. Mediha and Fuat would not be so amazed at how
Elif had grown, as they watched how their own children developed. Burhan would have picked the couple up earlier at the train
station had not Congressman Fuat had immediate formal duties
upon his arrival in Izmir.

"Welcome Mediha, welcome! We're honored, Doctor Fuat,
my best cousin," Burhan said, standing in the entrance with both
arms extended. The slender Mediha wore a calf length coat and
black heels with straps that showed-off her nice ankles. A felt hat
adorned her new brown bob. She fell into Adalet's arms and the
two hugged tight and long in the open doorway. The reunion
squeezed tears held back for the past few years. Clutching her
Kirkkilise friend to her breast somehow brought a keen reminder
of the extensive turmoil and fears Adalet had withstood – all too
often in loneliness ever since she was a young girl.

"Adalet Dearest, your house is like a hotel!" Mediha exclaimed. "And you can walk to the harbor to watch the ships."

"Oh, Mediha, it honors me so to have you as my guests," Adalet answered. "You've taken me in so many times in the past! Please come into the parlor good doctor. Warm yourselves" Fuat looked a bit leaner but handsome as always in his wool suit.

The fireplace with its copper hood took the center of the far wall and spread a radiant gleam through the high walls of the room. To achieve the hearth she wanted, Adalet had a smithy off a side street repair a small coal shovel that was topped with a copper handle grip, along with tongs and fork for the logs. The tools lent that touch of proper order to the fire. Adalet liked to curl up in this room on the divan under a knitted shawl, reading alone by its flickering light. So much of life had been hard to contain these past ten years. But, that was all behind.

"I'm not surprised to see your favorite color," Mediha said. "The green velvet of the divan and chairs goes well here in this old house. It favors the Ajem carpet." Burhan found the Persian carpet in the nearby town of Seljuk. The Christians left so much behind, that if one had even a bit of lira or fortune, many goods were accessible. For a few coins, she had claimed a gray-veined marble swan, as big as her bean pot and perfectly hewn. There was no telling how old the swan might be, for there were many marble relics in these parts. The Christians treasured the busts and torsos left over from the ancients. Muslims were forbidden graven images; and so, had shunned them in the past. Adalet sat the swan next to the hearth on the polished floor where it could glide in the morning sun that splayed down through the windows. The elegance inside of the swan made its grace and balance possible. She paid attention to that.

"Burhan Dearest, turn up the gas lamps on the wall," Adalet said. Burhan cast a generous smile over to his wife. She received it with gratitude. Adalet sighed and grinned back at him.

"Fuat, Mediha, take your seats and tell us, how was your long train ride from Ankara," Burhan said with a laugh. Adalet relished watching them enjoy the home she had created in the large gray and black stone house that couldn't be burned down. She placed green everywhere; and even ordered a green coat made for her own self. It went well with her black hair and almond brown eyes. The entrance was a portico rounded at the top. The place was a safe haven for the babe and her and the servant. The windows were high and tight, each guarded by a heavy iron grill that could not be opened from the outside. Doctor Fuat and Mediha would take the room on the second floor that had a view of the long bay. From the other window, Adalet had often watched children in the yards of the terraced houses on the hill. Elif slept with Adalet, although Burhan insisted she be left with the nurse when he came on weekends. His desire was enhanced by the days apart; and she found herself anticipating the sweet smell of his skin and its coarse texture as it nestled its way around her, igniting waves of that mysterious attraction to him. Naturally, she could never discuss that secret with anyone.

The four began exchanging vignettes of their children, of Kirkkilise, family and friends while she served tea and cigarette shaped dough leaves wrapped around white goat cheese and parsley.

"For dinner, I'm preparing freshly caught fish from the bay, and my special baked rice with chicken," she told them. There was also stuffed cabbage and white bean soup, among other dishes, to enhance the entree. "Our desert will be our famous fruit and nut pudding – to celebrate our deliverance from the flood of enemy Greeks!" The celebrated "asure" consumed one full day's attention this week, for Adalet would not allow anyone else to help make it.

"Well, that certainly sounds appropriate," Fuat said, brushing a crumb from his mustache, "Just as the ancient father Noah got the idea of building the ark to overcome the great flood on the earth, so did our Commander-In-Chief envision our united army." Adalet clapped her hand in delight that Fuat understood her intensions toward the celebration meal.

The story of Noah's ark coming to rest on top of a mountain in eastern Anatolia was one that other religions also believed. When she had been a girl back in Kirkkilise, every April, the cooks rich or poor would make pots of the dish. It was written in the holy books that the rains had beat down like thorns upon the wicked earth for forty days and nights. Asure pudding's ingredients were said to be the last morsels found on the ark at the bottom of the sacks and clay pots when the floodwaters receded and the great ark came to rest on a giant mountain's breast in eastern Anatolia. Noah had the nuts, wheat, lentils, beans, chickpeas and dried fruit made into thick sweet soup. It was eaten forever thereafter in memory of deliverance. On holidays in Thrace, the folk used to exchange this special pudding with Muslim, Christian and Jewish neighbors. At the unbelievers' holidays, the Jewish friends offered a wine drink with very low alcohol content, while the Christians would give their neighbors sweet honey cakes.

"We can't get fresh fish in Ankara," Mediha said later, tilting her modern head of hair. "And your asure – full of dried Smyrna figs and raisins was perfect!" Adalet made note to have her long dark hair shaped into a European chignon tomorrow night.

They had moved back into the parlor. The men sipped a brandy that Fuat had brought. Burhan was enjoying his glass with a smoke. Mediha and Adalet again took tumblers of black tea. "Let's hear about this fine wedding reception that we attend tomorrow night. Isn't it all so sudden?" Adalet asked?

Doctor answered. "Our Gazi deserves a marriage to an eloquent family after what he has provided for us."

"Have you seen her, Adalet? Do you know the bride, Latife's distinguished family?" Mediha asked.

"I've seen the bride's picture in the papers and heard kind things," Adalet answered. "About her wealthy shipping merchant father. I've few friends to gossip with here yet, but I read that she's very Turkish even though she is a graduate of the Sorbonne." Latife had studied in Paris.

"But, they say it was she who approached our Pasha," Mediha said, with twinkles in her eyes.

"Perhaps she cast a spell on him," Adalet answered, bringing her hand to her lips.

"You mean like you did on me, Adalet?" Burhan said through a puff of smoke.

"Friends, please," Fuat interjected, "The bride is devoted to him. Her father approves. She's the right type for us now."

"I understand she speaks French, Greek and English," Mediha said, nodding her head.

"As do many of us," Adalet answered. She still remembered much of the French she had learned from her tutors on Emin Aga's manor.

The reception, to which the two couples were invited, as there were others to accommodate all of the important people, was held in a salon in the notable section of Konak where they were served hors d'oeuvres on plates with gold on the edges. Besides the four, there were at least a hundred and fifty persons present.

The bride was not as tall as Pasha. Adalet thought that she was pleasingly fleshy with a round sublime face, just as a lady ought to be. Latife presented well in her short black dress. No headscarf. Quiet. Her liquid dark eyes seemed to gather all around her into a working mind. There were whispers in the hall of how she had resisted Pasha's amorous advances, holding out for the marriage bed, and that she would be one capable of fulfilling for the populous the image of the ideal twentieth century Turkish woman. Gazi Mustafa Kemal Pasha intended to show her as an example. Not only should women be educated, but free as any European or American.

Throughout the evening, Adalet could not help but to gaze at the professional soldier bridegroom. It seemed to her that he was surrounded with an aura. Firm and lean, his burnished hair was combed neatly back, highlighting brows that feathered at the ends above his eagle-sharp gray-blue eyes. She could swear that his every gesture softened each as he moved among the company. A poet might express the inspiration of his very presence – where everyone wanted to share his light, his mountain spring energy and his resonating voice, as captivating as a meteor across a summer's night sky. She had never felt adoration for a person, but she knew on that evening that she could never be truly devoted to anything less than what he represented: The future.

In Adalet's eyes, the bride was like the rest of the company, her light subdued compared to Pasha. However, out of all the women in Turkey who adored him, Mustafa Kemal Pasha chose her. Special, she must be; but was this Latife strong enough to bear a man with so much sun in him?

Fuat and Mediha left the next morning in order to catch their train back to Ankara. Fuat, with important things to plan, was still president of the Society for the Protection of Children, whose services of foster homes ranged into the thousands and thousands. There were not enough funds for all that was needed. Fuat had been communicating with important Turks in the United States who invited him over there for a tour to raise money for the Society. The Pasha's first transport of diplomatic friendship to bridge Turkey and the United States focused on the care for the widows and orphans of the long wars. The country's new leader had chosen Burhan's first cousin to carry out the mission. Adalet's fleeting images were shifting from Paris and its Eiffel Tower and River Seine. She began to dream skyscrapers and provincial towns with frame houses and white picket fences. Why not? Who could say where fate might take her? The revolution had taught her the necessity of vision before accomplishment. Doctor Fuat would be a suitable example of the best of the new Turkish nation.

Times were now constantly changing week to week. Adalet could easily retrieve the news each day from her house to the port or to the center of town. The people were anxious for news from Switzerland where the nations were making a new treaty. The Turkish Resistance and Independence War had virtually nullified the old Treaty of Sevres that sought to partition Anatolia and Thrace for control by western powers. Since the end of 1922, Ismet Pasha, hero of the battles of Inonu, had been working to design a treaty with the world powers that would grant what was left of the Ottoman Empire the sovereignty of a new nation. Finally, in July 1923, Ismet Pasha would achieve the Lausanne Treaty, registered with the League of Nations.

On October 29, 1923, the Republic of Turkey took its place in the world of nations with Mustafa Kemal as its President. Adalet and Burhan took Elif with them to these flag-waving events. The fireworks were endless.

When Adalet had lived in Izmir for over two years, she found herself happily preparing for the arrival of her mother and father. Sixteen-year-old Brother Sukru stayed in Istanbul where he and Maid Hanifey had lived the past few years with Brother Sabri. Sukru's education had been a casualty of the unceasing wars of his adolescence. Father Ahmet said not to worry; Sukru was suited to settling on the farm. That was his fate at any rate. Nefise was moving with her husband, Prince Ali Fuat, to lands that his Circassian family owned in the province of Chorum in central Anatolia. It was hard for Adalet to imagine her sister living away from the Center of the World; but with no sultan, being close to the royal family carried no special permissions and concessions. The fact that Ali Fuat had not been deported with the sultan and those attached to him was a reward for Ali Fuat's secret support of the National Defense before the Great Offensive was launched; and also because of his Circassian ties to his sister, who, as it turned out, was only been a concubine of the sultan.

Ali Fuat had lost one of his lovely Bosphorus homes during the chaos, and was trying to find a buyer for the other. The prince was trained in royal court law school, but the new government was planning to recognize only university-trained professionals; so Ali Fuat would oversee the management of large farms of wheat. He and Nefise would have a nice house built to hold the many children they hoped to have now that all the fighting was over.

•   •   •

Adalet's parents stayed the whole summer. Mother Zehra was pleased with her first grandchild, who was now actively getting into everything and speaking with the effervescent grace of a princess to whom Adalet could deny nothing. Zehra was not one to fool much with children. She would sit on the balcony off the upper bedroom and watch the ships anchored in the harbor. Ahmet went walking and riding with Adalet throughout the city almost every day. Adalet showed her mother how she could handle maids to keep a big house running. She wore the scarves and jewelry that Burhan would bring to her on weekends. It was evident that their beautiful daughter, Elif, was well trained. In short, Adalet did everything she could think of to make her parents see that she had made a good choice with her marriage.

One day, Adalet prepared a picnic. Father Ahmet and Adalet went to a wide and clean beach surrounded by olive groves and rocky crags jutting down to the sea. He reached for one of the green Smyrna grapes of which he had grown so fond. Father's face was weather worn and his goatee was almost white, but he still maintained himself with dignity. His mind was sharp and he walked miles without heaving for breath.

"Adalet," he said, "is your husband, then, a good one to you?"

"Yes, Father, as you can see, he comes by train almost every weekend just to be with us. He is a very smart man."

Ahmet stared at the hillsides to the south toward the remains of the ancient citadel. "Your mother has mentioned to me several times after Burhan's visits that there has never been an evening when she did not see him sipping raki and smoking cigarettes. Is this his habit?" Adalet's hair under her straw hat felt wet. She shifted her leg beneath her and stared at the waves that lapped at the shore. Father had never taken strong drink or smoked in his life, a social outrage to him. He even refused coffee. Adalet studiously began to cut up the melon, sliding out the pulp and seeds on the edge of the knife, slicing the rind as a boat beneath each wedge and dicing the succulence into mouth-size bites. Her father had taught her how to cut a melon like that when she was a girl. That way, a portion could be served without the need of a plate or fork.

He watched her. "Zehra looks for signs of Burhan's habits in her cups, but she doesn't say what she sees," he said.

Adalet remembered a recent day during tea when Mother Zehra sat talking in the back garden with the wife of the Italian Consulate, probing for her impressions of the Kushadasi governor. The silver haired Italian lady, who spoke Turkish fluently, was fond of Burhan. They often had drinks and dinner together and discussed the formation of the new government, the possible changing of the medieval Islamic code of rules to laws that would be based on freedom, equality and justice. To change the subject, Adalet began telling the lady how her father, Ahmet, had long ago been enthralled with the creed of the Young Turks, and had named her Adalet, "Justice," as an endorsement to their beliefs in an open society. The lady seemed to be impressed.

Mother Zehra had cut back in on the conversation. "I'm suspicious of a man who is determined to have his own way, who caters to his private desires. The Devil seeps into a person slyly and contaminates all who deal with such a one."

"Why, Zehra," the Italian replied, "Governor Burhan's ideals are not unlike the Gazi, in that, he is able to partake of his own pleasures and tend to the business of the country at the same time. Burhan is most in love with your daughter."

"I wonder," Zehra replied. "Perhaps I shall learn to trust him. In the beginning, I was suspicious that Burhan tricked my daughter into marriage because he wanted our money, and so that he could further avoid the army." Adalet was humiliated and broke out in a sweat. That Zehra would make such accusations to a stranger with no thought for a daughter's feelings was unconscionable. Nevertheless, Adalet did not reply, so as not to dare provoke her mother more. Zehra then looked over at Adalet and smiled, saying sweetly, "Perhaps I was wrong. Who knows? There is nothing now but change. Soon, I'll be back in my own garden in Kirkkilise, now that the Greeks have been pushed out for good."

"The world will have no more of wars, Zehra," the old Italian lady answered. "With the Great War and the horrors in villages –and in cities like this one– mankind has seen that to live in peace with a society of nations is the only hope. We have to embrace one another and raise the poor with us as we move into the twentieth century. There'll come a time when war will be known as pagan and barbarous."

Adalet knew that Mother Zehra never accepted anyone after she had seen negative symbols about them in her coffee cups or in the broad bean signs that she would cast across the table. She didn't speak directly against Burhan, but she neither did speak well of him; and to him, she spoke as a queen addressing a page. For his part in the relationship with his in-laws, Burhan said that, were it not for his child, he would prefer at present to stay in Kushadasi on weekends. Burhan was bound to woo Elif to love him best, but the child hadn't grown very close to him. He had been away for most of her young life, and she was so attached to Adalet. Burhan referred to Zehra as, "Your Gypsy Zehra," when he and Adalet were in private. Should Mother know that he said those words about her, she would pack up and be on the train within the day.

Adalet smoothed her long skirt, rose to her knees and placed the honeyed wedge of melon on its napkin into her father's hands; and then, she scooted around on the cloth to watch him eat his picnic treat. Beneath her, like a saddle seat, she worked her hips into the cool sandy earth. "Don't forget that my Burhan is a man of particular education, and special commendations for his valor before and after the War of Independence; and that he is now doing his respectable part for the Motherland. And he is your granddaughter's father."

"He is Doctor Congressman Fuat's cousin," Ahmet answered.

"Burhan also memorized the whole *Koran*, like you," Adalet

added. "He still remembers how to recite it by heart – though he is bound to be secular."

"I'd say that he is," Ahmet answered. He slowly brought up a hand a pulled gently on his graying goatee. "I haven't been able to persuade him to visit the Hisar Mosque with me." He looked over at the shining olive trees in the meadow beyond the road as if there might be some reply from there.

"Perhaps one day we'll all go to America like Fuat," Adalet said to shift the subject. Father always liked to talk about the doctor.

Ahmet turned back to her. "How long was Doctor Fuat there, Adalet?"

"Five months. He made speeches in at least eighteen major cities from New York, Washington, D.C. and Chicago. The newspapers in America reported it with photos of him with the highest leaders – in places called Youngstown, Providence and Pittsburgh." Adalet had followed Fuat's epic journey closely. He managed to raise a million lira for the orphans and widows of the republic. Imagine that. What was most surprising, was to learn how many Turks lived in America.

"Kirkkilise will be famous for Congressman Fuat," Ahmet said. "His mother, Seniye, did a fine job, Allah bless her."

Adalet took a deep breath. "He comes from a good family," she answered. Ahmet smiled. "Father, as you can see, things are well with us, too. Kismet will guide Burhan and me. As far as Burhan's religion, he is led to believe that religion and government must be separated. Yes, Burhan is learned, but he has so many duties that he has no time for chanting at present, and he believes like our Pasha that religion is a private affair."

"Do you still keep to your faith, Daughter?"

"Always, and in my heart, Father Dearest; but there will be no more harems, no more shame from being a woman, and no more wars."

"Gazi Mustafa Kemal has told us that the swords have been conquered by the plows," Ahmet added. He slurped the sweet bite from his fingers.

Adalet drew her hand along the coarse dirt and made a groove and dropped one at a time some of the seeds she had scooped out of the melon onto newspaper.

Ahmet wiped the sticky juice from his beard and smiled. "Inshallah, Girl, the seeds you will plant in your furrow will survive and come to harvest."

FIFTEEN

Signed Documents

Nuri said that Uncle Ruhittin taught him that one could accomplish anything if the mind is set on doing it – and also, if one can maintain enough fortitude.

Again this morning, Nuri and his sisters rummaged through the jumble scattered throughout the apartment. They've finished their picking through Adalet's things. Older sister, Elif, wanted the cracked porcelain teapot that had sat on the hutch. It was a final remnant from Nefise's palace days. Younger sister, Deniz, took the silver creamer and sugar bowl from Burhan and Adalet's high time in Izmir. They all made choices of selected laces and hand-made pillows and scarves. Leyla, the middle and closest to Nuri, found interest in the bolts of cloth and the crystal candle sticks with the brown cracks at the base. Nuri took the music box he had given his mother five years ago.

I unlock a door on the hutch against the wall behind the dining room table in the extended living room. "Nuri, can you help me?"

Kurt pokes his head out of the bedroom down to the right. "What, Mom? Dad and I are trying to get these boxes taped and stored up over the closets." Locks of hair hang over his forehead, wet with sweat.

"I want to know who's to get Mother Adalet's good dishes. Ask your dad to come in here, please."

I open the other doors. The whole set is in here. Adalet never gave her keys to anyone else except Filiz, Leyla or me. Things have a way of disappearing in a big family – borrowed and then not brought back. She also gave me the keys to her doors.

Kurt stands in the opening. "He says if you want to talk to him, he's working in the bedroom." Annoyed, I pull myself up, grunting loudly.

In the other room, I find some vacant space on one of the twin beds. Cartons are piled all over. Nuri is supporting a box against the edge of the opening above the closets that he had ordered built along the wall eight years ago. Kurt watches the bundle and holds his hands up to catch it if necessary.

When Nuri has shoved the box all the way into the space, he turns around. "What were you asking?"

"None of your sisters took your mother's set of good dishes, the ones she kept locked in the hutch."

"Those belong to us," Nuri says casually. "Kurt, if you hand me that short package over there, I'll slide it onto the top of the one we just put away." He points to the box on the table by the window.

"Us?" I ask.

"Didn't you know? I bought those when I first practiced medicine, when I went to Kargi. My mother and Elif's daughter Aysha were coming to live with me there, and I needed dishes."

"Kargi?" Kurt asks.

"Where I lived for four years paying back my medical scholarship. A little town at the end of a road at the base of some big old bald mountains."

Kurt sits on a box with "books" scrawled onto it. "Oh yeah, cousin Aysha must have been really young wasn't she?"

"She lived with your grandmother and me from age three to six and a half. Her father, Kamuran, was stationed on the Russian border. Kurt, hand me that. We still have a lot to do." Nuri is a bit irritated and tired. Kurt lifts the box.

I stand. "Do you want me to pack up those dishes then?"

Nuri catches under the case and speaks through heavy breathing. "No. Just leave them. We'll need them when we come back."

Kurt puts hands on his hips and turns back over his shoulder to me. "I told Dad to let me pack away those boxes, but he insists on doing it."

"Let him manage whatever he wants," I answer, chuckling as I walk back into the living room. These dishes are a kind of a joke on me. Here, all these years I thought Adalet was allowing me the key to the hutch because she especially trusted me; and come to find out, Adalet was only watching over them for us.

I contemplate the black and white photo on the wall. The young Adalet with the long straight dark hair parted in the middle with a white band across the top stares gently back. Around her neck, she wears a locket. In this house, Adalet hung only three photos: The colored one of Nuri wearing a cap and gown, the sepia-toned print of Mustafa Kemal Ataturk with his severe profile, thin set lips and pin-stripped suit and this one of herself, almost eleven-years old. Looks more mature than today's kids. The rest of the family, Adalet tucked into the album that Kurt is now looking through back there in the bedroom.

Adalet had been safeguarding Nuri's china for thirty-five years. I thought about the microwave I bought her as a present last summer. When I came here ten days ago, I found it back in its original box, behind Adalet's bed. I guessed that she was keeping it for me to use when I returned. She was a bit leery of the way it operated, anyway.

Kurt scuffs into the living room. His acquired slippers slap against the hardwood floor, a bit too big for his feet. The album he carries is made of thick black paper, its cover a thin copper sheet with the outline of a mosque pressed into it.

"Have you looked through this thing? Half of these faces, I haven't the foggiest. Do you know all these people?"

He holds it open. I glance across at it. "That big guy there in the suit and hat is your grandfather Burhan." Kurt takes a closer look at the picture as I stoop to take up a large bedspread from a stack of covers on the floor.

"He resembles Vedat," Kurt says. "Same tall and stout body's build and prominent jaw line. Dad looks like Grandmother."

"We'll sit down with the album, later. Right now, Kurt, help me cover the couch and chair. There'll be no time in the morning, with you trying to catch your plane."

Kurt scans the couch and chair. "Are you sure we want to hold onto these?"

"Kurt! Your grandmother always kept these covered to preserve them. She's had these since your Uncle Vedat bought them for her when they lived together."

"And when was that?"

"Nuri bought his mother an apartment before he bought this one. Let me remember —about twelve years ago— and see, the couch and chair still look like new."

Kurt shuts the album and places it on the coffee table and clutches one end of the spread. We unfold and watch it float down onto the couch, and then we begin to smooth it out and tuck in the seams.

"How old was Dad when Burhan divorced Grandmother?"

"It was right before Nuri got into medical school."

"Guess Dad was lucky to have a scholarship."

"Kurt, did I ever tell you the story of how your dad got his scholarship?"

"No, but I can see that you're going to."

"Uncle Ruhittin, these papers admit me to the exams for university, tomorrow morning at eight." Nuri said.

"You'll make us proud, Inshallah. You're smart enough."

"But, I don't know this city," Nuri answered. "Where is Suleymaniye Mosque from here?"

Ruhittin took his nephew to the window of his small house that sat above the Golden Horn, from where he ran a cottage fabric business with the help of his wife and children. After the Great War, there'd been no hope for him to have an education. Life had been rough, but he had survived the nightmares of the prison camp and accepted his fate as best as he was able. Taking in Burhan's son so that the young man could take some kind of test for the university gave Ruhittin some satisfaction. Things had not gone as well for his brother, Burhan, as Ruhittin had once hoped but perhaps Burhan's son, Nuri, would be able to find a better life.

Ruhittin pointed to where Nuri would have to head for the exam. Suleymaniye Mosque was across from the University of Istanbul, where the exam would be given. Its minarets were lit up in fuzzy lights across the Golden Horn and above the Galata Bridge in the section of Eminonu, some blocks back from the famous point of land that housed the Topkapi Palace, the Sultanahmet Mosque and the Saint Sophia. Those monuments of history glistened from the last gleam of the burnt orange of a disappearing sun to far out across the mouth of the Bosphorus and the Marmara Sea. The University of Istanbul sat across from Suleymaniye.

"Tomorrow, just keep your eyes on Suleymaniye's four minarets with its ten balconies. You head for it and you won't get lost," Ruhittin assured him. The young man, Nuri, stood listening respectfully. He'd never tell his uncle that he already knew all about the sultans. Respect was more important than showing what you knew. Suleymaniye stood for the highest point of excellence of the Ottoman Empire. Most Turkish children knew what the number of balconies on a mosque built by a sultan represented. Suleyman the Magnificent was the tenth sultan.

The next morning Nuri ran down among the small houses. Gardens flowered the hillsides for over a mile all the way from his uncle's house to the Haskoy landing – very near the remaining buildings of the Aynalikavak Palace grounds where his grandmother Zehra had been sheltered with Nefise, Adalet and Sukru during the Balkan Wars. Near the landing, there were young boys diving and splashing through the water. Nuri wondered how they stayed afloat. No one had ever taught him to swim. There on the Golden Horn, Nuri paid his five cents for the boatman to row him across to Fener, a cove still mostly inhabited – despite all the ethnic fighting of the past – by the indigenous Greeks from the Ottoman Empire. Istanbul had become a very cosmopolitan city, with one-half of it now settled by non-Moslems. The city had begun to sprawl back over the hills that sat above the waters. From Uncle Ruhittin's window, the Mosque had not looked so far away. From Fener, Nuri still had three or four miles to accomplish, and time was getting short.

He ran along the Golden Horn, around the repair stores and through the crowds that were anxiously pushing to and from the Unkapani Bridge, and then, he sprang up the winding stone streets, always keeping his eyes on the four minarets with the ten balconies. He felt quite alone in his task as he pushed through the busy marketplaces among a throng that moved like a river of humanity that had no interest in his problems. The mosque loomed before him like a mirage; but he kept going, calling himself lazy for not starting earlier.

His lungs were aching and he could no longer feel his legs by the time he ran through the gate of the Istanbul University Biology Institute. He darted up the steps and to the heavy doors just as they were being closed. In desperation, he banged on them with his fists, catching his breath so that he would be able to speak.

A short dark man with heavy eyeglasses came to crack open the door. The man wore a blue cloth jacket from the Biology Institute, the oldest university in the country. "You're too late," the janitor said curtly. "Go home. Be on time next year." He started to close again.

Nuri put his leg through the door. "Please, sir! For God's sake, I beg you, I've been lost."

"Many are lost," the man hissed. "Learn to be on time. We begin the exam."

"Sir, I must take the exams!" Nuri was determined he'd have his leg smashed by the door rather than let it close him out.

Then, a bit of luck happened: Someone from the inside ordered the door to be locked; and while the man turned to acknowledge his superior's command, Nuri slipped his thin body inside and moved like a fox along the walls toward the main hall, and away from the janitor. The doorkeeper made no more effort to stop the skinny youth. As the keeper of the door, the guard was occupied with his big brass key.

• • •

Back on the streets of Kirklareli – once named Kirkkilise--several weeks later, Nuri learned from a friend that his name had been posted as one of the lucky from the thousands who had taken the exam that day at the university. Nuri had not only passed, but he was listed as ninth out of six hundred on the medical school list. That would enable him to have a full scholarship – which meant an unheated room and two meals a day. It was grand to have it.

Nuri took the train back to Istanbul and to Uncle Ruhittin's house. At the university the next day, he learned that he was also eligible to enter architecture school, although he had not qualified high enough on that exam to be awarded a scholarship. He signed up for architecture anyway, for they told him that if a student gave up a full scholarship he might receive it instead.

He registered for the medical school and learned to his delight that the award not only included room and board but also some basic clothing. "However," he was instructed by the secretary, "you must return with a worthy relative to sign collateral. Your full scholarship must be repaid in the case you don't finish." Nuri could hardly contain himself. "Furthermore," the man said, "you'll sign now, agreeing to work for the government for a determined amount of time once you receive your medical degree." Nuri left, promising to bring back a solvent relative.

He tried for several days to contact his Uncle Sabri, called "Cripple Sabri" because of his First World War wound; but Sabri and his second wife and seven children were living on a farm near a village quite a way from Kirklareli. He couldn't get to Istanbul. Nuri's grandfather Ahmet was too old to travel and had difficulty in communicating. The old man had grown rather deaf. Sukru said he was too busy with his farm labors to worry about somebody else's education. Doctor Fuat was a congressman in Ankara – and Nuri hardly knew him anyway. After the last disappointment with Burhan, Nuri was afraid that the famous Doctor Fuat would be hard to contact. Nuri had heard that the heir of Emin Aga's daughter, a son of the one named Gulifer, ran a factory, but he had no tie with them. Nefise and Ali Fuat had a big farm – off in central Turkey. Even if Nuri had known where his father Burhan was living, Nuri had vowed to ask nothing more of him.

Nuri related his discouraging predicament to his uncle.

Ruhittin listened carefully and then stood and hiked up his pants. "No problem. I'll sign for you!" He said it with the air of a pasha. Nuri knew his uncle owned little, but Ruhittin was so absolutely positive and full of resolve that Nuri became hopeful. The two set out for the administrative offices for the scholarships.

They passed by the cluster of gravesites and mausoleums surrounded by a tall iron fence. Nuri noticed there were candles burning on the tombs; prayers enlisting help of the holy dead for the living. He thought to pause and burn a candle for his future; but Ruhittin had already begun to cross the street toward the administration building. So, Nuri imagined placing a candle for himself on one of the tombs, and then hurried for the second time in two days to the old large Konak house that had the extensive and colorful gardens. They were directed up the two tiers of white marble steps and down a hallway.

Nuri saw the reflection of his thin frame bouncing along to keep up with his uncle. Ruhittin was a tall thin man in a slightly wrinkled jacket and blue cap who hadn't shaved that morning. Uncle's shoes needed polishing, but maybe the secretary wouldn't notice.

As they entered the office, Nuri hoped the signing would go quickly, and that he could begin his preparations. The portly secretary in a shiny black suit with a vest, sat at his desk outside the door to the inner office marked Director. Over the rims of thick black glasses, the secretary glanced sideways at Nuri and Uncle Ruhittin with a deliberate air of disapproval. "I am here to have the collateral papers signed so that I can receive my medical school scholarship," Nuri said, giving his name as well. To make matters worse, Nuri was sure that the secretary eyed him as if he did not believe that Nuri was doctor material. He pulled himself up so that he would appear taller and neater and cleared his throat before continuing. "My uncle must get back to his important position at the factory. Please, may we get on with this quickly?"

The man reached over the shelf beside his desk and got some papers. "You own your house or business, of course," he said, looking directly into Uncle's face. "You can fill in the information and put the house as security."

"I don't own a house," Uncle Ruhittin said quietly.

"So you apparently have property?"

"No, sir."

"A car, a boat, a horse, a cart, a goat?" the man asked with rapid arrogance.

"Nothing but a wife and children and a stubborn will, Sir!"

"Well then," the man said with a chuckle, "Without some kind of ownership, how do you think we can receive your guarantee for this boy's scholarship?"

Uncle turned red. The three didn't move for five long seconds of silence. "We will return in an hour," Uncle finally stated. "Come, Nuri."

Nuri followed the quick steps of his uncle, whose feet sounded as if they were trying to crack the brick of the walkway as he moved out onto the cobbled street. Nuri caught up with him. "Thank you for trying to help me." Nuri said breathlessly.

Ruhittin gave him a hurt glance. "Come! We go where we can think what to do."

Nuri followed his uncle into a store. Uncle Ruhittin, who did not drink alcohol before the Great War, began to drink raki as a relief for his mind and nerves after he had returned from his long captivity in the prison found camp. After the war, he was never again carefree like they said he used to be, and was often prone to anger and depression.

Outside at a wooden table, Nuri sat and watched his uncle drink one then another. Nuri had experience with what drink would bring, and was about to get up and leave when this man that his father called "Ruhi" said, "OK, let's go. I've got all the documents I need now!" With that he jumped up and took off toward the door.

Nuri could do nothing but follow, although he was hesitant. He only prayed that there would not be a scene that would dash his pos-

sibility for a scholarship later on, for it was impossible to tell an uncle to go away and forget it.

Ruhittin strutted into the administrator's office and demanded the papers again. Nuri stood back near the door. This time, the secretary pursed his lips and looked Uncle over head to toe and shook his head. He could probably smell anisette, the famous property of raki.

Uncle began to speak in a loud voice. "As for documents? I am the only document you need. This boy needs no guarantee. His parents are the founding stones of the republic!" Ruhittin moved closer and looked the man in the face, spreading both of his hands out on the secretary's desk. "His mother raised him while building this country with her mind and hands! Documents? His father, my only brother, helped blaze the trail to the first roads of freedom!" Uncle pounded once on the desk with a fist. The man sat for a few seconds and then pushed back his chair and stood, his eyes wide and unbelieving. "I spent six years as a slave in the guts of Egypt and Yemen so that fat asses like you could parade around in an office today wearing a suit!" Uncle continued. "Who do you think gave you the rights to have such a job as this?"

A white-haired man, with a very straight back and square shoulders, came out of the inner office and stood at the door. It was the director. "Director, Pasha Sir," the clerk said, This man is causing trouble over the signing of the collateral for the youth's scholarship."

Uncle Ruhittin looked at the director. Nuri sighed. All was lost. He would never be a doctor here or anywhere else. Why had he enlisted Uncle Ruhittin?

"Pasha Sir," Uncle said, addressing the chief directly, "Do you know why I own no home, no property, not even a horse? Can you believe it? Can you imagine my dreams when I was a youth in Kirklareli, such as my nephew here? My mother gave her life giving birth to me. When our country went to war against the Allies, I offered my life to the Motherland."

The man walked around the desk and toward Ruhittin. "Did I hear you say that you were a prisoner of war in Egypt?"

Ruhi stepped toward the man. "Three years, Sir. Three in Yemen. But as you see, I am hard to kill. My best years were buried there while people like these were cheating the government," he said, turning to indicate the secretary. "My property? It's the will to survive for our children." Ruhittin wheeled around and took Nuri by the arm and pulled him to his side. "I can but give my name and oath to the Turkish Republic," he said. "I guarantee this young man will finish his scholarship. If not, I'll work my lifetime to repay it."

The director took Ruhittin's arm. "Calm down. Step into the office with me for a moment."

With the director's door closed, Nuri and the clerk sat glancing back and forth at each other without expressions. Loud talking inside the director's office was little more than a jumble of noise. At length, the secretary made a comment. "Director Doctor Pasha always speaks loudly like that. His hearing was injured years ago." He then bent back to work on his desk.

And then, luck showed up the second time: After ten minutes, the two men came out. "Let him sign the papers!" the director told the clerk. "I was a prisoner of war in Egypt, too. What this veteran has said is absolutely true. His word is gold. See to it immediately." Then, Director Doctor Pasha and Uncle Ruhittin pulled themselves up straight and saluted each other.

There were only these two things of Adalet's that I hoped to take to Virginia, but I didn't say anything while the selections were going on. Adalet's daughters should have first choice. Not that there was that much material of value left. Adalet had given away almost all except the necessities in her last few years. I'm sitting on the bed wrapping tissue paper around the marble swan with the broken wing. It was always on the floor in the living room at one end of the couch. I was happy today to see that no one had claimed it. I wonder why, for it was a neat piece of sculpture. Maybe no one wanted it because of the damage. This gray-veined marble's so common in Turkey. I lay it onto the folded rectangle of fuchsia velvet embossed with gold and green silk that is cut into tulips and leaves. I think the cloth could be several hundred years old. It's lain balled-up since last week. I didn't let on that I wanted it. I secure the fabric in tissue and tape it around the swan. I'll take them in carry-on luggage. Back in Virginia, I'll have the velvet and silk framed. It could have come from one of Nefise's palaces. Who knows?

"Look what I found stuck back in the bottom closet," Nuri says, coming into the room.

He's holding a hand-carved wooden box with a heavy top held on by brass hinges. The open lid looks to be full of papers. Nuri sits beside me.

"What are you going to do with that?" he says. "It will break, you can't take that back."

"I know. I'm going to carry it in my hands." I fold the fabric over the swan's head and hold it in my lap. The swan is like Adalet – elegant and quiet. She had given it the place on the floor where it could peep out unobtrusively at the various comings and goings in a subtle grace. "Do you remember two years ago when you, our friend Margaret, and I took your mother in the wheelchair to the Dolmabahce Palace?"

"She wanted to go on the Bosphorus one more time. Sure," Nuri answers. He touches my hand on the head of the swan.

"And I wanted to see the palace where Ataturk had spent his last days."

Nuri sits back, balancing the box in his hands. "Ah, poor man. He died too soon. Liver and heart spent from too much hard life."

Kurt has slipped into the room beside his father. "Ataturk? He just wore himself out. All the fighting, stress, politics, drinking. What were you saying about taking Grandmother out on the Bosphorus?"

"She had so much energy that day, Son." Kurt crosses his arms and listens. "We also boarded a ferryboat from Beshiktash to the Prince Islands out in the Marmara."

"How'd she take that?" Kurt asks.

Nuri twists around to him. "She loved it. We took a horse carriage and the long tour of the Buyuk Ada – the Big Island."

"She bounced along wearing Nuri's black sunglasses like some tourist," I add. Kurt eases in and leans up against the wall. I smile at the men, and then continue. "In the ferryboat on the way back, Margaret, Nuri and I went to get tea and cheese toasts. When we came back to your grandmother, there she sat – surrounded by about eight men – exchanging ideas with them like she was giving a press conference or something."

"Oh, my mother always kept up on what was going on," Nuri says.

"I guess they were talking politics," I say. "Whatever it was, they were treating her with respect; and she just looked radiant and intelligent. But she was perfectly at ease."

"I'll bet you wished that you could understand Turkish well enough to get the details."

I nod to answer Kurt, realizing he probably wished to be fluent in Turkish many times, too.

"Look here," Nuri says, showing us the open box. Inside are letters and cards. Kurt steps over and shuffles under the letters and pulls out a faded photo of our kids.

"It's Sara Ayla and me."

Kurt bends over Nuri's shoulder. "Gee, we must have been twelve and four."

"My mother saved our letters, some from me, your mother, you and Sara. I'll bet a couple of these are almost thirty years old," Nuri says quietly. Kurt reaches over and takes the box from his dad and sits on the bed looking through it while Nuri and I go to find a carry-on bag for me.

It's then that Kurt discovers a very important document signed by Adalet.

A few hours later, Kurt has gone out with Orhan for one more drink in the Bosphorus moonlight. Nuri and his favorite sister Leyla are talking softly in the corner of the living room.

Nestled in the padded hutch wedged into the windows of the kitchen, I am finished for the time being with the journal where I have jotted Adalet and Burhan's journey together in an outline form. Across from me is Adalet's spot, where she always sat. I light the candle that I bought for her two summers ago and scoot it to the end of the glass table and then click off the overhead light so that I can bathe in the glow.

Through the windows that wrap the nook, I look out onto the hundreds of lights and think how – of all the lights that must be turned on in Istanbul at this moment, these I see from my windows are only a few. I imagine all kinds of lights all over Turkey, over the nighttime world. I remember the gold lights on Ataturk's shrine and museum in Ankara. I could see them at night from my hotel balcony. There were also lights on the relief that honors the female founders of the republic.

I sink back into the booth. Let's be honest. Regardless of all of Adalet's contemporaries' fortitude in building a new secular republic, there's still the same old religious and social conflict today, still the fanatics with swords in their eyes. There're also conservatives of good will, but Ataturk might be disappointed to see so many women on the streets in black coverings. Granted, a lot of them are Arabs and immigrants from Iran and Saudi Arabia. And, there are still plenty of old houses and palaces where life floats up in its waves of soft music, gatherings of progressive ideas and sleek people having drinks around pink tablecloths. Candlelight and talk is fairly free here today even with the traditionalists. Istanbul is still a place with wide enough heart and mind to take in people and trends from all parts of the world. The masses are still restless, still anxious, still driven for survival on the streets and highways, on the move in and out of spaces, filling up all niches in a frantic rumble, trying to stay on top of their fate. But tonight, in this amber, looking out on a cobalt and golden Istanbul, I can almost think Ataturk's motto of "Peace at home, peace in the world!" is a nice thought if not a reality. There was a lot of sacrifice in order for these skyscrapers to be standing here tonight in the moon's calm glow. The same is true of America, as a matter of fact. But, does the contemporary world care?

•   •   •

The candle's flame jumps around on the kitchen walls like an unfocused film. It seems to me that Burhan's and Adalet's marriage fell apart with the confusion of the times – not unlike the Ottoman Empire crumbling after the First World War. Considering the family opposition, they were trying to survive the best they could – like the country in general, I suppose.

SIXTEEN

Marash

Southeastern Anatolia, 1928-29

By the time we came to her, the baby had delivered itself.

Life in Izmir had shown such promise. And then, Burhan had suddenly decided to walk out on it after three years. "It's already been decided. I'm tired of working for the government," he had said on that afternoon. "We'll take Elif and go to Kirklareli and open a shop." The name, Kirkkilise (or Forty Churches) had been changed in 1924 to Kirklareli (The Place of Forties). Forty was the sacred number of changes, renewal and wisdom.

"But Burhan Dearest, our life in Izmir is so good, and we have another child coming. Nothing will ever be as it used to be back there," Adalet argued. Izmir was putting itself back together fast. There were many women's groups and activities that she had come to enjoy over the past three years with laws passed such as separation of religion and government. A man could no longer by civic law have more than one wife at a time. Education for the masses was unified.

"Exactly. We need change," Burhan answered. "I said to myself that my wife needs her family around her with another child on the way."

"What does Fuat say of your decision? You never spoke of this to me before!" she protested, unable to stop the tears. "No! You must not resign, Burhan. Your next promotion could be from Kushadasi to Izmir!"

"Do you think one such as me can take orders easily? Do this, do that!" Burhan fretted around the room, picking things up and throwing them down. "A man never has time for his own life. This traveling, this being separate – it is not good for my nerves." There was of course the familiar smell of raki in the air. When Burhan drank a bit too much, he was inclined to temper. Adalet thought that Burhan's disenchantment lay with his assignment that posed a challenge to his idealism and the belief in the republic's new society. If Turkey was really moving toward a democracy, should not all be treated with respect and equality? Unfortunately, there were still many in positions of command like the narrow-minded governor of the province, who reigned with authority over her husband's powers. The province chief was one who wanted to pull the country back to the Ottoman way of pyramid hierarchy, where position meant control of those below him. He lacked vision of progress. Burhan couldn't tolerate it; and his disappointment was frightening. If Burhan couldn't learn to accommodate, he would never be a leader. Look at Kemal Pasha's life and how he has had to deal with inferior methods and motives. If one didn't temper enthusiasm with reality, one was doomed to fail.

"Did you fight with the province governor? Is your position secure?" she asked.

"What kind of position did I have in that Kushadasi mud box full of flies and mosquitoes? Just because that man loomed above me in rank doesn't mean he can dictate my life. I resigned!" Burhan flung off his tie onto the bed. "I was a freedom-fighter! I would leave rather than be pushed around by a conservative!"

"You fought with him – and now you have lost your post!" Adalet grabbed him at the back of his shoulders. He pushed her away and she fell against a bench. That was the first time he had become physically rough with her. She pulled up and sat down on the footstool. "How can I tell Mother and Father? How can we go to beg shelter from them when we have another child coming?" she moaned. Sobs flushed into her hands at her cheeks. Burhan had shoved her, with the child inside her womb! She leaned over with her sodden face buried and let the emotion drain from her. As it did, she began to rationalize in her mind for Burhan's actions. Perhaps it was not all his fault. As a good wife, why had she not first of all shown him that she understood his disappointment? Maybe she had not been encouraging him to grow patience and perception these last six months when it was obvious that he was becoming more and more frustrated. Now, it was too late. Facing these ideas, she began to choke and cough, wiping her face on the hem of her skirt.

Burhan paced around and then came and stood over her. He gently touched the top of her dark bob and began running his fingers through her hair. "I'm sorry," he said quietly. "You yelled at me." She inhaled a sigh and nodded.

Burhan brought his hand down the back of her neck and around her shoulder as he eased around to the front of her. "We get our own place! Build a house! This one is now worth much more than when we bought it," he said with sparkling eyes. Without apology, he pulled her up into his arms. "We'll have a shop on the spot where my father had his forge and market – and we will have a big family."

After that, Burhan wouldn't discuss what had happened in Kushadasi. In fact, he would storm and leave the house when she tried to speak of it. Adalet wanted him to go to the district governor and petition for reprieve. That made Burhan furious. "Damn province governor's too weak to even take a drink! Damn governor's wife in her long black scarf!"

Adalet harbored suspicions. Raki and wild women had lured her husband into a bad situation. Maybe he couldn't make amends. Men were so weak when it came to that. She told herself that Fortune had given her Izmir for a while in time; but she would never lose what that experience had made of her.

Actually, returning to Kirklareli, working together to rebuild in the heart of Thrace, her family would be like a gold bracelet linked around her at the birth of her second child.

·   ·   ·

With the second child, Leyla, and then the next child Nuri's birth there, the three years there weighed Adalet down with depression and infections that took months to recover.

In time, with the grain and tobacco shop not doing well, Burhan began to order houses built, which he would sell. He was a creative man whose nervous energy wouldn't allow toleration of the ordinary. With each contract, the family would feast; but then the money would be suddenly gone – and Burhan wouldn't talk about it.

There came the day that Burhan slapped Adalet so hard that stars seemed to spring from her head like prickled points of amber. She learned when not to push her questions and ideas on him. His temper caught fire as quickly as a match across slate.

"Are you so dense, or do you actually not realize, Girl," Mother Zehra asked, "that your husband is seen hanging around tea houses known for gambling?" Zehra declined to read Adalet's fortune at all in those days. "I will not speak ill of a son-in-law – even if he does carouse all hours of the night," Zehra would repeat, lifting her brows. "I also refuse to tell my daughter how she wasted her promise by going against her mother and father. I will not dwell on why, when others make their way for my counsel," she added, repositioning her red velvet slippers on the cushioned foot rest, "that my own daughter refuses to heed my advice."

"Mother," Adalet hastened to finally be able to tell her, "Neighbor Seniye has spoken to Congressman Fuat. Burhan's to be appointed assistant to the province governor in Marash."

"To the southeast? To those 'Mountain Turks' regions? What kind of life can that be?"

"Near Antep and within a day's ride to the Mediterranean," Adalet answered. "We could even take a boat to Cyprus for a holiday. Aunt Azime thinks that Burhan has been uneasy doing these boring tasks. His intelligence isn't challenged, and that if I help him, he once again –"

"Don't bring up my sister – who manipulated this marriage behind my back! She brings me treats, serves me tea and calls me

Dearest One, as if I will ever forget it –since I continue to see with my own eyes the disappointment–" Adalet noticed as Mother stopped. Zehra was focused on Adalet's hands that poured the lemonade. Zehra brought her rosy lips together tight. Adalet's nails were jagged at the tips from digging in the herb garden, and her hands were rough from helping the maid scrub the diapers. She had forgotten to bathe her hands in olive and rose oils when she finished.

There were always more important things to do, what with not only taking care of her own three but also watching three extra children, now motherless since Sabri's wife, Servet, died of consumption. Poor Sabri was as devoted and in love with his wife as Father was of Mother.

Sabri's nerves, that had stood him well in the war in the east and his strong will that did not fail him with the pain of his crippled leg, had totally given way at the death of his wife. Furthermore, an accident happened at his shop around the same time of his wife's death. For some reason, a box of gunpowder that he sold from his shelves exploded and a man was killed. Poor decent Sabri who wouldn't hurt anyone was arrested and spent some months in jail. With family connections, he got special attention from the authorities because he was a war hero and was released. However, Sabri's whole idea of himself had shattered. He then abandoned his children in his mother's house, and in Adalet's keeping, while he went away to recuperate for almost three years. Had it not been for the maid Hanifey as a constant help, Adalet could not have done it all.

"Oh, Mother," Adalet said, taking Zehra's plump hands, "They say that Marash is famous for gold and blood-red peppers and the long trains of Taurus Mountains that encircle the town on the high plain."

Zehra squeezed back and grinned. "Not to forget the famous mastic ice cream and soothing salep hot drink made from goat milk and the orchid roots," she added.

Adalet kneeled and looked in her mother's eyes. "Of course," she said. "And when I visit the waterfalls down the slick edge mountain in a silken rainbow, I'll say a blessing for only you."

Zehra smiled. "And they say," she continued, "the town takes on a lavender glow. That's protection if you breathe it into the deepest part of you."

Adalet's son, Nuri, had become so attached to Hanifey that he thought she was his second mother. Adalet's breasts stayed infected for so long after Nuri was born that she had to milk them. Hanifey concocted such a good milk tit that there was never any use to try the breast-feeding with him again. When Burhan and Adalet were leaving for Marash, two-year old Nuri thrashed and wailed for Hanifey. Adalet took him into her arms and attempted to bury his head in her bosom, but he kept reaching back for Hanife as they drove away. Adalet wept with Nuri because she, also, knew Hanifey like a mother. If Zehra had not needed Hanifey so badly, the faithful maid would surely have come with them.

Off and on during that year in the rust-red and ash-gray plains of Marash, Adalet looked out the window of her duplex house toward the mountains mixed with the colors of weathered copper and pewter buffed to a sheen – and yes, some were even that sandalwood shade of her cup of the sweet sahlep that she sipped while waiting out the cold evenings once the children were in bed. The old citadel sprawled over the top of the high mound, shaped with unyielding giant cones and canisters meshed into its thick walls. Marash had tolerated the Hittites, Byzantines, Romans, Arabs, Crusaders and Ottomans. And then, those plains endured the French occupiers, who swarmed in with leagues of Armenians called "La Legion Armenienne," goaded on by the victorious Allies – who wished to entrench a Christian state in Anatolia. Such a confusing time. So many factions seeking the spoils of the sultans. Local Christians took up arms as well. In the winter of 1920, National Revolutionary Forces fought the intruders back until the French retreated, letting the bloody battle between Turks and Armenians play out until the creeks turned purple. Twelve years had swept change so radically and rapidly.

The battle for Marash led the rest in the War of Independence. Even the sultan, let alone the Europeans, didn't know what to make of that one, Mustafa Kemal. The British and French argued over who should control southeastern Anatolia. First the British left and then the French, taking five thousand Armenian soldiers with them. Allah bless, all but fifteen hundred of them died on the seventy-five mile march to the border of Syria. When she had heard the terrible details of the battle, Adalet could not help but sob, remembering what the Bulgarians, Serbians, Montenegrins and Greeks did to the Ottomans and Albanians in the First Balkan War. So much blood lost. Over a million Turks died in the Balkan Wars and the Great War.

Adalet looked out the window to the night sky. The stars twittered as they had done through the centuries between blankets of clouds spreading out from the mountains. That would bring rain tonight and would pass and the blue would come tomorrow again.

During that year in Marash, Burhan made an effort to prove to be a worthy husband and father. Adalet continued to be determined to make her marriage a success. Whether she was in love with him ceased to be an issue; for she had her children, and she busied herself there with teaching the new Roman script and language to serious girls. The young students who came to Adalet's home to learn wore colorful blouses and skirts. Their unveiled heads were wound in white muslin secured with dark red and lilac woolen cords embellished with bright flowered tassels that ringed their faces. Adalet taught at the table in the dining room while her own children played through the house, stopping as they pleased to join the lessons.

The broad duplex house was two stories, on grounds that had been the American Board Missionary School of Marash College. The locals reminded Adalet that missionaries had proven to be mischievous to the country in their support of the Christian population during the troubled years before the republic. Ottomans had allowed missionaries to establish their schools all over Anatolia – some twenty-five before 1880. In their zeal to Christianize Anatolia, they became channels of the insurgencies.

With the exception of the gramophone, all of the walnut furniture brought to Marash from Kirklareli was portable, broken into sections and loaded into a train and then truck for traveling and an easy set-up. Adalet had faithful servants to help her with the duties of the home; and it was lucky for her, because the new baby made its way into the world when they had been there only six months.

"Burhan Dearest, I had a dream last night," Adalet told him one morning when she was in her eighth month. Burhan had been absently eating his white cheese and olives while he read.

"You and your dreams and visions amuse me Adalet. Tell it," he said, laying aside the newspaper and reaching out to stroke the side of her bulging belly; for he was hoping for another son – one who seemed a bit more like himself, who was not so much the mother's child, one who did not play at dolls and sewing. But secretly, Adalet already knew that Nuri was destined to become a doctor, just like Fuat. She enjoyed watching her child cut open the dolls. He would examine their insides; and then, sew them back up to heal them. It was written on his forehead. As simple as that.

Adalet offered the pot of honey to Burhan. He always topped off his breakfast with a bit on toasted bread and black tea. "I dreamed," she continued, "that I walked into the room and there was the gramophone sitting on the table, and the sun was glinting off two brass plaques attached to the front," she told him, reaching over to smooth down the lapel of his riding jacket. He pushed back a strand of hair fallen to the side of her face and smiled at her as she continued. "One of the plaques held the name 'Deniz' on it and the other 'Mahmut.'"

"Ah," he said, picking up his leather riding crop and his silver cigarette case. "If it's a son we'll name him Mahmut."

•   •   •

When the time was ripe, Burhan had gone for the midwife and didn't return for hours. The servant and Adalet had been singing in the playroom with the children when she felt the first wave of pain. By the time she came down and into the dining room, her water was breaking. The pains took Adalet to her knees, and then onto the floor.

A week later, after baby girl, Deniz's, birth, Adalet was sitting up in bed, eating the famous Marash gum-mastic ice cream to celebrate, and talking with visitors about her dream. "The meaning," she told them, "is that Deniz will one day marry Mahmut and they will make music together."

"You are fortunate that I am your neighbor," the doctor answered.

"Oh yes," she said, nodding also to the pharmacist who had come with the doctor to pay respects.

"Had it been more than a single wall that divided our two houses," the doctor added, looking to the pharmacist, "my wife would not have heard the chair hit against the door and definitely not been startled by Adalet's scream as she went to the floor. By the time we came to her, the baby had delivered itself."

"Doctor had only to cut the cord and hand my little girl to me," Adalet said, beaming over to her side where Deniz lay sleeping, wrapped tightly in her blanket. The other children had been born with heads of thick curly hair. This one's black hair was straight as a stick and long as a bob. She was filled with the blood of the Crimean Tartars from Father Ahmet's side of the family. Deniz pushed into life without help. This one would be headstrong and demanding. In fact, on the day that she was born, Deniz was screaming for more breasts when Burhan finally came back with the giggling Kurdish midwife.

SEVENTEEN

The Female Bird Makes the Nest

1931-1936 Bilecik, 1936 Kars/Karaköse

They entered fog tunnels as they came up out of the valleys.

Life had been good during the years they had lived in Bilecik. Three children were born: Vedat, Sedat and Oznur. Nationalism was riding high in the belief of Pasha's principal of Populism. Adalet loved the name he gave of the "People's State" – not to forget the name the Parliament conferred to Pasha in 1934. Mustafa Kemal was now "Ataturk – Father of the Turks." The newly-scripted citizens were hungry to read the newspapers and magazines coming out all over the country in order to hear of openings of state factories and banks that would make possible the goods needed so badly. Industrial growth continued to be on the rise, as did the cities that formed around them. On the Black Sea, the city of Zonguldak began a Mining and Engineering School. The country was putting itself back together with energized workers to whom the Constitution gave the rights to form unions. Development of the people's land by the people. The common worker laid railways, dug irrigation projects and erected the banks and business centers that made the increase of import and export possible. All was led by the nation's hero and untiring cheerleader.

But there were continuous fights erupting within the bosom of the land. In eastern Anatolia, the Kurdish and religious insurgencies flared up often, followed by news of deaths and transports. In Thrace, anti-Semitism caused many to flee for their lives. Even Pasha suffered assassination attempts. Such terrors prohibited true democracy. Would there never be an end to bloodshed and hate?

Adalet took heart that, under the Constitution, women could not be discriminated against. The civil law prohibiting a man from taking multiple wives was passed ten years ago. Women now had the freedom to choose their own professions. They could testify in court and enjoy equality as far as inheritance, testimony in court and divorce matters were concerned. Finally, in 1934, women won the right to vote and to be elected to national office. Here in 1936, there were eighteen women in Parliament. While Burhan and she daily supported all of the freedoms and equalities and the building of the new nation, their growing family could not predict from one day to the next whether it would take its cup with joy or sorrow. The equal man and woman of this clan had many issues not settled by arguments, silence or tears. Burhan juggled his charms among the coffeehouses and at the podium. Adalet found herself studying him to find that weak spot in the fabric of his character where she might enter as a stranger and thereby communicate quietly at the table of his peaceful soul. But, he was always on guard and would not let her in. Most of all, she wanted to discover the way to fix him so that all of his potential would come to pass.

But, after six years there, Burhan had left the children and Adalet in Bilecik in 1936 – not only so that the children could finish the school year but also because it fell to her to sell the house, some of the furniture and the goat and the cow. There were other necessary duties such as preparing warmer clothing suited for the mountain pastures of the ancient town of Kars. After all, it was located near the northeastern border with Russia.

Following a month of his being in Kars, Burhan sent a whole round of Kashar cheese back to the family. The pale yellow mass as big as a festival cake with gaping holes weighed nearly as much as a garden-wall rock. He had filled the holes with hard honey candies. The children were delighted with it.

Adalet was actually relieved that her husband was gone from Bilecik – where she was sure that everyone knew how he had been tripping around the town at night like a fox after chickens. It would take a while for him to get such a reputation in Kars. The children and she would be with him before he would have time to find trouble for himself. Or, so she reasoned.

Burhan's letter that came with the cheese had set her mind to wondering what he might have been doing to hurt himself. He didn't give any details, only that he had unfortunately taken a fall that had broken his leg, and that they had sent him across the border into Russia to have it fixed. Since Burhan was the second in political command there, they would have taken proper care of him. Medical treatment in Kars was apparently wanting. Specifically, he had been sent for care to Azerbaijan, to the city of Baku. His wound couldn't have been very serious though, for he said not to worry, that he was recovered. The details of his injury were mysterious, which was not so unusual with Burhan's adventures. He mentioned some useful and old articles he bought in Baku before he returned. True to his entertaining self, Burhan had added an interesting observation of Baku's political climate. "You might wonder how Communism has changed the Russian State," he wrote. "Let me just say that from what I saw, the old rule was like a cane with the embellished silver handle, with which the tzar found his way through daily life. Under Communism, one in charge carries the same cane except that now the top is flipped to the bottom. The silver handle is in the mud." Adalet laughed out loud.

In preparation to join Burhan in Kars, she had ordered some new dresses from Beyoglu in Istanbul, and took care to lose a bit of weight; for, it was hinted that she had tempted her husband to seek other pleasures by staying homebound with the children. After all, even Ataturk attended parties. Pasha's marriage to Lady Latife had lasted only two years. People said it was because Latife could not understand his role as father to the country, his impulsive character, his need to be with the people and that the nervous wife simply let her husband slip through her fingers.

Adalet decided that since she personally would never want another husband, she should try with new resolve to meet the needs of Burhan – beguile him again, arouse in his eyes that flame. His desire for her had been gone for so long now that she could hardly remember the way his eyes touched her once, even from across an open yard. But, now that childbearing was done with, she should be able to give him more attention.

Adalet recalled Aunt Azime's words to her so many years ago: *The female bird makes the nest.* How she missed Aunt. Adalet failed in Azime's dream of her as the wife who could inspire all of Burhan's talents and ambitions. However, that last spring back in Bilecik, Adalet told herself that she would find a way.

And then, after she received the dress, she received the dispatch from the province governor, the Vali of the province that included Kars. The man, whom she had not even met, must have been desperate to send her such a letter including the paragraph, " …would kindly ask that you and your children come to Kars as quickly as possible. Your husband, my assistant, is lonely. There is a rumor about the company he is keeping with our Chief State Accountant's widowed daughter. I am sure it is all some mistake but your presence here will rectify the matter…"

Immediately after getting the letter, with the exception of Elif, who had graduated middle school in Istanbul and was in a school for female teachers in Edirne, Adalet hastily packed up all of the children and set out for Kars. They hauled the few belongings that she did not sell onto the several trains they had to change on their three-day trek. Well over six hundred and fifty miles across the northern part of Anatolia, they rode through hills so thick with leaves that they couldn't see the sky, and past farmers' wives by the roadside selling tubs of fresh apples or grapes. It seemed incredible to Adalet that in only twelve years the people in the country sides and towns and villages would have the freedom to live their daily lives without a thought – as if the three years of the Greek occupation and the terrible wars' devastation had not happened. Mother and children entered fog tunnels as they came up out of the valleys. Around rims of mountains, they could look off to plains with the texture of dried blood. The plains spread to distant giant gorges stretching blue into the clouds. The low hills were alive with blooming mustard. Sometimes the earth would look as bare as a cement colored moon. And yet, suddenly there would spring an ambush of yellow or purple wildflowers. When they stopped at a station they would eat and fill water jugs.

Nefise and her husband, Ali Fuat, met them when the train stopped in Kirikkale —"Broken Castles"— a town in central Anatolia east of Ankara, where they made their home.

Ali Fuat and Nefise brought food for the picnic hour and then, loaded their hands with hand baskets full of breads, chicken, sour cherries and a personally embroidered lap-napkin for each of them when the train blew the signal to depart. Sister was still petite, though she had fleshed out quite a bit. Above her heavy-rimmed eyeglasses, Nefise pulled her light brown hair back into a bun on the top of her head. She was gray at the temples and ears but her cheeks flushed ruddy as she laughed. Nefise was amazed that Adalet could handle so many children, since she had not even a one of her own. However, neither time nor trains wait. The half-hour was spent. With the children and the prince encircling them, the sisters clutched each other tight until the engine began to hiss and steam. How cruel was Fate to have separated these two who, in each other's company, caught the winds of girlhood again. Truly, Adalet and her entire original family were as separate as the tines on a pitchfork.

Trained to link hands when traveling, Adalet's brood sailed toward the train car with Leyla chained to Nuri, Deniz, Vedat and Sedat. Her hip saddled Darling Oznur. At the step to board, she turned and took the picnic basket in her other arm and fell back against the corner of the doorway. Leyla lifted off the child and Nuri took Nefise's provisions. At least, their belongings stayed packed in tightly bound carpets stored in the baggage cars. Adalet caught hold of the iron bar at the opening and leaned to watch until her sister's form dissolved into the sun.

Led by their mother, the chain filed down the single aisle to their compartment, which wasn't much larger than a closet with windows. Adalet placed herself between restless Vedat and Deniz. Leyla tended Oznur in the opposite wooden pew. Nuri and Sedat squeezed in at the open windows.

Soon, they were caught up in watching out the windows as the land rolled by: Two donkeys munching by a stream, a man in baggy pants, and a woman in a daisy green and yellow scarf beating a lamb's wool carpet on a rock by a creek, with five other carpets cleaned and spread on the banks, drying in the sun. They rumbled on past men and women gathered on both sides of roads, waiting, patiently, for something to happen or someone special to come along, or hoping perhaps for nothing at all, just waiting. They sailed through the erosion of mottled hills, villages tucked into piedmont slopes and around herds of sheep led by brusque kangal dogs parading like sultan's palace guards. The hills wore away into huge rocks. Finally, transported by a smaller train where their compartment was more like a big wooden box that skimmed on narrow rails, they moved up through the summer pastures and rolled above small earth-roofed houses built close to the ground.

Storyteller Adalet knew how to keep children from being bored. Opening the basket on the floor between their feet, she told them all to take what they wished. When they were settled back into their places, she said to her most restless child, "Deniz, do you know that I had my first trip on a train when I was your age?"

Deniz snapped her jet black eyes and lashes. "Where were you going?" she asked, scooting forward to the edge of the lean bench.

"Who went with you?" Nuri asked.

Taking in a long breath, Adalet answered, "Your grandmother – my Mother Zehra.

"Where did you say you were going?" Vedat said quickly, grape juice running down his chin.

Adalet reached across and took Oznur from Leyla's arms so that the older daughter could eat her bread and cheese in peace. Oznur settled comfortable into her mother's arms as Adalet sat into the back of the seat for support. The others had all been waiting for a reply without speaking.

She continued using Mother Zehra's mysterious tone of voice, "With my mother, my older sister, Nefise, my younger brother, Sukru, along with the maid, Hanifey – whom you kids know is still my parents' maid – fled, yes, for our very lives we left our elegant home and village forever." There was a silence as she looked at each of them as if searching for clues of understanding and interest.

"Fled?" Leyla repeated with awe.

"Yes. We ran for our very lives from my grandfather, Emin Aga's village of Bedre."

"Why?" Sedat ask, sliding his thin limbs to standing.

"Sit back down my boy," she said with a chuckle. "For this story is too exciting and tiring to take on your feet. And, it's a long one." She knew that once she was finish with it, they all would be ready to sleep, even sitting up on these wooden seats that were little more than cartons with backs. She waited until Sedat fell back into his place and squirmed into Nuri's side. This long journey from Bilecik to Kars could take at least three more days. Her children were well trained but they must be carefully managed so as not to become overwhelmed with weariness. Good. Oznur's head had fallen into the pillow of her breast with the sedative limpness of the brink of sleep.

The Storyteller allowed the sound of the train to create the mood of her tale, along with the roar of the iron wheels against the rails and the squeaks and chirps of the wooden cars as they dared the curves and hills and the laborious huffing of the smokestack on the coal-fed fire.

"You see, I was only eleven-years old, a child born between Nefise and Sukru. With our mother and the maid Hanifey, we had raced from Grandfather Emin Aga's mansion in Bedre toward an evacuation train in Alpiya, some twenty kilometers from Kirkkilise, that is the town you know as Kirklareli."

"Did you make it?" Nuri asked, his eyes wide with anticipation, for of course, he knew that they had, otherwise his mother would not be with them now.

"By the grace of Allah and in the nick of time, we did. Sit back and I'll tell you about the train ride to Istanbul. How could I ever forget it?":

For hours after the train's engine sounded its screaming note and pulled its load reluctantly from the station, Hanifey and I had swayed against each other. Off and on, I dreamed that I was tumbling on a sea. Five then six then seven hours, the train lugged its load through the soggy night.

"Are you all right, Love?" Hanifey asked me, bending over my shoulder.

"My legs ache. Will we stop soon?"

"Don't wish to stop. When we stopped two hours ago, we got wet and cold again."

The train did stop a second time. The people didn't want to go out again; but there were soldiers at the doors, ordering everyone off. The knitted bodies unraveled. Our groom Hassan moved back up with the family and helped Mother Zehra down the steps. Hanifey and I were pushed onto the platform. Out of nowhere, there were soldiers pulling at Hassan. "You! Come with us!"

"These women are in my care! Hassan cried. "Here is Emin Aga's daughter, Lady Zehra – " The soldiers' faces were blank and hard. Two of them jerked Hassan away from Zehra and began to lead him away. "Your duty calls!" one of them said. "We are more clever than you think. The escape train will be emptied of all who can fight."

"He is our protector!" Mother screamed, veering after them, grabbing onto Hassan's coat. I felt a wail gather and start in my chest and quickly cupped my mouth.

The soldiers paused to yell at Mother; and then they pulled her hand from its grasp. "Control yourself, woman. We need men!" They moved off, and Groom Hassan sank into the quilted pattern of cloaks and scarves.

Nefise and Sukru had come down from the train. I pried toward them while Hanifey went to Mother Zehra. "We couldn't get out of our seats!" Sukru said. His voice was like a puppy's whimper. When I laid a hand on his forehead, it felt cool and damp. "You need to drink some water," I told him, searching for anything that had caught the rain.

"Where is Mother?" Nefise asked.

We three children made our way to Mother and Hanifey just as Mother grabbed an officer by his jacket, asking, "Brother, is there news of Bedre?"

"Bedre? That village? In harm's way, for certain. Smoke all around."

In an hour, we were back in the train, having to fend for ourselves. Mother had us to be near the doors long before the soldiers ordered the crowd back on. We had lost our places; but even without Hassan, we managed to grab seats where we could see one another but not together. I pushed in next to a window and became lost in how it mirrored the profiles of the people beside and behind, and how in the wet glass, everyone blurred.

The pitch black of the long night against the window gave way in the early morning to the shade of dull lead. Fistfuls of plump rain beads slung onto the glass, quivering but a second before shredding apart. Again and again, I could almost feel the tear of the wind against the tiny drop. I couldn't stop imagining the low hills that protected my Bedre: Rain, dripping over white chimneys, rock walls and golden oak leaves, filling trenches in gardens and echoing up from the wells. Rain now made slimy and red. A bloodbath is what the man had said. I tried to banish it with words that I once heard from an imam, the holy leader of our mosque: "One should lay the mind away from harm." But, the officer's words kept coming back.

A woman next to me asked, "What will become of our men?" The woman wasn't really looking at me or anyone else. Just asking a question into the air, her eyes were bloodshot. Her cheeks were as ruddy brown and as coarse as her wool sweater. I couldn't bear her look at her or think about her question and turned away, clamping my lips, straining to see familiar houses and mosques. Everything that fell back from my sight now looked like nothing but gray oily outlines smeared against the night.

•　　•　　•

Adalet paused in her story. The children's faces were rapt and their mouths hung open.

Leyla stretched her way up out of the pile of the younger ones and said, "I need water."

"Yes, let's all have a drink from the jug," Adalet answered.

"Did your father and grandfather's staying home protect it?" Nuri asked while waiting his turn with the jug and tin cup. Sedat wiped his plump red lips and passed the cup to Nuri.

"No, but you have to wait to learn about that." They were ready to listen more. "Now," Adalet said, "Let's get back inside that escape train!"

In the late afternoon, the train gave a lunge and changed its roar, slowing again. The huffs of the steam engine staggered and stumbled until the noise collapsed in a heap. The heavy load came to a halt. The rumble of voices in the crammed car became shrieks and shouts. The engine spewed, the bell behind the smokestack clanged. "They are attacking the train!" someone yelled.

People began to push and jostle but there was nowhere to run. Each segment was packed. The two times we were stopped before, more people had pried on board.

The cries rebounded all around us. I tried to find my family. I spotted Hanifey but not Mother Zehra. People were shoving toward exits, some, crawling out of windows, shouting things like,

"Take to the forest!"

"Hide in the Ergene River!"

"Save us Abdullah Pasha, our eastern Thrace commander!"

Near the door, Maid Hanifey had managed to grab Sukru. The woman who had been beside me was gone.

I twisted around, and then pulled my knees up onto the wooden seat and held onto the metal rim at its back so I wouldn't be knocked off. People in panic were dangerous. I had seen a white-haired lady disappear beneath feet.

For an instant, I glanced at the pink and green roses of Nefise's headscarf slipping between a brown jacket and orange vest. The headscarf bobbled toward the opening. I tried to climb out of the seat and was thumped back onto it. Closing my eyes, I waited. The women of my family had never been away from home without a man. If all the men were taken, Thracian women will protect themselves, I heard one time. Even in the thickness of noise and fear in the air all around, I vowed to stay strong, could fight if need be. If I had nothing but hands and a scarf, I would not hesitate to strangle anyone who tried to hurt my family. "Allah, I will find courage," I said aloud. But how could I defend them if they were pulled away?

When I opened my eyes, the car was quiet. The seat where Mother Zehra had sat was empty. Passengers were gone from the pews on both sides of the aisle, but I could still smell their sweat. Out the windows, I saw that the train had stopped at a station. A bleak dawn was showing through fog though the rain had ceased. There was a beige stone teahouse beside the platform where passengers wandered about. "We are sheep without a goat," I whispered, remembering my Father in his words. When I went toward the windows, people were milling onto the trestle and tracks and crowding around the doors of the blue wooden station. The sign said, "Chorlu." Heads poked out of six windows stretched across the front. Muddy children ran through the gate of the teahouse garden and reveled past the ticket station. Soldiers moved among them. They had stopped the train again to search for deserters. One of them yelled to the others as he passed an open window of the car, "We need men to fortify Catalca! Thrace is lost!" Catalca. That was the low mountain range near Stamboul!

Earlier, I listened quietly while two old gentlemen in the seat behind me talked on and on about what had happened: The Bulgarians controlled the land behind. The army was not sending men to the west from where they had come, but east to where they were headed. Around me, the stunned refugees kept crying, the homeland, the homeland, gone, so fast, but how can that be? Back in Bedre two months ago, the old men had been talking in the marketplace about the sultan's Thracian army's being untrained and hungry. They said that the new canons were worthless. Without instructions, how could they be used? Our Ottoman hierarchy of pyramid rule demanded that everyone except the ones at the very top depend on superiors to *make decisions. I supposed that everyone assumed the threat would go away. The regime didn't care; so naturally, the men turned to essentials, gathering harvest before the rains, securing windows for the Balkan snows. Oh sure, they knew that for two hundred years, the Empire's power, supremacy, land had been spilling out like wheat from a sack. But, who could realize, who could believe a rumor of the death of six hundred years, of empire, of caliph, of harem, of Sirs, the local rich – like Grandfather, who controlled the rest? Since the train left Alpiya, it had traveled almost eighty miles. Because of delays, Istanbul was yet more than a day away.*

Alone, I looked through the window on the other side of the car. A cluster of women sprawled about on the second set of tracks. They were talking and looking back over their shoulders suspiciously. Standing near them, a woman in brown slippers and no leggings was screaming through her tears at a soldier on a stallion. The soldier resembled my brother, Sabri. But he was not. My eyes stung with tears. Was Brother Sabri still alive? Had he drowned in the blood basin? I sat down in a pew.

Some people were unraveling from the rest and crossing through the mist over into a park. Some were running toward a forest and others to a river beyond the field. An ancient stone bridge arched where a dirt road ran the edge of the field and met the river.

I couldn't see to the other side of the river nor over the rise of the bridge. Didn't those people understand? If the enemy were really attacking the train, wouldn't the soldiers be firing their guns? If the people ran far from the train, it would leave them behind.

I stared back at the tea garden. Where was my family? Perhaps they were somewhere buying more water and bread. Around the garden, three huge oak trees spread into the canopy of fog. The leaves on the trees were curled and tinged brown but most of them clung to the limbs. Soon, snow would cover them through a long winter, and then March winds would tear away the withered leaves. Green buds would sprout. I prayed aloud again, trying to sound powerful like Father: "Let this war shrivel and die." My voice was deep against the walls of the empty car.

A strange and sudden noise answered me. I whipped around. The sound was coming from inside the car. Again! Like a kitten's cry. Heart pounding, I pulled up and stood on the seat. Stretching left then right, I gazed over and under the mounds and gullies of the wooden pews. The whine came again and louder yet, spreading into a wail.

Hopping down, I darted up toward the sound. On a seat, a tightly bound wool blanket, a blue and white cocoon with a mouth stretching too wide for such a little red face. Some mother had forgotten her bundle in the panic. My sight shot back down the aisle of the car. Where was this baby's mother? How could she have just pushed past without stopping for her? What if the Bulgars had been attacking the train?

So carefully, I lifted the infant and smiled into its face. In my watery eyes, the little red face smeared. I squeezed her eyes tight, blinked away the tears. "I am here, little one," I said. The tiny black eyes stared at my nose, and the squalling stopped. Its petite mouth yanked at the air as the baby caught its breath. So seriously the eyes studied mine.

I shoved my finger into a pocket, coating it with bits of sugar from a sweet cake that Hanifey had given me and stuck it into the puckered mouth. The baby's sucking made me tingle.

The face of the baby was somehow familiar. Of course, knew this one. It belonged to Lady Naciye and her husband who was Mother's brother, Uncle Mustafa. This child was my four-month-old cousin. I had before seen her twice and knew her name. "Hello, Cigdem," I said.

Holding the baby tightly on my chest, I sat rocking, rolling the sugar onto my finger. Cigdem's tongue flickered like a tiny fish. I began to sing an old nursery tune that Hanifey had sung to Sukru: "Dandini dandini danali bebek...Kinali bebek..." I no longer felt exhausted like when the train stopped.

With Cigdem tucked in my arms, I scooted to the window. Down at my feet lay a string of amber prayer beads that someone had dropped. I picked them up and dangled them above Cigdem's face. For a moment the baby seemed fascinated, but then, began to whimper again. I placed the beads around Cigdem's neck. Scooting my *back against the window, I pulled my feet up onto the seat, made another sugar finger and then sang a rhythmic chant. "Um, um, um, uh, um, um, um, uh." The baby and I rocked in this way until the clamor from the outside became a roar as the people pushed and shouted, coming back to the train. Extending myself across the length of the seat, I rolled back and onto my side, almost covering the bundle with my body. "No one can take this space from my family," I whispered to the little bullet-shaped baby.*

"You would protect us that way, too," Sedat whispered, his head on Leyla's shoulder. Leyla wrapped an arm around him and hugged him close.

"And she sings that same chant to get us to sleep," Leyla added. The children exchanged glances and giggled quietly so as not to awaken the sleeping Oznur, who now lay across Adalet's lap.

Adalet continued with her story in a whispered tone.

I didn't have to fight for my family. Hanifey had not only safeguarded my seat, but also managed to claim two spaces across from it. Once the train began to move again, we all discussed what should be done for the baby, as its mother Naciye was nowhere to be seen. Hanifey took charge, saying, "I'll make a sugar tit from the few grapes we have left." She ripped at her petticoat. "In these underskirts, I have enough cotton for a week of diapers."

"Until Aunt Naciye comes," I stated, "Allah has given me charge of Cigdem. I found her. No one takes her from me." That suited Hanifey, who was content to take care of provisions for the little one. Mother grunted. "Just as you wish, Adalet. I certainly don't need another burden."

Nefise sat scrunched up across from me with a tight and blanched face. Sukru's head rested against my chest while he slept. On my left, Zehra begrudgingly held a conversation with a young Gypsy. I knew that in ordinary times, he never could have forced his way into the spot next to her. The Ottoman Army considered him undesirable, and so the soldiers had not taken him. It was accepted procedure, for the belief was that Gypsies were better at "borrowing" guns and

ammunition to sell than waging war with them. Gypsies liked freedom too much to let themselves be confined by the rules of the army.
When the young man noticed me staring at him, he smiled, bringing a roasted chestnut from his pocket and offering it to me across
Mother Zehra's belly.

"Beg pardon, Elegant Lady, I am Talat. May I share this with
you?" Repositioning the baby, I nodded, extending my hand. Zehra
scowled at the exchange, but let it go. I was well aware that Mother
Zehra would never take food from him. But, a chestnut was delicious
and filling. Perhaps Talat's pockets and hands could be indeed filthy.
Nevertheless, the hearty morsel covered with shell was clean. When I
slipped it in my pocket for emergency food, I felt Zeyneb's good luck
piece, the evil eye charm. Zeyneb was our groom's daughter and my
playmate. She had given it to me for luck just before we fled Bedre. I
gave her my gold locket with my photo in it. When I thanked him for
the chestnut, he nodded and turned back to Mother.

"To be frank, Elegant Lady, respectfully, I say it's sometimes luck
being undesirable."

"Undesirable? Surely you are not," Mother Zehra answered.

"Oh-ho! Don't jest with me, Respectable Lady. You know that
while you Ottomans tolerate us, you have no trust that we would
fight for your ways." He paused to note the surprised effect that his
words produced on Mother's face. "To be sure," he went on lightly,
"you are correct. We would desert. I'm getting out of here today. Like
a wheel, I'll roll on. Some fellows on horses told me that the creeks
back to the west run red. The Bulgars came in like slashing winds."

Talat shot a look over to me, who was held fast not only with
the way his mouth formed words but with the animation radiating
about his face. He held a spark of life that no one else on this train
had the will or energy to produce. With these words, he could get
tossed from the train.

"Ah, yes, many dead, old men, young – babies like this one of
yours –your first of many I hope, bless you–" He paused to kiss his
fingertips and touch his shiny forehead. My face flashed red. "Yes,
those poor ones," he continued with an air, "Ah, now they are memories in a wounded eye."

He lowered his head and looked sorrowfully into Mother's face. He neither shared the love nor the fate of the homeland. Talat continued with a whisper, as if he was drawing us into a secret. "They said the mud was slippery; and not only from the rain." He leaned in closer to Mother. "They claim the creek swelled maroon with blood."

Adalet took a break and let the children use the porcelain chamber pot that was pushed back under one of the wooden seats. She asked Leyla to then pass out pieces from the two loaves of bread and for Nuri to slice up the yellow cheese. Sedat offered around the rest of the grapes.

"Does that friend, Zeyneb still have your locket?" Deniz wanted to know.

Adalet just chuckled and shook her head.

EIGHTEEN

Istanbul
(Istamboul, Stamboul)

1936, on the train to Kars; 1912 Balkan Wars

After four long days and nights. Could it be true?

When Adalet and her brood all had their fill, Leyla once again took the petite blond-haired Oznur onto her lap so that her mother could continue her story of the escape from the Balkan War without interruption. Adalet leaned forward toward the children, who huddled closer. She closed her eyes and listened to the roar and grind of the train. When the sound carried her back, she opened her eyes and began quietly.

The sensation of the dream covered me like a foamy tide roll-ing in from the sea, as if I was spinning out of a black cave at the edge of some strange coast. The sound began to wash over me, ca-reening from a thick, greenish fog in the distance. The tide was full. I was trapped beneath it. A seagull's shrill like those at Igneada on the Black Sea coast urged me to free myself. The squeal changed to one from my old Greek neighbor's hungry pig. The tide vibrated and shook my chest. The pig with its throat cut continued crying.

I jerked awake. The baby! My arms tightened their hold. What if I had dropped Cigdem while I lay back asleep? Cigdem's screams made a discord against the steam engine's whistle. Mother Zehra was talking, but I couldn't understand. The garble of excited voic-es in the car mixed with the baby's cry and the whistles. I took in a breath to clear my head. My hair was oily and strung down across Cigdem's cheeks and I brushed it back with my hand. A pungent smell of burnt oil and wet iron made me nauseous. Hanifey handed across the sugar tit. I took it and held it to Cigdem's mouth and her screaming stopped.

"Sirkeci Station, Istamboul!" Mother repeated that over and over. She leaned into my shoulder. Her face had brightened. Stamboul. The shrill continued as the metal grumbled towards its halt.

I stared through the window at a huge side of a building moving past — beige and red bricks, tables set outside a restaurant beneath broad protruding eaves, a series of round windows, each with a necklace of bricks, some painted white. The sun was sparkling on a silver clock hung over a platform. It said 2:10. There was no rain.

"After these four days, I doubt I could have survived a fifth," Mother said, puffing out each word.

Hanifey, who was standing on the seat, hauled down the luggage. Mother checked the latch on the leather bag that the maid handed to her. The young man Talat had disappeared. Mother handed the luggage to Nefise, saying, "Soon we'll be out of this noise and stink — and not having to keep intimate company with strangers."

I studied my mother. It was a hard trip for one treated like a queen. For myself, I liked Gypsies' stories and songs. Though that one, Talat's, words were most disturbing. But the young man was interesting in his red bandanna. At Thracian festivals, black olive pit Gypsy eyes swam with stars. Their breath filled the air with tales of wild animals, wicked hoaxes, fantastic, strange lands.

Nefise and Sukru were on their feet. "Sit," Mother told them. Hanifey and I didn't move. "We have no need to push through the doors to pandemonium in the fist of confusion," were the words that Mother added with a sense of importance.

Mother had never been to Istamboul, though, of course, Grandfather Emin Aga had come regularly to represent Bedre and to sit on the very Sultan's Council, and pay the taxes that he had collected from the serfs who worked and lived on the fields surrounding the manor. Mother had never made the journey with Father when he took over Emin Aga's duties after their marriage. I realized that my mother most likely was not in a hurry to have to face the city without husband or father. Mother Zehra hid her fear in her disgust. It was awful for Mother these four days of being jostled about like a peasant in such a mixed crowd. She did not like people to touch her. Rarely did she even kiss Sukru, let alone me — though she would occasionally give Nefise a peck.

The fact is, I was light-headed almost to the point of being giddy to finally be in Istamboul. And, the fact remains that I had no choice but to lay aside whatever horrors there might be at Bedre — since there was nothing I could do about such a big subject that was entangled with Bulgar and Greeks — the Rum, which was what we Turks called the Ottoman Greeks, whom we considered left over from the Roman Empire. I wanted to believe that Father and Grandfather had somehow been able to escape. As for now, our family was in the Center of the World, and Mother Zehra had gold coins tucked in her bosom. I had heard that people would always care for those with gold. Grandfather and Father had friends who would take care of us in Stamboul.

In my arms, Cigdem's whole face was sucking at the tit. She would need a wet nurse. Would she be a motherless child as Aunt Azime called Burhan and his brother?

Our little troop was the last out of the car. As we walked across the platform toward the restaurant, I held Cigdem on my shoulder, patting her on the back. Her squeals filled the air. There were various noises clustering around in the partially covered station. The shiny engine rested its pug nose mere inches from the very end of the line. White steam drifted from under its black round belly. There were almost as many shops inside the station as there were in the whole of the main street of Kirkkilise and it was larger than the town center. I counted a newsstand, a teahouse, a greengrocer and several other shops whose wares looked strange. All of the uproar echoed against the walls and bounced in and out too quickly to record themselves as single sounds. After a few minutes, the crowd that left the train thinned out, but there were still many who stood in bunches, who looked to me to be confused and lost.

The young boy, Sedat, had fallen asleep with the rocking of the small cabin and the dull combination of wheels against rails and

the rush of wind orchestrated by the pointed black engine's thrust forward – so that the sound enveloped them as if they were held in the belly of a great waterfall. Leyla tucked a balled-up sweater under the boy's head. He did not stir but bobbed a bit like a cork, folded knees to chest and elbows to chest in a space beneath the window on the wooden floor. Oznur had been passed to Deniz, who slumped back with her against the pew. Deniz's eyes were intent and sharp. She would not sleep as long as her mother told stories. Vedat sat next to the window on Adalet's side, watching out as the hills and mountains came into view and slid back. He absently nibbled a paper pack of sunflower seeds. Sometimes a village appeared, sailing like a collapsed ship on the foothills of a mountain on the copper plains. He touched his nose against the glass. Occasionally, children ran to have eye contact with those privileged to travel out of sight. These would yell and gesture. Vedat made funny faces and waved back, wondering if those children would leap on and ride if they could, if they would dare leave home for the venture.

Ten-year-old Nuri drew his brow together as he waited to hear more of his mother's flight when she was only his age. He did not see her as being anything else except his mother. Storyteller that she was, he wondered if she was making up the story as she went along. Of course, he vaguely knew about that Balkan War, but it didn't really affect him personally. Those things happened so long ago. He thought that his Grandmother Zehra hadn't changed much. Nuri rubbed his close-cut stubs of hair and wondered if he even liked his mother's mother much. Zehra sometimes called his siblings and he, "Burhan's brats." He was glad that they were going to Kars, glad they would be living as a family again. He wanted to show his father that he could be useful. As the oldest son, he was responsible to see that his mother arrived to his father in a happy state. The time in this stale cabin felt eternal.

"Mother," Nuri said reaching across to take Adalet's hands in his, "Please go on with the story. What happened when you finally got to the station in Istanbul?"

Adalet searched over her children and sighed. Such a long trip for them. Soon the train's passage would pass into whether or not her little family would settle this time into a happy nest. This time it would be different. She had a resolve. Each of her children was talented and special in his or her own way. Burhan would learn to love being their father more than he cared for carousing. If the whole country could pull together with all of the disagreements from so many factions, surely she and her husband would do so as well. She clutched Nuri's hands and smiled at him deeply. This family was missing a strong leader. Even Doctor Fuat was becoming frustrated with helping Burhan begin again. She hoped that help from the heavens above was waiting at the station in Kars. But, she wasn't sure what to expect anymore.

"That's where the rest of the miracle happened," she said, bolstering up her spirits with the memory of it.

"You mean finding Cigdem?" Leyla asked.

"No, its more than just finding a baby on a train," Deniz said as she readjusted herself so that she could sit up. Leyla gently tucked her hands under Oznur and ladled the sleeping body over to her own lap without disturbing the child's dreams.

Adalet laughed softly. "You're right, Deniz. It's always what happens to the finding that brings the story around to miracle." She reached for Deniz and brought her across to her knees and brushed her coarse black hair back from her face before she continued.

All at once, Mother was pushing past Hanifey and was headed toward a table near the outside back corner of the restaurant. An old man in a white skullcap beneath a fez bent toward a seated woman there. The wailing woman's face was in her hands. Why was my Mother concerned with them?

Mother slowed as she approached them, and then, placed both of her hands on the backs of the two and began telling them some-

thing! Mother actually helped the woman rise. They seemed to know each other. The two people with Mother wheeled around. I stared as I hugged Cigdem tighter.

The woman let out a squawk that echoed above the commotion in the hall. She flung her head back and her hands up into the air and bolted toward Cigdem and me! But then, in mid-air, she tripped and pitched forward on the burnished tile, saving her face and head with her outstretched arms. Frozen, I stood with my mouth open while Nefise ran to the woman, calling, "Aunt Naciye!" Cigdem's mother. Nefise began pulling Naciye up onto her feet. The others came to her. Sukru nudged into my leg and almost knocked me off balance, with the baby in my arms.

Aunt Naciye sat with one foot under her hips and a leg thrown out of her rumpled skirt. Like a machine, Cigdem screamed and gasped and screamed and gasped. Naciye's hair had fallen down the sides of her ears and over the forehead onto her nose. Tears streamed down her swollen cheeks. She lifted both arms toward the baby. "A miracle, a miracle," she kept saying.

"So, it sounds as if, even though enemies were in your village back home, that your trip was wonderfully exciting for you," Leyla said when Adalet sat back to get her breath and to wipe the sweat from her face.

Adalet brought her hand to her mouth, repositioned Deniz, and chuckled. "Well, and so I always loved to travel."

"Me too!" Vedat said.

"Too!" Oznur mimicked. They all laughed to see the blonde girl had awakened and took turns passing her around, hands to hands.

"Practicing for living with your father, I would say," Adalet added. They all rocked back and forth with the little wooden train as it swung around the side of a steep grade and descended amid shrieks and squawks of its wheels and brakes toward the wide valley. They all turned to see through the windows of their compartment door. The same to the other side, out the windows of the aisle a lush basin far below the gorge on which they spun in their wooden cocoon. The sun had begun to settle down and spread among the uneven mattress of the mountains beyond the sandy valley.

Adalet hoped that the train would stop for water and coal once they reached the bottom. She would replenish the basket and let the children stretch their legs. Night would carry them miles across Anatolia while they slept.

"Actually," Adalet began in her mysterious voice so that they would know that she would tell the rest, "That adventure to and in Istanbul was the best trip of my life – so far!"

"How could that be?" Nuri asked.

"Because, my son, at the Bosphorus Strait, though hungry and tired, two fortunate families from ravaged Thrace had come safely to the Beautiful Heart, the home of palaces, the Seat of Osman where the faithful mingled with Europeans and their Western ways."

As our two families waded through the throng to the outside of the station, I felt as if my eyes were not large enough to hold the wonder. I walked a little lighter now that Cigdem was in her own mother's arms. The dome in the station floated up at least half as high as the dome of the old mosque in Edirne. This station was as splendid as a palace, with tiled walls and chandeliers. The colored glass windows were ornate and as tall as a man on a horse. Marble covered the entire floor. Two policemen blew whistles and directed the people through the wide double doors.

Along with a crowd, we emptied down the outside steps and fanned out. Mother Zehra raised her voice above the commotion. "Keep moving. Let us find a space where we can get a breath. We have to get to Sultanahmet Mosque."

Aunt Naciye answered, "You know best, Zehra Dear."

Outside, the station's shape resembled a Genghis Khan helmet. On either side, a clock tower rose to the height of the smooth tile dome. Below each tower, the brick and marble building spread at half the height, each side with eight double oval windows topped by a round one, all under the wide eaves. They said that the Orient Express line ran from this spot all the way to Paris.

The old gentleman with Naciye was her father. He tapped his cane as he bent his way across the marble square in front of Sirkeci Station. He stopped under a white lamppost that held three white globes, and gestured back for the rest of us to follow him. Hanifey walked with her arm around Naciye, who was feeding the starving Cigdem under a shawl as she went. Nefise carried Mother's suitcase and walked beside her. I came with the other bag and Brother Sukru.

As I watched Aunt Naciye with Cigdem, I was a bit surprised that I had given up the baby so easily, that, in fact, I was rather glad to be without the load now that we were really in Istamboul. Aunt Naciye's father had called me "a heroine," and Naciye agreed.

As we walked through the gravel beyond the uneven cluster of trees, we saw it: The mystical Bosphorus Strait! It was more brilliant than any turquoise ring Mother had ever worn. Wide as pictures of ocean ports, crowded with ships and boats of every size and kind. When the big one with the paddle wheel bellowed, Naciye's father called me to his side.

"See that, girl?" he said, pointing with his cane. "That is a ferry boat. She will cross with passengers on both decks; and she will land at Beshiktash on this European side, or across the strait in Uskudar, points you can see from here."

"There's a small boat in the ferry's pathway," I remarked.

"Fishermen and sailors know how to finesse past big ships that wallow in their paths. That ferry crossing the channel will reach Uskudar in fifteen minutes."

"What's that place?" I asked, raising my arm to a cove directly across from where we stood. "It looks far."

"Karakoy. This is where the famous river called the Golden Horn empties into the Bosphorus."

It was too much to take in at one time. The station's steps were crowded and there were many people. The vista stretched as far as could be seen. In the distance across the strait were the green hills of Asia.

People in all manner of dress filed about us and emptied in and out of boats. Some bought or sold fish at the shore. Near the large wooden buildings at the water's edge, a group of men talked amidst a flock of sheep. Some were shepherds in bright blue and yellow tunics and turbans. Others on the square wore fezzes and dark suits under long coats that billowed out in the wind. Those had business papers in their hands. A man scurried by in a dark purple suit with a matching hat. It even had a brim!

"Around toward the left," the old man continued, "would be the famous Galata Bridge. Separates Stamboul from Pera, where the foreigners live. It crosses the Golden Horn."

"The Sweet waters of Europe," Mother added, joining us along with the rest of the group. "My Ahmet told me about it many times." At the mention of father's name we all shared a heavy moment, each drawn back to Thrace. In silence, we looked out onto the water. I felt rather ashamed that I was once again behaving as if this were a holiday when those back there could be perishing; but none of the events of the past four days seemed real – including now standing on the shore of the Bosphorus.

The old gentleman broke the sad spell with his words: "There is nothing more important that we can do for our loved ones except to survive here in this safe place." It was true; but I wondered what would become of us if the invaders crossed over the fortifications at the low Thrakian mountains of Catalca.

Shyly, I studied four soldiers smoking and talking in a group. They did not look to be worried. I turned back to the wide blue ribbon of water. Everything appeared so calm. I imagined being on the top deck of the big ferry, well on my way to Uskudar on the other side.

"Do you know how to get to Sultanahmet?" Mother asked the old man.

The old gentleman waited. Two carriages rode by loaded with passengers who had disembarked from the ferry. "It has been five years since I was last here," he answered, bringing his hand to his short white beard and stroking it. He looked back over his shoulder for several seconds, and then continued. "Back up that hill behind the train station, all the way to the top, you would find the Topkapi Palace built by Sultan Mehmet." He nodded to Sukru to be sure the boy was listening. "Sultan Mehmet, the-Conquerer –

of 1453. Constantinople. Byzantium." He cleared his throat before continuing. "Topkapi Palace – the Padishah's palaces and grounds are on a point overlooking The Bosphorus, the Sea of Marmara, and Uskudar across in Asia." He straightened and faced Mother. "Just behind the Topkapi Palace gate stands the Aya Sofia, the renowned Byzantine wonder. Behind that – Sultanahmet."

"Emin Aga has influential friends that we hope to find, in due time, of course," Mother said. "Are you sure there's shelter left for us at the mosque?"

"Inshallah. Allah is merciful! Those in need of shelter from this war will be so many," Aunt Naciye said. She spoke with a sharp tinge.

Cigdem began whimpering again; and so, I lifted the baby from her arms. Patting Cigdem on the back, I rocked her, singing the chant close to her ear. Cigdem closed her mouth and listened.

"But I have heard the mosque is great, is it not?" Hanifey asked.

"Grandest in all Istamboul," the grandfather answered. "A town square unto itself – a school, hospital, gardens and grasses broad as fields of wheat. Arches stretching across doors taller than three men. Wider than four." I could hardly wait to see it.

"So we may find a corner in which to sleep," Hanifey said with a sigh.

The old man nodded. "When I was a bit younger and journeyed here, it took me half an hour just to walk all the way around Sultanahmet. I did not count, but there must be several hundred porticoes and balconies – three and four stories high. The inner courtyard is full of fountains for drink and ablution. The courtyard alone is as large as Karakoy over there. Many doors open at Sultanahmet, my little ones." He smiled at Sukru again. "And it has kitchens, too!"

I thought that the first thing I would do when we got there was to find a green spot, a cool drink of water and a bit of bread and cheese. My body ached all over. But, I remembered to be grateful to be alive and still well. We had all survived, except perhaps who knew about Father and Grandfather, of course. I did the best that I could do, which was to say a silent prayer for them and then make plans.

First, I would see to the others, that they had what they needed, and then I would drink and clean myself in the running water at the mosque; and eat whatever was offered. After that, I would run through the grass and sing.

But no, that would not be proper. People would think that I was a crazy. This was a time of mourning. So, I would find a quiet corner of garden and cover my head and rest. Perhaps, I would sleep for a long time.

"How shall we ever get up there in this noisy throng?" Hanifey asked him. She motioned with her arm at other disoriented groups from the train. "All these weary people."

"There is no carriage to be found for hire this day!" We all turned at once to see who had given this un-asked-for advice.

Gypsy Talat! Behind him stood a drab man in a dirty coat and a frayed skullcap. The poor man had hairy cheeks and a cropped black mustache. Big red ears stuck out from his cap. There was a leather saddle-like thing across his back.

"This man will carry your bags," Talat said with a grin. He raised his hand and rubbed his thumb against his fingers. "For some reasonable honor to your poor agent – me," he continued, bringing his fingers to his forehead, and then sweeping them out with a bow that was grand enough for a circumcision celebration juggler. Gracefully, he raised himself and spoke with both hands across his heart. "I'll escort you to where you can catch the ride up to Sultanahmet."

Naciye's father snapped back at Talat. "Who asked for you to bring us a porter to carry our luggage?" Naciye stepped to his side and motioned Talat and the luggage porter away. She looked to Mother Zehra and raised her brow.

Mother took a curt step and caught Naciye by the arm. "My Girl, my brother Mustafa would have me care for you and his baby." She gave a quick jerk of her head to Talat, who waved the porter toward the bags.

Without emotion, the hairy-cheeked man lumbered over and began to let Talat load the luggage onto the saddle strapped onto his back. Gypsy Talat did not stop until a small mountain had been piled up and tied on – just as if the unfortunate man were a working mule from the farm. I wondered why anyone would want to become a porter.

The elderly gentleman pursed his thin purple lips, then leaned over to Hanifey and spoke under his breath. "Young men like this are not to be trusted!"

"Our Lady Zehra needs to rest as soon as possible," Hanifey answered with certainty. "And, she knows how to deal with all sorts of people, shifty or not."

Our little straggly band followed the two men. I held Cigdem low against my chest so that I could see above me and at the same time, watch side to side, as wagons and horses came from all directions. The too many people on the streets hurried, dodging in and out of the tangle of bodies and vehicles.

As it turned out, the stand was just across the wide square that was no wider than Grandfather Emin Aga's cherry orchard. But it was a relief to be taken care of. The porter stood by. Naciye's father insisted to pay him, but Mother Zehra would not hear of anyone doing it but her. While she argued with Gypsy Talat over the tip, I stared across a wide cobbled street that divided itself into four directions. Every corner was bustling with people in suits and jackets, pantaloons, turbans, headscarves, black caftans, long flowing skirts. They all had places to go or something to sell. The area was so vast that the streets and boats and carts had absorbed the crowd from the train. There was a grill of smoking chestnuts at the corner, shiny carriages with dancing mares, roasting ears of corn down by the ticket booth at the strait, shoes on a cart and fruit on a wagon. Hanifey was buying a newspaper from a man with no legs, who sat on a cushion at the curb.

Suddenly, Nefise screamed. "Sukru back!"

A cart moved up onto the sidewalk. Sukru barely missed getting run over by the wooden wheel. The boy pushing the cart didn't even glance back.

And then, at first we just heard the clanging; and next, we saw what created the clacking roar. Sukru jumped up and down.

"Look, the streetcar! Just like the pictures," I called. A man in a uniform ran in front of it blowing a horn to warn people to get off of the tracks. Who would have ever dreamed of anything as wonderful as that?

Mother placed a settled amount into Talat's slender hand. He grinned, saying, "The right price always takes you where you want to go."

As he turned to leave, he slyly winked over his shoulder at me. No *one else saw what he did – except big Sister Nefise, that is, who widened her eyes and took on an expression of concern. I just shrugged as if to say, "This is the kind of shameless thing to expect in this place!" I couldn't wait to see what would happen next.*

The children tittered with delight to think of their mother getting winked at by a young man. It appeared even sillier to picture portly Aunt Nefise as a young lady. Adalet hoped that her children would have a chance to live in Istanbul someday.

Leyla opened the food basket again and the others crowded in, digging for what was left to eat. There was still some water in the jug under the seat. Vedat, remembering that, was already crawling between legs to fetch it. As for Adalet, she was still lost in the reverie. She had spun it out to sew up the long hours. But it was mostly true and she hoped they would remember some of it. If not, they had been entertained. She sat back from the chatter to reflect silently on the young man whom she had met on the train:

And many experiences flooded into my world to teach me what I should know. However, in my heart and in my mind, I would ponder for a long time on that Gypsy Talat – his spunk and spirit in spite of not having a country to call his own. In time, I'd surmise how Gypsies have to make their real home inside of themselves. And, they have to live with a sense of humor to ward off grief. I had learned that one must be the active character in the tales of his or her life. I never saw Talat again. But, I didn't forget.

NINETEEN

The Dance

The arguments at home began to fester like an unattended thorn under the skin.

The one-passenger car plus engine that Adalet and her children had ridden from central Anatolia to Kars reduced its speed. The Transcaucasus five-foot Narrow Gauge Line, Russian built, that had been ceded to the Turks after the wars ended its trail across the border in Baku. Rolling toward the elegant hub across the plain below the massive mountain with the ancient citadel cradled on its peak, the transport and company seemed to coast on stratums of thick steam and dull moans.

Burhan had not been able to meet his family at the train station. The regional governor, called, "The Vali," and his sister did. The stout and bushy man made much over the children and Adalet. The vali maybe talked too much to make up for his height, but he showed himself to be of a good heart. However, Burhan had written to Adalet of his irritation that this boss still insisted on using outmoded titles and protocol of the past. Conventional systems such as the pyramid hierarchy and inequality based on social status, sex or wealth still needed changing all over the country. Such Ottoman ways should be discontinued, and leaders should show the example. The vali was discretely apologetic for his letter mentioning the state accountant's widowed daughter along with Adalet's Burhan, and he asked her to be a judicious wife and not to mention it to her husband.

Finally, Burhan's assistant arrived, and took the family to their new home, which was a sand-tone, staunch Russian style. The rectangular-cut rock house commanded a corner near the middle of what seemed to Adalet to be a rather dreary town. The cast of the town not only belayed the era's ruin of military forces but there was also the moody sky open to the onrush of dark clouds. Burhan assured Adalet that the heavy snows in winter had the effect of giving the town a fanciful touch. Having grown up in Thrace, she could imagine that, and also the heavy tunnels of winds blown down from the frigid north.

When they arrived at the house, Burhan presented Adalet with an angular brass samovar on square feet and a sizable silver tray with ornamented handles, both from the Russian city of Baku. Both were created in the time of the tzar. The tray had three large initials carved into the center – a whimsical trace of someone or some family whose existence had vanished, leaving only three flowery letters that served in the present as nothing more than embellishment. Burhan also bought slippers in Baku for the children, and for his wife, a gold ring with an oval opal in its center. It fit perfectly. The white stone gave off a greenish cast. She treasured it, especially pleased that he remembered her preference for green. She was surprised to note that Burhan's broken leg was healed quite completely. One would have to wonder if it was ever broken at all. Perhaps her foxy husband dreamed up an excuse to take a jaunt to Russia.

In the early months that they were in Kars together, Burhan gave the impression that he was anxious to take his wife and children out in the buggy, showing them the wide streets and the relics of how it had been as a Russian town. New Kars had been laid out with a plan. Could it only be yesterday that Adalet heard the news that General Kazim Karabekir had liberated Kars from the Russians and Armenians? She must ask Sabri if he fought near Kars when he was an Ottoman lieutenant. Twenty years ago, she would have never pictured herself living on the border of Armenia with six children.

"Town sits on an ancient caravan route, famous for honey,

furs and cheese," Burhan told the children. "Name used to be called 'Kar-su (Snow-water)' because of the many water ponds that result from the melting snow."

"Summer is short," Adalet added. "That's why it's named, 'Snow'."

"Tomorrow, we'll take a picnic and ride up to the castle built by the Seljuks in the twelfth century," Burhan offered. Adalet knew that he would make sure they got the history of the place so overridden by one conqueror and then another. The Mongols and Tamerlane destroyed the Armenian principality of the tenth century around 1386. Persians hacked it into the earth and then the Ottomans rebuilt it in the sixteenth century; and then the Russians got it for around forty years until the Nationalists led by Kazim Karabekir Pasha took it back in 1920.

Adalet saw Kars as a junction of the wide plains and the iron toned mountains, rebuilt numerous times on faith and determination under stormy skies that were in the habit of changing from one hour to the next. So much war over cold stone.

Adalet had set about fixing up the house to make it comfortable and preparing for the long winter. She preserved jars and jars of pickles that included an array from red peppers and cucumbers to honey melon. Winter blew in early and the snow began to pile high above the children's heads. The cold and snow held them hostage and away from school many days. Trying to warm them, Sedat said the abode was as lovely as living in an ice palace.

In this far place, she did not trust anyone to keep her children, especially the servants whom she hardly knew. This kept her from going out of the house without the young ones on most occasions. Burhan had political events to attend several times a week. Adalet liked to be with people, but her first duties were to her brood. Burhan did not take her excuses well, for he thought his wife should be with him on social occasions whenever he desired to have her at his side. She accused him of being jealous of the children. He told her that she was using them as a reason for ignoring her wifely duties. He would not understand why she refused to leave the children with the servants for half the night.

Burhan said to her, "Your youthful dream of going to Paris would have been an utter failure. Look at you, who can not now in this new age fix up your face a bit like modern women do – and, as the progressive Turkish women are doing." Burhan thought rouge and mascara brought life to faces that had grown drab from a focus on too many kitchen walls. Adalet didn't like the feel of cosmetics to begin with and did not like the artificial way that a made-up face looked back at her to end with. A painted face had nothing to do with a woman's freedom or justice.

One afternoon, Burhan brought home a mirror in a wooden frame and hung it in the hall. It was almost half as tall as Adalet. "We are the leaders of the Cultural Revolution," he said, adjusting his bow tie in it. "It is up to us to set the example of dress and deportment." Ever since the "Hat Reform" back in 1925 when the fez was outlawed, Burhan had taken to wearing a brimmed hat just like the president. "We can check our appearance before going out the door," Handsome Burhan added, preening a brow with a finger.

It wasn't just that Adalet couldn't train her maids to care for the children properly. The truth was that there were still bandits around. The town filled itself with Azerbaijan immigrants who spoke a rather different dialect. There were Kurds from the east as well. Adalet needed time to get used to living with her children among so many strangers. At least, she could still use her gun if there was trouble. How would she ever get over it if something bad happened to these youngsters brought to the far end of Anatolia?

By the time the springtime rolled around, Adalet decided to let it be known to her husband that she was able to get out more with the children, and that they all would love to take outings with him like they did in the late summer; but Burhan's mind was somewhere else. After a while, with his disinterest, she began to feel frantic. Since their home was only a block from the courthouse, she started dressing up, adding a bit of face powder and taking the children with her to visit their father two or three times a week. Sometimes he was busy and they had to wait. Sometimes he was away on chief of staff business and the secretary didn't know when he would return. Occasionally, Burhan would be able to invite them into the big office with its divan and desk and serve them tea and sweets. By the third week of those visitations, Burhan told Adalet that he preferred to see the family at home. The office visits interrupted his demanding schedule.

The children withdrew into quiet corners and busied themselves when their mother and father's battles became routine and harsh. Adalet complained about Burhan's nocturnal activities, where she had overlooked them in the past. She felt resolved to force him to behave by attacking his weaknesses openly. Between them, the skirmishes quickly settled into fights for position and control – like a game in which each side wounds the other. From the children's eyes, Adalet knew that they were the keepers of the scores. There could be no winner in this case but she had no idea how to behave otherwise. She and her husband had differing personal and family ideals. She thought about how Kemal Pasha, as president of the republic, simply got rid of political opponents who became blocks to the path of progress, for the sake of the nation. But, even with equality and justice, how could a mother of seven without means and family support be able to provide for them on her own? Perhaps there was no real justice for those who gave birth.

"There is the Children's Day ball tonight, Lady. Do you have a dress?" This was a sore spot with Adalet, this adult half-the-night ball in honor of Turkey's future. It should, instead, be a large family gathering with food and music at the school. April twenty-third had been the day chosen for it because that was the day the republic's first congress had convened. It was none other than Congressman Doctor Fuat, who had started the celebration. And he had come up with the idea because of his continuing work with his Children's Welfare Society. Ataturk liked Fuat's proposal of it from the start because Pasha knew that the youth were the hope of the republic. Children should be encour- aged and honored. Adalet could not see how parents' leaving the children behind with a servant would in any way honor them. But, Burhan had not been willing to present her ideas to the vali, who thought a classroom program during the school hours was quite enough, and that children should always be put to bed early.

Adalet followed Burhan from one room to the other, making comments that he pretended not to hear. "I have a dress, yes, the Istanbul dress with black lace. Why should I waste it on you? I try to please you. I've made you the father you said you wanted to become, haven't I? But you – you can't find a reason to admire me. Nor do you spare time to spend with your children! Who is your reason this time, Husband?"

He spun around in the hallway and drew back his hand and held it poised. "You make yourself so sour, approaching me looking like an uncooked quince!" He closed his hand to a fist and let it slowly drop. "What should I say? Will you fix up your face and present yourself to the people here tonight or not?"

He had threatened her again, had he? "Of course I choose – No!" Adalet pulled her hair down from its bun as she scuffed across the floor. With her other hand, she wiped at her face. "You do not give a proper invitation!" With that, she jerked toward the bedroom, her eyes glistening.

He stood silent in the threshold, with both of his hands clinched.

"You have not said you want me at your side!" she screamed. He stepped closer and shut the bedroom door.

After several seconds, she took a breath to speak softer. "I do not like my lips reddened." The children were gathered at the end of the hall outside.

"Adalet lokum, my sweet peach of a girl," Burhan said, walking up to her and putting his hands on her shoulders. "Of course,

I want you with me. If you decide, come in a rig; and I will happily see you there." He paused for an answer. Getting none, he turned and left quietly, pausing only at the hall mirror.

Adalet screamed down at him through the window like some street woman after coins. "You are not to stay out all night!"

The children gathered around their mother's weeping. Adalet was ashamed to show herself to them in such helplessness; but she could not rally wisdom to know what else to do but rail and cry. Leyla bought her tea and Nuri combed and pinned her hair back up while Sedat recited a poem. Oznur just snuggled into her breast. The children, each in their uniqueness, loved her best of the entire world. Adalet had not imagined such loyal affection before she had her offspring. Of course, there was Nefise, but she had her exciting life of palaces and lands that were always so far away. The sisters kept in touch by mail. How much of the truth of your daily life could you pen in a letter?

Had not the province governor and his sister arrived at the stone house a while after Burhan left to implore Adalet to come to that fateful ball, she would not have gone. And had she not gone, she would not have noticed that the vali's chief of staff was absent from governor's table. Nor would she have seen Burhan appear an hour later on the dance floor with the walnut-haired state accountant's widowed daughter. And had not the vali then asked Adalet to dance with him so that he could cut in on Burhan and exchange partners so that he could then dance with the accountant's daughter, Burhan and Adalet would not have gotten into an argument back at the table. Vali Governor and his sister would not have been obliged to take Adalet home early – where she waited up until the late night turned into a foggy glaze. There would not have been the battle where she demanded a divorce and threatened to take Burhan's children from him and have the courts award to her whatever money she deserved in the settlement by law. Those words shocked Burhan so much that he promised to do better, and asked her for another chance.

• • •

Which she gave to him. After six more weeks, he was relocated in the same position as chief officer to the governor in the nearby town of Karakose. The family went together to set up a house yet another time. However, things between Adalet and Burhan had not gotten any better. She could see that she was presenting herself to her children as nothing more than a pitiful wench. Soon enough, she realized that it was in her cups and in his face that this man needed to be left alone to do whatever it was that he would do – whether she was in his house or not. And so, Adalet determined to take the children back to the place that they had previously bought in Kirklareli.

Once again – she and the children must travel over two thousand miles across Anatolia from the northeast to the northwest. Adalet would go from Kars, Karakose with no choice but to throw herself at the feet of her mother and finally admit how right Zehra had been from the start. No more would she hide the horrible kismet that she had chosen for herself. Adalet considered that perhaps her continuing situation had worn away the friendship of the good jinni that had always accompanied her and given her visions of the right way to go.

But – as it turned out, the gift of sight had not left her.

TWENTY

Sewing

Colemerik, Hakkari, Southeastern Anatolia, 1938

Seven children required a lot of money. The pay for her job was not much, but every bit helped. She tried not to regret that Burhan had not progressed up the ladder of his profession.

Again, Adalet reached up her right hand and turned the wheel and began pedaling with her feet, quickly bringing her right hand back to guide the material so the seam would be straight, keeping a steady eye on each even puncture the needle made into the dark blue cotton with the white flowers. Her machine clacked along with a rattle like a wooden-wheel cart on a cobblestone road. Burhan had asked the province governor of Hakkari to requisition this machine last August after she passed approval that allowed her to teach in a school. She recruited two additional teachers. Adalet's three children helped her cut and sew uniforms.

The reading and writing program that Ataturk began ten years ago in 1929 was now used throughout most of the country. From the beginning, Burhan and Adalet learned the Latin alphabet quickly and then began to teach it to others of various ages. Kemal Pasha had led the teaching example personally, standing in his pin-striped suits and wide-brimmed hats in the public parks throughout the towns and villages, taking chalk in hand to the blackboards. In the cities, the program that should have taken five years was largely accomplished in five months. They learned that the roots of the Turkic language were not in Persia, France or Arabia but in the Asian Steppes of Turk's nomadic ancestors. By the time Adalet and Burhan arrived in Hakkari in the summer of 1937, the national literacy rate had risen from nine to twenty-two percent.

But, few here in this southeastern appendage of Anatolia could read or write in any language. The Kurdish people of the plains and mountains had always found means to survive with the nothing that the Ottoman Empire gave to them. The women had no voice with these Shia Muslims who lived under the rules of conservative religious warlords. As long as Allah allowed these rugged men a small herd of goats, sheep and a family, most of them saw need for little else – after all, here the inhabitants had the green-gray Zap River Valley. They felt no need to read about the history of this soil. There were songs sung into the wind, and legends told around the fires of longings, heroes, deaths and ancient prophets such as Noah and Abraham, who had also camped in this land. Endlessly, or so it seemed to Adalet, they appeared satisfied to gaze off to the jagged edges of the mountains that cut the blue sky like a blade, while they shielded themselves in the shade of a scrub pine from the blaze of the summer sun or the bite of the winter rain. But however delicious the pistachios and toasty flat bread, Adalet could not be contented staring into space toward the Mesopotamian borders for hours at a time hoping for something fantastic to appear on the horizon. There was too much to be done.

Adalet stopped pedaling, then cut, and trimmed the threads with the scissors. She held to the light the cuff already prepared for the sleeve of the dress, examining the stitches. The sleeves would fall just below her elbow. The cuff would give the dress a bit of style. Burhan might be proud to see her in such a springtime frock. She, like the minority of other enlightened women, did not wear a headscarf unless she went around a sacred spot. Her flowered dress would have a neckline that came down in a point toward her bosoms. Half of her arm would be bare, and her ankles as well. These were modern times. Of course, in the cities like Izmir, Ankara and Istanbul, women like the Turkish Women's Union wore all sorts of fancy hats, shoes and short skirts that fell just below the knees. These members met regularly and were determined to wash ignorance from the walls of Turks' history by starting libraries, museums and theaters. Pasha said that

it was the females who would lead the nation, and he meant to enforce that idea legally. Now, there were female judges in courts throughout the land to make decisions for society. The ladies of the Union could be seen in the newspapers and on the streets and in the parks with open smiles on their faces. Freethinking women didn't have that look of unspoken regret and the downcast eyes. Adalet had been a Women's Union member eight years ago in the town of Bilecik.

Kurdish women in Hakkari would have a harder time coming into the modern world, for in this almost forgotten edge of the country's farthest southeastern boundaries, a wife was a servant to her husband's family. But, this was still true – not only here but also in other parts of the countryside – and, those women were trained to be gratefully bound to someone who would have control over their every breath. They were deemed fortunate if they had produced children to insure that they were of some value to the mother-in-law, who would continue in the tradition of treating them like dirt, in the same way the mother-in-law had been dealt with as a bride. Adalet hated that cycle. Brides waited their own moment of power when their sons would marry so that they could be mothers-in-law. She vowed she'd not be a part of that tradition. The best that Adalet could hope for in this desolate place was to open a few doors by teaching reading and writing. There were only three teachers for the school here. Adalet taught her oldest son, Nuri, in the fifth grade. He would be the top student of five who would graduate.

Adalet stood and held the flowered material to the sunlight coming in through the windows. She felt fortunate to have a two-story house. After all, her husband was not the governor of the whole province or even the local governor. He was again the vali's chief of staff. Burhan was happy to have a dry place downstairs to keep his horse. Most of the houses here were one floor. The heavy winter snows would have been too bland without a view.

Adalet required a lot of light to create the primary and middle school uniforms. She was determined that eleven-year-old Nuri and thirteen-year-old Leyla would be able to keep up with their education. Seven-year-old Sedat knew his alphabet. Adalet held the half-made dress to her chest. Sedat was in the other room softly singing a song that he made up: "*Come out to Anatolia and dance... Come by ox-cart or truck... It is not far...*" He was a thoughtful child who preferred to play alone. Yes, he would be a poet, she supposed. She could see it in the deepness of his eyes. Elif would soon graduate. The other two children were back in Kirklareli with Burhan's half-sister, Sabiha, whom Mehmet Nuri the blacksmith had carried in his arms from Izmit to Kirkkilise so long ago. Sabiha was a gentle soul, a widow with a great love of children. She had not one living child. Burhan's children were like her own.

Adalet glanced at the four tall windowpanes, then went to them and looked over the clay pots sprouting green, which she had set on the boards of the sill outside. Her Nuri and Leyla sat down in the dirt yard on the top of the rock steps playing backgammon. The two got along well together. Leyla was Teacher's Helper in the school. Adalet's students aged five through twelve would soon take their examinations. Some would qualify for certificates – Inshallah.

She held up her flimsy dress against the window's glare. The material had been sent to her from the office of the President of the Turkish Republic. Adalet was told that Pasha had received the report of her school here in Colemerik, Hakkari last September, and had ordered this fabric sent to her for a nice dress. "Make your self happy, Wife," Burhan told her, bringing it through the door. She imagined that Ataturk had taken pleasure in awarding her, for he respected teachers so much that he once said that he wished he could be only the Minister of Education – were it not for his many other duties too numerous to mention.

The gaiety of the flowers on the dress would cover some of the rolls of loose flesh that she had accumulated with the births of seven children and the fifteen years of nursing off and on. Perhaps she could become more slender now. She had determined to have no more children after Dear Oznur was born. Oznur was the seed of Adalet's joy, and more like her than any of the others. Here in Hakkari, Adalet missed her other children. But, she would see all of them at the end of this school year. Seven children. She remembered when she had only one – and a maid to take care of that one.

Again, Adalet slipped behind the sewing machine to peer out the window and to check on Leyla and Nuri down in the yard. They had apparently started another game of backgammon. Pushing it open, she leaned out and called. They both raised their heads and waved from where they were sitting on the top step. "Are you hungry?" she asked.

"We are playing two out of three!" Nuri yelled. "We've each won a game!"

"I'll come and burn the charcoal in the samovar when we finish the new round," Leyla called back brightly. They full well knew it was getting on to be teatime.

After motioning to them, Adalet turned back to the Singer sewing machine. Staring at it, she thought: my small factory. Once again she reflected with pride how successful that Ataturk had been with establishing factories all over the country to increase jobs for the populace and create necessary materials for everything from everyday life to necessary goods to build the nation. A first factory in the country, the one in Kirklareli, in fact, was brother Sukru's good fate, for sugar beets thrived in Kirklareli to his fine profit. Sukru had married a village girl and she proved to be a good partner for running Father Ahmet's farm.

Adalet occasionally wondered if her father would ever relent and leave her and the children some inheritance. Her parents never gave her money when things went foul with Burhan, even for the children's sake. They maintained: "You made your choice and have to bear the results."

Her little black machine was shaped like a skinny puppy with a gold seal of a sphinx on its side. With it, she had not only produced black dresses and shirts with white collars for all students at her school, but also clothes for some of the poor children in Hakkari.

She moved over to the chair, picked up Leyla's dress, sat down with it and took up the sewing basket at her feet. The dress needed a new button before it was washed. She sorted through the large matchbox that held buttons until she found one that would do. When she had the needle threaded, she attached the button. When she was done, she leaned back and closed her eyes. Her finger came down on the threaded needle. She jerked up, grabbed a scrap of material and dabbed at the blood, not forgetting to bless her hand as she did. From the basket, she took a small pair of scissors and cut the thread at the base of the button, and then stuck the needle down into a round ball full of pins where it would not prick the hand like an unseen thorn. She had made the pinball from a worn-out pair of stockings that she had bought eight years ago in Bilecik.

Bilecik, she sighed. Oh yes, there was a lot to remember about Bilecik.

TWENTY-ONE

Illusion

Colemerik, Hakkari, southeastern Anatolia, 1938
Flashback to Bilecik 1931

To forget sadness, easy as a spool of thread, Adalet would often unwind her years in Bilecik.

She and Burhan had been happy there in Bilecik —or at least for the first three years— and had often planned to stay permanently. Fertile Bilecik nestled along the Karasu, the Blackwater River, nearly two hundred miles west of Ankara, on the ancient trade route, and today within a day's trip to Izmit or Bursa. Adalet chuckled to herself and shook her head. Since Bilecik, she'd lived in Kars and Karakose, gone home to Kirklareli, and then made the trip back across Anatolia from her hometown to here in Hakkari.

Adalet bent and scooted the sewing basket back under the table. Leaving Leyla's dress on the arm of the chair, she rose and shuffled across the room and pondered the picture of Ataturk. The president's office had sent the picture to them when they were in Bilecik – after she made the spring sheep cheese and sent it to Congressman Doctor Fuat in Ankara; and he, in turn, presented it to President Kemal as a gift from admirers. When Gazi Kemal asked who made it, Fuat told him that it was from the acting province governor of Bilecik, his cousin, Burhan. Ataturk replied that Fuat should request to have Burhan sent to be a cheese-maker at the President's Forest and Farm – a large agricultural area Pasha established as an example and healthy food resource for the citizens. Burhan kindly regretted the invitation, saying that his duty in Bilecik would not permit him to come.

"Burhan, why didn't you just write to Pasha that it was I who made the cheese?"

"No need for that. A woman who won't leave town to go to a cultural meeting with her husband certainly wouldn't find time and space in her life be a national cheese-maker." Burhan laughed at his joke.

Adalet would have treasured a letter of thanks from the president for the cheese. But her husband was not likely to share attentions with her. He was even jealous that she could play the lute and he could not. At least, she had claimed this picture of the Gazi and hung it in the parlor before Burhan could take it to his office. Adalet stared into Ataturk's eyes. He gazed directly back, his head slightly slant, his brow furrowed in deep thought. His hairline had receded and thinned, and perhaps, through the years, he was accused of too many women and all-night dinner meetings. Fuat had told them the Gazi smoked too many cigarettes for a man with a frail liver and heart. Poor man bore the weight of the nation. He would always be her personal Pasha in spirit; for without him, Turks would be left with a country so small that one could ride across from end to end in half a day. Without her belief in his ideals, there were times that she would have given up. President Gazi Mustafa Kemal Ataturk had seen what was written on his forehead years ago – and he had been true to his destiny. If he had developed an odd temperament and a few strange behaviors in his last years, as they rumored, Adalet figured it was probably justified. She often told her children, "Our Pasha's path will not lead us astray."

In Bilecik, at least for the first three years, Burhan's late hours and secret outings tended to be with other professionals. He had a horse and access to a car. Adalet understood that her husband was just another man in a country of men who were actively engaging in the struggle to survive each day a bit better than the day before. Of course, many of those men were like Doctor Fuat who neither smoked nor drank – nor gave his wife Mediha any cause for concern about fidelity. Doctor rarely raised his voice, as his mother Seniye had often remarked – unlike Burhan, whose mood was hard to determine and whose temper went unbridled in the house. The children had learned to judge when to stay out of the reach of his hand. However, as a civic leader, Burhan played his role well, and he also provided amply for the family. Outside the house, Burhan was generally respected as an intelligent speaker of a remarkable wit – one who was fond of teasing the ladies and partying with the men.

In spite of getting passed over for her cheese making, during the five years in Bilecik among those rolling green plains, Vedat, Sedat, and Darling Oznur were born. There, for the first three years, Burhan drank only socially – and he hadn't struck her with his heavy hand for a long while.

Their two-story house came with an adjoining shelter for the horse and buggy. The first floor was stucco, with curved iron grills on the windows. That section was used for cooking, dining and guests. Servants were fairly easy to come by. The second floor was of an irregular shape that protruded over the rest, with six large panes in each window so that there would be plenty of light; and wooden beams graced the tan stucco. The surrounding countryside was green, particularly the garden to the front and the back of the house, where the children played among the flowers, chased the chickens and brought the cow home for milking.

"Wife, order a dress from this man who's come for coffee," Burhan said one day. "He's a noted tailor in Pera, Istanbul." And after that, Adalet ordered a dress from him several more times. With Burhan's winnings from the Thursday night card game somewhere out in the town, Adalet had dresses made of the same material for herself and the two-year-old Oznur. In that child's eyes, Adalet saw her own spirit in a way that she did not with the others. She intended to guide Oznur personally, and see to it that she got private lessons – not only in languages but also in the arts. Oznur should go to Paris.

•   •   •

"I am actually the province governor here, because 'Himself' is gone most of the time," Burhan told his brother-in-law on the day Sabri arrived in Bilecik from Kirklareli, along with Mother Zehra and Father Ahmet.

"Adalet tells me that you write most of the governor's communications," Sabri said.

"It's my job," Burhan answered. "By the way, you'll be interested to know that I've surveyed the area looking for land that will grow substantial fruit or tobacco, or even hashish poppies if you wish. I have several ideas to offer you, which you can get for a good price from those who owe me favors." Money was hard to come by with the world depression still having its effects on exports of tobacco, dried fruits and cotton. And taxes had to be reckoned with before any profit could be realized.

"Good. And once the tobacco comes in and we look forward to a harvest, I'll build a factory to process it," Sabri added, taking a lokum that Adalet offered from a plate of treats made for the sweetness of the occasion. The whole family was talking of settling in the area. The dream filled Adalet with happiness.

However, as fate would have it, Sabri and her parents returned to Kirklareli at the end of the year, signing all of the property Sabri had purchased in Bilecik over to Adalet; for he had gotten ill, and could not even see to the land's being tilled. Burhan and Adalet had been living in Bilecik two and a half years by that time. Her family's departure was a bad omen. Adalet's illusion of togetherness proved as false as a rotted tree – when comes the springtime, the shell with solid facade gives no shade.

After another year in Bilecik, Burhan's ways began to be more unpredictable. He was still his tall and stout self, with his round face, wide hazel eyes, and thick locks of dark hair brushed back. He kept his bushy eyebrows neatly trimmed as well as the tiny mustache under his nose. Adalet pressed his suits and cleaned and ironed his shirts. She would not let the maid do those things for him. He rarely thanked her, but she was pleased if he was in a reasonable humor. He bothered her little about intimate needs.

They never discussed the subject. Women friends told Adalet that after a certain age a man lost his need for that business – and Burhan was almost thirty-eight. For her part, at thirty-two, she was relieved not to worry each month about another baby. They did have reliable servants. But, the loose social life seemed a waste of time.

That last year in Bilecik, Burhan got so that he didn't press her to go with him much at all. However, he would come in from a late-night outing when he won at gambling, rousing the house and insisting the children get out of bed to taste a "celebration halva" that he made when he had sauntered home. It was when he became cruel-tempered that Adalet took shame in front of her children. Father Ahmet had never raised a hand to any of his family. Adalet had thought that rough behavior was over and done with; but it started happening again. And, the bazaar episodes had gotten increasingly frightening. One time, she even had to cover her bruised face when she was compelled to answer the door when a neighbor knocked.

Maybe Mother Zehra saw it in her cups. Before Adalet's parents left Bilecik on the train back to Kirklareli, Zehra had told her seriously: "Burhan will only get worse as time goes by. Unless he, by some miracle becomes religious, he will never change for the good."

"He has the children, a steady job he likes, and he is a charming man," Adalet answered. She'd never let Mother know for sure.

"Children, wife and profession are dammed if a man is ruled by his passions," Zehra answered. Adalet knew that Burhan loved his children, although he had never been one to bother with playing with them or joining them in a meal. He had no need to preside as the head of the family table. Unfortunately, he had never had the chance to learn how to be a loving father, and she counted it his loss and their loss. Maybe Burhan would mellow, as he grew older. Adalet remembered pleasant days with him in the past. What was she to do except to keep the house going and food on the table? In truth, most fathers spent little time with their offspring unless they worked together in a business. It was an unspoken subject among wives how often men ran after loose women. Adalet could see that her children didn't know how to feel about their father, who was such a handsome public figure and such an unruly beast at times in privacy. The family of nine hid the shame – even pretended it didn't exist among themselves. Young Nuri happened to tell Adalet about the day when his Father sent him to the market for a bottle of raki.

"Be quick about it, Son," Father said. He was sitting in the chair in the back garden. I raced all the way to the market center. It must have been angels that kept me from holding the bottle to my chest as I ran back. I tripped and began to fall on the stone walk. The bottle flew out of my hand. When I saw Father's bottle broken with the raki splattered on the ground – and with me having nothing from the fall except a skinned knee, I plopped down at the side of the street and cried until an old man with a beard and cane came by. He said, "What's the matter, son?" My hands and face were full of slobbers. I told him that I could never go home again. "Look," I said, pointing to the broken glass and wet mess spilled up against the wall. "My father's raki is ruined, gone; and I've no money for another." The old man sat down beside me on the curb. He told me my life would be long and full of harder things to bear than a broken bottle. He told me that he knew the gentleman, my father, Burhan; and that he was a good and decent man, who would forgive.

When Nuri came home and told his father what had happened, Burhan gave him another lira; and told him to go back, and to walk on the way home. Nuri was surprised that Burhan did not whip him or at least yell insults. Adalet thought that the surprise hit Burhan when he saw the fear of himself in his son's eyes and when he recognized how much courage it took for the boy to come to him and tell the truth.

That experience didn't change Burhan, though. Mother Zehra proved right, that it did get worse; and in the last two years that they were in Bilecik, Adalet picked up disturbing snippets of gossip. She put the bits together like the patchwork spread that she continuously cut and sewed together from remnants of materials used and discarded throughout their years of marriage. The piecework fashioned itself, without much problem of design, with whatever scraps were at hand in any given time. Parts of it were reds, yellows and blues and parts were brown, beige and black. By Bilecik, it had almost grown to be big enough for a full-size bed. Adalet's pattern was simply a round piece of cardboard from which she traced circles of white linen. Over that, she laid a piece of remnant. Next, she cut and stitched it together in coarse black thread that gave the look of half-inch spokes holding the center fast. She attached the pieces together one by one as they became worn out from use. Sometimes, she just used scraps that were hardly large enough to be of any service. The rings formed into varying colors of foursquare cubes connected to the whole. There was order to these moons of color. The practical result was a flowery cover-up growing larger as the years rolled by. Adalet tucked it into every travel's trunk.

Mother Zehra had seen Adalet and Burhan's life in the patterns of the coffee dregs and broad beans. No doubt she had already tried to cast a spell on Burhan to rid him of the thorny jinns who plagued his life – their life; but if she had done so, Zehra's spells did not hold. There was no denying the too obviously absurd signs that Adalet surmised in that last six months of Bilecik. Burhan was most surely one of those foolish men running after women, partying and gambling away their daily bread. And raki was on the cursed needle and thread that connected it all.

In truth, her delusion about Bilecik was like Turkish coffee without sugar.

TWENTY-TWO

Vision

Colemerik, Hakkari, Southeastern Anatolia, 1938
Flashbacks to Karakose, 1936; Kirklareli, 1937

"But," Adalet said aloud, chuckling in her throat, "Even after those years, here I am in Hakkari still with him in this isolated valley cradled by giant mountains."

Adalet spoke to herself as she covered her sewing machine with a pillow sheet that Nefise had sent to her from her Chorum farm. It was garnished with Nefise's endless garden of thread flowers. Adalet brushed past the doorway and out of the room.

As she passed the children's bedroom, she peeped around the corner at Sedat. He sprawled on the floor and hovered over his slate, inventing some adventure with a fat piece of chalk. Maybe he would share his picture later. Burhan seemed to show special interest in Sedat's creations, and the boy loved to please his father. "In ten minutes, you must come," she told him in a singing tone.

"Yes, Mother Dearest." That was always Sedat's answer. It was a joy each time to hear it. Adalet tried to hold the chime of his voice in her ears for as long as possible. Four-year-old Oznur napped deeply in her crib in the corner of the room she shared with Sedat.

Adalet went down to the kitchen and began to prepare afternoon tea, taking out the glasses and saucers, and lifting from the cabinet the lemon cake that she made yesterday, and then, unscrewing the knobs on the lid of the samovar so that her daughter could fill the belly with charcoal. After that, she sat waiting. In a bit, she would call Leyla and Nuri in from the yard. Later, the children would be set to do their school lessons while she ironed Burhan's shirts. When they were finished, all four would help her to cook the evening meal, for she gave each of them special jobs. Perhaps tonight, she would read again to them the novel, *Little Wren*, by the famous Resat Nuri Guntekin. They loved to hear about the orphan girl who wandered through life looking for good kismet and someone to love her. Last winter in the evenings, she and the children cried together as she read to them about how the girl was betrayed by her own true love from childhood. The orphan became a schoolteacher in Anatolia. Her heart was bigger than her mind at times. It was told that the night before the Great Offensive that Mustafa Kemal Pasha calmed his nerves by reading the same novel while waiting. The novel was new then. Last winter, Adalet and the four children would sit and read on the divan under the big brown and white goat hair rug near the huge iron stove that burned dried cakes of animal dung. There was not enough wood left in this region. Manure fuel didn't burn hot enough to warm a house. And, its smell was not something Adalet had been able to get used to. But nevertheless, they liked to huddle together and listen to the tales unwinding regardless of the fizzing and snapping inside the ugly black stove. Burhan would come home at near dark for his supper, and then he would go back out to the officers' club to smoke, drink and play poker, leaving Adalet and her brood to their tales and songs.

"Mother, shall we have tea?" middle child Leyla said, coming in from the garden and pushing past the kitchen door.

"I get to stoke the furnace!" Nuri yelled, pushing behind her. The belly of the samovar would hold the red-hot charcoal. Adalet had already set it to burning earlier in a small bucket outside in the yard. The brass urn appeared rather like a magic fire to the children.

"I want the biggest piece of cake," Sedat called, running down from the upstairs bedroom.

"Ayii – come" Adalet laughed, jumping up from the reminiscing in her chair and dashing to them. She unscrewed the top from the samovar while Nuri took the small hand-shovel and a bucket from the side of the fireplace and went out to get the hot coals. Oznur danced a jig around her mother's skirts.

"I said I was the one to burn it," Leyla demanded when Nuri came back inside. She took the bucket from him; and with small iron tongs, carefully lifted the charcoal from the bucket into the pit of the samovar. Adalet poured water from a pitcher into the belly around the tube and replaced the top. Sedat came with the small teapot. He had let Oznur spoon the dry tea inside it.

"That's right," Adalet said to Nuri as he nestled the top into its place onto the shiny boiler. Sedat then fitted the teapot into its nook at the top. They settled around it, waiting for the steam to rise from the holes around the small pot at the top, signaling that the water was boiling.

Adalet said to them, "I was lost in memories when you came in." She sighed.

They were all seated around the table except Oznur, who had climbed into Adalet's lap and Leyla, up getting the cake.

"Which memories?" Leyla asked, placing the cake. She began to cut and lay it onto the plates that she had previously brought from the hutch.

Adalet wasn't about to relate to them all of her recent thoughts, so she told them, "I was thinking about our trip over the mountains from Kars-Karakose to Trabzon on our way back to Kirklareli the last time."

"That was a year and a half ago," Leyla said. "Before we came here to Colemerik, Hakkari."

"We were taking a truck out of Karakose, all of us riding with our mattresses, pillows, and clothes wrapped in kilim rugs. Deniz and Vedat too – all of us in the back of that big black truck," Nuri said.

Deniz and Vedat had begged to stay behind in Kirklareli with Sabiha when Adalet and the children came to Hakkari. It was true that those two were the rowdies of the brood, and travel went smoother if they were separated from the others. But it was also true that Vedat proved to be Sabiha's favorite, and the widow found Deniz to have the most interesting personality. Adalet felt a deep respect for Sabiha, who never wavered in her support of her half brother and his wife. Most important to Adalet, she was a stable friend. Where Zehra, and sometimes even her maid, Hanifey, criticized Adalet's marriage, Sabiha entered each situation with her radiant face and healing hands and un-condemning voice. Sabiha was one to seize every opportunity to widen the children's horizons, such as dressing them up and taking them with her on Saturday afternoons to the Kirklareli free classical concerts by the military band in the town's central park. Certainly Deniz and Vedat were safe and nourished in her house. Sabiha wanted to also keep Oznur and Nuri, but Adalet could not bear to part with Darling Oznur and Nuri's help was indispensable.

"Mother even had the front hall mirror wrapped inside a mattress in a kilim!" Leyla laughed. "Anyway, it was a truck standing in for a bus," she added dryly.

"Oznur was in my arms," Adalet said, watching the twinkling eyes of her children. She could see the six of them along with herself and three other passengers on the way out of Karakose, the children seated on their colorful loom woven rugs watching out through the wooden frame built up from the wall of the truck's bed, the sky overhead blocked out by the canvas nailed down across the top.

"And the next thing we knew, the tire exploded!" Sedat squealed. "Like a gun shot!" Adalet was surprised that the boy remembered it that well.

"Then the driver pulled into a National Guard outpost," Adalet added, reaching over to take Sedat's hand in hers. He squeezed back with the one hand and sipped his tea with the other. He had already slurped up his cake. He would want another piece, and Leyla would protest; but his mother would give it. He was such a good boy that she could refuse him nothing.

"That driver said the outpost would be safe from the bandits, said we couldn't go on until a new inner tube for the tire would come," Leyla interjected, wiping a piece of cake into her mouth with her finger.

"We were going to camp out all night under the stars on the kilims!" Sedat said with a wonder in his voice.

"Mother, it was after about an hour in that place you started objecting to the driver," Leyla said. "Telling him we had to get out of there, that you would not stay the night."

"A powerful vision – it found me, showing blue and citron fire hitting that outpost," Adalet said. "My spirits gave me a warning, and told me to leave – Allah Knows! I had all but one of my children in my care! To think what could have happened to us!" She shuddered, bringing her hands to her face and saying a prayer between her teeth, spitting out the hideous thoughts.

"The driver got angry," Nuri said when Adalet finished. "He didn't want to go, said we couldn't go; but you told him to stuff hay into the tire and it would get us to a town."

"He was ranting, calling you 'crazy woman' but you wouldn't let him rest," Leyla added. "You told him your friend was the province governor and your husband second in command – and that if he didn't do as you asked, you were going to have him punished for delaying on the road."

"What you finally told him was that if he was not man enough to fix the tire, you and your children would stuff the tire yourselves!" Nuri exclaimed. "And that Leyla would drive his truck!"

"Our kismet was not to stay there that night, I knew that," Adalet said. "We had been spared the flat tire all the way through the hills. The tire's blowing – Allah bless us! –had not happened until we came to the plateau– and so near the guard outpost that we fairly coasted over to it." Oznur slid out of her mother's lap and onto the floor with a loud sigh.

"We were not more than twenty kilometers away from Karakose," Nuri said.

"Hey! And we rolled all the way to the next town on hay! Hey, hay!" Sedat sang. His rhymes and puns. The family wit. When the steam started climbing up the sides of the teapot, Leyla went to the samovar, took off the pot, turned the spout at the base of the brass container and filled the pot with boiling water. She replaced it on the top where it would brew and settle the tea. Nuri got up and went to the shelf and took up the tea tumblers on their up-turned saucers. The two of them would make tea with Leyla first pouring varied amounts of the brewed tea into the glasses depending on how strong each one was to be. Nuri would open the handle, adding boiling water to the tea in the tumblers.

These are good children, Adalet thought. Conscientious children need lots of instruction and constant attention. How could Burhan be so unlike his first cousin? Doctor Fuat and Mediha lived a different life in Ankara. Mediha had not seen Anatolia like Adalet had, but she had her children and responsibilities, too. Adalet wondered if she and Mediha would ever spend time together again, but she doubted it. She knew that Congressman Fuat was disappointed in Burhan's lack of promotion as well as in his varying temperaments. Fuat had helped Burhan find new positions too often when he had overstepped his hand or used questionable judgment.

"Allah cares for those with faith," she told her children, looking into each of their faces. Since they had experienced the result of her vision, Adalet hoped they believed. Even Sedat had remembered.

In that town on the next morning, they had heard that during the night, bandits had raided the guard outpost where they had been. Everyone was robbed and killed. The shack was burnt to the ground. The three other passengers on the truck had not come with them.

After that, they had taken a real bus and rode through the high mountain country of Gumushane with its lush pasture lands where cold, white mountain streams flushed through the dales and gullies in abundant rush. There were sheep, goats and cows in the dewy high grasses. Adalet wished to stop and bathe in the famous hot springs, but it was impossible. They rolled down from the peaks and plateaus – careening around twisting switchback roads with no guardrails so that it seemed the bus would spin off into the air before plunging to a doom in the gaps and rocks – into slopes sparkling with the famous Rize area tea plants. The shiny-green leaves of the shrub trees covered whole hillsides. Peasant women pickers with deep baskets dotted the arbors like flowers.

Finally, they wheeled into Trabzon on the northeast Black Sea coast, where they eventually got aboard a steamer. The seven of them filled up a large cabin, and Adalet would have gotten some rest had it not been for her children's stomachs being sick from the waves. They had never been on a ship on the sea. Such plunging and rocking. Finally, after four nights and five days, they were brought to Istanbul.

They staggered off at Karakoy. When Adalet looked around it seemed to her that nothing much had changed from when she had first come to this spot at age eleven, except the few automobiles rolling down the cobblestones. She hailed two wagon taxis. They had to overcome exhaustion to make the final leg of the trip.

After spending the night in a hotel in Sirkeci, a train carried them home to Kirklareli. Adalet had not complained about the long trip with the six children, for she kept thinking how their lives had been spared in the mountains.

After that eventful trip and the near escape from death, Adalet and the children had stayed in Kirklareli for one school year. Zehra and Ahmet claimed that they were too old and also, that with Sukru's family, it was too crowded. Burhan's half-sister Sabiha once again offered to gladly take in Adalet and her chicks. There had been a scene, of course, with Mother Zehra's not missing the chance even in front of the children to say, "What did I tell you? A hard life you've brought down on yourself!" Father Ahmet didn't yell, but he remarked that Zehra had seen mountains and explosions in her cups and had said an hour's worth of prayers over it, and that Adalet should thank her stars that there was someone praying for her safety. When the children told them all the details about Adalet's vision and the outpost, Zehra raised her brows and said, "Well, at least you got that from me."

TWENTY-THREE

The Ruse

Adalet lay on her bed stunned with the truth in what Azime had said to her.

From Karakose, Burhan repeatedly wrote to Adalet. He telegraphed the province governor of Kirklareli. He wrote to Aunt Azime. "Adalet, you have been given these beautiful children to be sure," Azime told her, "but daughter! Who gave these little ones to you?"

"Allah," Adalet answered.

"Not without a great deal of help from my Burhan!" Azime retorted. "Your husband – whom you wanted so much that you could not keep yourself from running to him – is a man of great use to the cultural change," Aunt continued, walking up under her grape arbor searching the leaves for the last grapes left of its season. "You say you are for progress, for social revolution," she said, one hand on her hip and the other balancing a purple grape between her thumb and forefinger as if there should be a great decision made as to whether or not to eat it. "And yet, what kind of wife is it who abandons her mate at the end of the earth when he is at the peak of his chances for promotion? What should he be expected to do with such behavior?" She bit the grape in half and studied Adalet as she chewed and swallowed it. "Hmmm?" she said. "What is your chosen other half to do now? His bed is cold; his dinners are cold. There is no one to make his fires. There is no one to comfort or encourage him as he fights to upgrade the thinking around him."

Adalet exhaled the breath she had been holding and stared down at her hands empty in her lap. "As the lady Latife lost our great president," she said.

"Latife!" Azime chirped, throwing the other half of the grape onto the grass. "You are more able than she! And Ataturk had the whole country waiting to be his wife!" She raised her finger and pointed to her niece. "You." Adalet focused on the long finger with the curved red nail as it joggled at her.

"Burhan gets distracted by foolish habits when he drinks alcohol," Adalet told her.

"Distractions like what?" Azime asked.

"Gambling," Adalet shot back. "And other women," she added more quietly.

Azime walked over and placed a bony hand under Adalet's chin. "You are all that poor boy has ever wanted, all he has ever had," she continued.

"Mother warned me that his bad habits would only get worse," Adalet said.

"Your mother and father will never be able to appreciate the destiny you have to play out. You must do what you can as a wife to this man so that he can raise the nation and help to provide a future for your children." Adalet knew that Azime was referring to what Pasha had said about the women of the republic being the backbone of the nation in that ...*everything we see on earth is the product of women.* Pasha also said that giving education and freedom to women would raise the morals and ideals of the men who lived with them.

"The future actually depends on women like you," Azime added.

Adalet sat on the sun-bleached gray wooden bench under the shriveled and yellowed grape arbor; and she didn't answer her aunt.

Azime studied Adalet for a few moments and then added, "And don't forget, Adalet, you were the one who set this marriage off on a wrong foot in the first place when you deceived Burhan with your family in Istanbul in the beginning of your marriage!"

Adalet flinched. She hadn't known that Azime knew about that time. Burhan must have told her, or perhaps her mother, who had been so angry at how the affair, which the family had planned so well, had failed. She looked up at her aunt with teary eyes. "I'm sorry my Dear Aunt but I must go lie down for a while and think what I should do."

Adalet lay on the bed and thought about her difficult struggle with her husband. Perhaps she should take responsibility that the marriage had been robbed of its trust so long ago. She had been so confused and young. She had no trouble envisioning, as she had done many times that morning in Istanbul back in 1918, when Burhan had been invited to come to the lady Saadet's Bosphorus house on the pretense of his having tea with Sabri. The events of that morning had always left her with a tinge of guilt, although Burhan and she had hardly discussed it after that, and never even during their worst arguments throughout the years. Perhaps the hurt had been just too deep for Burhan's manly pride. Perhaps it had festered in his heart like a splinter:

It was around eleven o'clock in the morning. I had the heavy head of one that has not slept, and the uneasy heart of one torn into two pieces. Earlier, I had heard the honorable judge arrive. The district judge was necessary for the planned setting to work. The scenario had to fall within the bounds of the new legalities of divorce. The voices of Sabri and Saadet echoed in the hall. They were cheerful. It felt good to be in sync with my family. But, it was sad to trick Burhan in that way. Nefise and the prince comforted me. I vaguely wondered if the two of them were in love with each other, as were Burhan and I. "This uncomfortable hour will soon pass," Nefise's Prince Ali Fuat assured me.

Just before the silver clock on the mantle struck the hour, I eased down the staircase in a blue and rose-pattern long-sleeve dress. It touched the stairs behind me at the back of my black heels. I had tied on a blue silk headscarf to show respect to the judge. In the drawing room, the four others waited for me with the judge.

Sabri no sooner introduced the judge to me than we all heard footsteps on the porch. My heart raced. Lined up in a row, all of us faced toward the front door. I moved to Sabri's side and hooked my hands into his elbow. He gave me a relaxed, hearty nod. I fixed my eyes on the brass doorknob, repeating in my mind the words that I must recite. The new law required the judge to ask the wife specific questions and for the wife to answer using certain words in the presence of at least two witnesses and the husband.

The door's bell jangled my whole body. The servant came to the foyer and waited for the signal from Saadet before going to the door.

When Burhan entered, he hesitated a few seconds, and then looked to see the five of us plus a judge dressed in his official robe in the drawing room. Burhan stared at them, and then focused on me. I knew he must see the guilt all over me. His eyes narrowed in suspicion. My gaze dropped to his polished black shoes as bit my lower lip, trying to swallow the hardness in my throat, wishing my plight done with and over.

Burhan moved through the opened French doors of the drawing room, and then stopped just inside. Burhan would, of course, know something was amiss since the hostess, Saadet, had not gone to receive him. "Allah Help," I whispered under my breath. I was trapped either way. Sabri turned toward the judge.

The judge spoke. I raised my head. "Are you Burhan born in Kirkkilise, the son of The Blacksmith Mehmet Nuri who made the pilgrimage?" Burhan's mouth fell open. He stood awkwardly, holding a bouquet of pink roses wrapped in white tissue and tied with a pink bow. The judge repeated the question louder. Burhan lowered the hand with the roses to his side. He slid his glance back and forth over the five of us. He started to answer something but his voice got stuck in his throat and he coughed. The judge spoke again. "You have been asked who you are!" The judge's demanding tone startled me.

Burhan took one step forward, and then stopped, standing with his legs spread and his head back. "I am Burhan and my father is *that whom you say." His voice was steady and flat. It seemed that I was seeing him at the far end of a tunnel.*

The judge and the others turned to me. I centered my eyes on the judge's black silk vest. He asked the second required question. "Are you Adalet, daughter of the Esteemed Ahmet Giray and Lady Zehra, Daughter of Emin Aga of Kirkkilise, formally of the destroyed village of Bedre?"

Barely, I managed to force a breathy, "Yes." I did not move my head, but could feel the heat of Burhan's eyes upon the coward and cheater I had become.

"I am the Most Honorable Judge Murad Zade, chief court official of the district of Beshiktash, Istanbul," the judge said with his power of command voice. He was next going to ask me the hardest question.

"Given my authority by our Lord Sultan Vahdettin," the judge said, "I have been summoned here to proceed with the dissolution of a marriage between said Adalet and said Burhan. Therefore, I ask you, Adalet: Why have you brought me here?"

I sucked in breath and held it as if I were a frozen wall. Up until this moment, I had determined that I should and could manage the ruse we were enacting; and now, in the glare of my husband's eyes, I was numb.

Sabri pulled my clinched fingers from his elbow and brought his arm around my shoulder. He held me against his side, whispering loudly into my ear. "Say the words, Adalet Girl!" His voice was as tight as his hand that squeezed my shoulder. I stumbled on the words that we had earlier rehearsed.

"I..."

"Yes?" the judge asked. I focused on the carpet that lay near my toes.

"Speak up, Adalet!" he insisted.

"...Do not want..."

"What?" he asked sharply.

"...That man Burhan... for a husband," I whispered hurriedly. There were seconds of iced silence.

And then, the roses came skidding across the polished floor and flipped like a dozen of exclamation points onto the carpet at my feet. I jerked from Sabri's grip and jumped back. It was as if they had exploded, petals scattered and thorns glistening from the naked stems. Suddenly, I flinched again at an outburst from across the room – a yell like a soldier rushing toward battle. "Aiiieee!" it was.

We stared dumbly at Burhan and his savage sound.

"So!" he shrilled. "Trickery! Fool that I am, I am not the fool you take me to be! I will not be tricked!" Burhan took three clomping steps toward us. He halted abruptly, clinching fists white at the knuckles, tight as rocks.

We recoiled as he raised an arm and pounded at the air between himself, the judge and the five of us. "You are trying to cheat me!" he shouted. "I will report it to the high courts! I am Adalet's legal husband; and I say on intimate authority that this woman – here –" He pointed to me as if I were an enemy. "This –" he went on, "Who has spoken, is not the lovely woman who is my wife, not Adalet, daughter of Ahmet of Kirkkilise and crazy Gypsy Zehra! Moreover – I propose that you, most honorable Judge Murad Zade, take these people under arrest for false pretenses!"

With that, Burhan whirled around and pounded his shoes abruptly out of the room and the house, slamming the door behind him, while not one of the family could think of what to say.

Finally, the judge broke the stiff air around us. "What sort of ruling I am authorized to declare, I am not certain. The law is so new, you see; and with the Great War and Ottoman defeat, it could take months to receive a decision on this matter."

The most honorable judge bowed and patted the pocket of his jacket, indicating that he was quite ready to leave. "But, you understand," he pointed out, "For the time being, this divorce has not gone forth."

A second later, Adalet fainted dead away onto the carpet and Burhan's scattered roses.

TWENTY-FOUR

Pasha

Kirklareli, 1937; Hakkari, 1938;
Kirklareli, 1938

How quickly all could be swept from life.

It continued every week, while in Kirklareli, that Adalet got the news. Burhan continued to beg for her write to him, as over and over he wished to ask her forgiveness. Sometimes it took such a shock to make a person mend their ways. Perhaps she had not been compassionate enough with his needs. Maybe they both deserved forgiveness.

Burhan arrived in Kirklareli in the spring that year, vowing on his mother's grave that he was reformed. He convinced Adalet that she was his only kismet, and pleaded that she and the children join him in his new position in the southeast in Colemerik, the capital of the province of Hakkari. Burhan promised Adalet that she could be a great help to the republic in that place. The whole area lagged far behind the advances the republic had made in education, women's rights in society as well as in the basic living conditions. In many parts of the rest of the country, most certainly around the cities, there were new factories, women judges, new schools and even women in the military and law enforcement. There were symphony orchestras, art galleries, museums, ballet and youth and adult programs to usher the country forward with the progress of the new century. Burhan kept repeating that in Colemerik, Adalet could work in a school as a teacher. She had already been teaching adults and children skills like the new alphabet and giving them information such as hygiene, health, literature and music in other places. She had done it wherever she went for fifteen years. And in Hakkari, progress was needed where things had not much changed.

So, of course, for the sake of goodness, let alone progress, she had forgiven a man of such repentance. Allah be blessed that she loved to travel – for she left Elif in school, and conveyed Vedat and Deniz, who didn't want to leave their friends and Kirklareli school, to the loving and attentive care of Burhan's half-sister, Sabiha. Burhan went on ahead to prepare a place for them in that farthermost southeastern Anatolian town.

With Leyla, Nuri, Sedat and Oznur, she had set out again, back more than a thousand miles: a train from Kirklareli to Istanbul, a ferry across the strait to the Asian side of the Bosphorus to Haydarpasha Station and another train crossing of Anatolia. That time, they headed southeast to Diyarbakir, and then a bus up to Tatvan.

From Tatvan, they took a ferry over the wide and awesome blue and deep Lake Van, where the shoreline was scattered with remnants of so much history – Urartu citadels, Seljuk mosques. Atop the deck, they saw the island where stood the famous Christian church from the tenth century. With no Armenians left living there, it looked ghostly, sad. The sky seemed to wrap the little nest of her and the four children, along with everything around them, in the same color as the huge lake. The copper and gold of the arid land melted onto the blue of the water. They gasped at where the ruins and rocks periodically rolled down from the cobalt mountains.

When they landed at Van, four National Guard met them. Burhan had ordered a mule caravan to be waiting, one animal for each of them, to carry them more than a hundred miles through the desolate briers and scrub-tree hills that led at times to ledge-paths above copper valleys and rims of wild raging rivers. They slowly worked their way step by step all the way down to Colemerik, Hakkari.

In the beginning, the children thought it was a special delight to weave down the arid vales astride the animals. All of them were sore after the first day. They spent five hot and difficult days jog-gling along the footpaths of the rugged terrain of hills and hol-lows, and four nights camped under the shelter of carpets and cliffs. The guards kept a watch out for bandits along the road.

Hakkari, 1938

The four children and she had emptied the brass samovar of its water. All of them had had a second helping of lemon cake. The late afternoon Hakkari sun had pushed through the open windows and flushed every crevice of the room with light and shadow. Leyla wiped Oznur's hands and face with a wet cloth while Nuri and Sedat cleaned the table. Now, they would all rest until the sun began to retreat behind the mountains. After that, she would have Sedat practice his mathematics with her while she started the lentil soup. Burhan would be home by dark. Perhaps she'd have the red peppers stuffed with rice.

A bit later, she sat in the shade and thought about children – those she left behind in Kirklareli, those who were inside the house reading and playing games, and those who came from the town to her school. She mused on her own childlike love of adventure, her belief in making any situation work. Had the coming to this distant appendage that hung like an outstretched palm between the coun-tries of the Persians and the Iraqis, where the summers were brutal with heat and the winters brittle with cold, truly been her kismet? This certainly was not the environment Adalet thought would be in the cards of fortune for Burhan's and her back in Izmir or in Bilecik. The Kurdish population here had welcomed them. The school was going well. Hakkari wasn't a new beginning. She hoped it wouldn't be the end. Perhaps her next move would be nearer to Nefise. Life amounted to continuing on the path laid before her. So much had changed through the years. So much was lost.

Little did she know that her marriage would stumble on – go-ing back and forth for six more years.

•　　•　　•

After a year in Hakkari, Adalet and the children returned yet again to Kirklareli. A few months after being there, they heard the shocking words cried out in the streets: Gazi Mustafa Kemal Pasha had died. The news came on a frosty and steely-gray day, November 1938. Adalet had read about it over and over at the time, trying to believe that it could be true and hoping that it was a lie. Pasha lived for the republic's future. Now, the future existed and he did not. What did that mean? She had pictured him: His body in a coma, Gazi Mustafa Kemal opened his gray-blue eyes for several seconds for the last time. Apparently, he saw nothing to hold him longer, for he closed his eyes again and left the country on its own – for the first time in almost twenty-five years, ever since he had become a hero at Gallipoli. On the previous day, he had simply said, "Goodbye," before going into a deep sleep. It had been barely a week and a half before the fifteenth anniversary of the republic.

All of Anatolia and Thrace was a flood of tears for three days and nights. The whole landscape was draped in black. Folk with torches lined the railway that carried him from Izmit to Ankara. The people lit the final trip of that one who had been their moon and star for their difficult way, the one who taught them to search for the innermost strength within themselves.

Before the November of his death, it had been widely rumored that Ataturk was very ill. And so, Adalet had been more shocked than surprised with the news. And furthermore, Adalet had been given a dream. It came a few nights before the president died. In the dream, she was in her home, and a knock came to the door. When she opened it, there stood Pasha.

"Can I come in?" Ataturk asked.

Overwhelmed and overjoyed, she brought him in and gave him the best seat in the parlor. He sat there in his nice suit with the tie and handkerchief in its pocket, his fine hair slicked back. There was not even a speck of dust on him anywhere. He gazed at her as if he could pierce her heart. Adalet picked up a small box wrapped in gold paper and handed to him what was a present of her special cheese. He held it on his lap and smiled at her. "Adalet," he said, "I am very tired. Would you give me a drink of water?" She gave him the best glass in the house, filled with cool water from the spring. He drank it down and told her, "Thank you for everything." And then he appeared to vanish into her hearth fire.

To those who asked Adalet for the meaning of her dream, she told them: "Pasha has left us; but it is up to those who are enlightened to feed the nation's thirst and continue to teach the children."

Sometimes, it was almost easier to be a partner to the ideals of building a new society that did not necessarily conform to the standards of the past than to be a wife to a man who could not adhere to the basic loyalties of marriage.

But, in truth, there were always two sides to every story.

TWENTY-FIVE

The Fortune

Istanbul, September 1993

Nothing appears to be broken.

Nuri and I leave the noise and dust along with our shoes outside the padded green leather covering hanging across the entrance to the Sultanahmet Mosque – known in the West as the Blue Mosque.

Barefooted and glancing up at the namesake turquoise and cobalt tiles, we tiptoe across the musky carpets. The muted light of the low-hung chandeliers and the cavernous hush gives off the sense of being inside some clapper less bell. We relish this respite before we say good-bye again. Tomorrow, Inshallah –or as my kin back in the States would say it– God willing, we fly home to life in Virginia.

This time, our coming here was, of course, strained. Three weeks ago we were burying Adalet. One morning in that first week, Nuri was awakened by what he thought was her hand on his shoulder – the way in which she gently awoke him when he was a boy. I had been trying to feel her presence in the jumbled materials that she left behind. I searched for an essence of her in the mother goddess statues in the Ankara Museum. But, I could not feel her spirit within me the way I wanted. Tomorrow, I leave Turkey with only memories. And there's the burden of that promise I made to her that I might not have the wherewithal to keep. Plus, the family dynamics are falling apart. Coming back will never be the same.

At least, we have that paper that Kurt found in the box when we were cleaning out the apartment. Adalet signed it and left it where she knew only we would find it – knowing that no one else would be interested in looking through the old letters from us to her. The document verifies property rights. Adalet was clever to the very end to make such a security, knowing all too well the confusion of family and inheritance.

Several hours later, Nuri trips on ahead to get the car. I dawdle in the huge open square, looking back at the soaring Blue Mosque before turning around toward the salmon-colored Saint Sophia, the classic Byzantine Church meaning "Holy Wisdom." The huge cathedral was turned into a mosque by Mehmet the Conqueror and remained so for four hundred years. In fact, it served as a model for Sultanahmet Mosque. Ataturk fixed up Sophia and opened it as a museum in 1935. So, we have the Red Mosque and the Blue Mosque facing it off here in the square.

Continuing my amble across the cobblestones between the two giants, I muse on the wonders found in this one square mile, old cistern and ancient hippodrome lingering alongside modest hotels and quiet shops.

The sight of a cozy tea garden leads me to wondering what can I serve guests who might drop around to say goodbye this evening. There's coffee and a few cookies left in the kitchen but not much else. A weathered fruit seller moves across the haze in front of me and parks his cart up against a tree.

As I approach him, he nods and pulls a plastic bag from a nail on the cart. I smile, scanning the goods. "Oranges, apples, bananas," he prompts in Turkish, pointing to the fruit. He picks up an orange, and motions that he will put it on the dented metal scale sitting on top of his cart. I wave my hand back and forth, palm to the ground in Turkish negative. His oranges are a bit dehydrated. Apples aren't bad, but the bananas already have spots. The in-season fruit is heaped in a neat pyramid. I point to the tan pears, and ask for one kilo. As he begins filling the bag, I change my mind. "Iki – two kilos," I tell him, jigging my fingers in the air. That should do it.

Balancing the loaded bag in my right hand and my handbag over my left shoulder, I skirt from the square to the curb. Nuri waits on the far side of a second street. I leave the Saint Sophia side and pass the ancient Underground Cistern entrance on the other side. With the bag flopping against my thigh, I cross to the median. The "Walk" sign blinks yellow. There is a red Volkswagen in front of me at the head of a line of cars in the left inside lane. An off-duty policeman sits in the passenger seat. The right lane is empty. The policeman motions for me to go ahead and cross. As I step past the VW, the light flips to green.

Out of nowhere, a black car swoops around the VW from the right lane. Its brakes squeal. There's a dull thud of metal against my thigh. I'm lifted arching backwards off the cobblestones. For a second, sky blue washes down onto my face.

The next thing I know I'm splayed on my back onto the street. My hand goes to my thigh and clutches a mushy fistful of cold and wet. Numbed and sweating, I push to sitting and stare at the shiny grill of the black car. At the same time, I'm checking limbs and chest. There's pulp and skin on my right hand. I seem to be all in one piece, with only a slight tinge in the right leg. No blood.

I'm suddenly aware of the shrill voices and the many kinds of shoes surrounding me. The noises create a kind of drumming pulse in my ears. I sit completely splattered with pear sauce, a curious spectacle, a tourist nailed by one of Istanbul's millions of cars. The plastic bag lying near my foot is gutted, as if the bag of pears exploded.

And then, Nuri is here, kneeling, holding my arm and waist. "Lee! Are you okay?" His voice quavers. I let him know I want up. Light-headed, leaning against him, I take some steps and we make it the rest of the way across the street.

Police arrive. They're talking with Nuri. The black car's driver flashes his indigo eyes at me. I'm his bad luck – unfortunate kismet.

"We'll go to the hospital," Nuri says quietly, coming back to me and reaching out to smooth the hair off my eyes.

"The bag cushioned me," I tell him. I just want to get out of this mess. Back at the flat, I haven't even finished packing.

"We should get an x-ray," he insists.

"I'm fine," I say firmly, stepping to the sidewalk. Aware that he notices that I'm trembling, I add, "It's just the shock." Forcing a dry laugh, tell him, "Good thing I bought two kilos instead of just one."

When Nuri and the black car driver start filling out police forms, the crowd looses interest and disperses. Two matrons in scarves, green coats and no-nonsense black heels linger on the sidewalk near me, whispering and looking. I catch wind of their words and hear "armut." They are amazed about what happened to the bag of pears. I am too, as a matter of fact. The old saying of Adalet's comes to me: *I go out each day to see what is written on my forehead.* Fate is written on the winds and will meet you head-on. I glance over to the women and shrug. They nod back knowingly.

Leaning against the rock wall waiting for the forms to be completed, my breath comes normal. I dig in my purse for a mint. Stuck to the mints is a small folded piece of paper. As I suck on the mint, I open the note. It's the one given to me three days after Adalet died. With all that's taken place the last few weeks, I totally forgot about it.

Now, it all comes back, the September rain:

The rain that day several weeks ago had finally begun to let up a bit in the early afternoon. My niece, Filiz, had driven her sister, Beliz, and me down from the city's finance district. We went along the roadway by the Bosphorus Strait, and over by the wide estuary of the Golden Horn.

The car pulled into the old Eyup district, a hodgepodge and muddle that crawl from the water's bank and on up into the jumbled hills. We three trudged through the maze of Friday's people and goods, around the tub-size flowerpots and the various vehicles parked on the sidewalks. The conservative section centered itself around the mosque named for Eyup Sultan, a relative and disciple of the Prophet Mohammed who died there in the seventh century. Eyup's tomb was a shrine. To honor Adalet in tradition on the third day after her burial, we came to meditate on her soul. The idea is held that a soul could be left wandering the ethers, confused, needing a little extra support.

Filiz, Beliz and I found a corner for us in the small, fenced-off women's section. In front of us, the large area for men filtered a gray light. A little man in a baggy suit entered the hall adroit as a sprite and immediately proceeded to bend his knees, hands and head to the floor while we began to talk quietly about how Adalet had respected education and freedom, how she was good with advice and coffee fortunes, that she always had a stew bubbling, a smile.

When the three of us left the mosque, we stepped into a chilling, thin rain. We hurried down the main street until we paused in front of a battered Ottoman-style teahouse laced with a façade of overhanging roof and lattice wood. Squinting through the dim glass, we saw a shadowy room furnished with rough slatted chairs and tables. Lamps lit the walls. The sign on the door read "Acik", Open. "This may be the place of the famous fortune teller," Filiz told us.

"A coffee-cup reader?" I asked.

"They say his shop is on Eyup's main street," she answered.

Not only getting out of the rain but also having a professional reading was certainly appealing. Adalet surely would have nudged us to get in out of the chill. Reading Turkish coffee cups was another thing that Adalet taught me. I surmised that in the art of fortune telling, images and symbols have clear meanings, but the value of the fortune itself depends on the reader's inspiration from who knows where.

We opened the door to copper goat bells jangling on the knob. A customer at the far end of the room lifted his glass and slurped the last tea from his tumbler. "What an assortment," Beliz whispered. We paused in the entryway, looking around the room. Faded newspaper clippings, photographs, antique knives, shovels, ladles, oxen yokes and pitchforks. The conglomeration plastered the walls and hung from the ceiling. Near the back of the long narrow shop, a small flame glowed from a single burner on a partially enclosed hutch. A huge brass samovar steamed on the counter. A pyramid of white demitasse cups and saucers and a whole tray of small fluted glasses waited across the space in the dusk.

The tea drinker stood up and slipped coins into the hand of a bearded man who seemed to be in charge. In seconds, the customer brushed past us and left without raising his head to look at us.

The bearded man scuffled toward us in baggy gray trousers, a brown sport jacket over a woolen sweater and black leather slippers over socks. His white skullcap covered the tops of his ears. A salt and pepper beard hung to his collarbone. He opened his hands, gesturing welcome. He pointed to a table.

As we sat, Beliz let him know we wanted coffee with readings. He bowed his head and brought his hand to his heart, introducing himself as Rasim Hoja, the owner. The Hoja title indicated that he was a respected scholar or teacher of Islam. He would read our cups, he said, lacing his fingers into his beard, his eyes on each of ours in turn. His raspy voice floated on a scale of smooth halftones. He brought three small demitasse cups of coffee, two with sugar, one without.

After drinking the thick coffee, we turned demitasse cups top-down in the saucers. Rasim Hoja returned, and in no uncertain terms indicated that he would read Filiz's fortune, Beliz's, and lastly, mine. With a few battered books under his arm, he pulled up a chair. He told Filiz to hold the saucer still while rotating the cup three times, and then to ask a silent question. He took the cup in one hand, the saucer in the other, and examined the dregs. After Hoja took a pencil from his jacket pocket and waved it like a wand over the cup and saucer, he mumbled what seemed to be a prayer. He then read aloud in Arabic from an old poetry book and also from a sacred text.

My nieces' fortunes took forty-five minutes. Hoja leisurely performed his impressive rites. Beliz translated what he saw in Filiz's cup: "You were famous. You no longer create something that you are very good at doing." Beliz and I exchanged looks. Yes. Filiz had been rather well known on the stage ever since she was a girl until nine years ago when she gave up acting for marriage. In Beliz's cup, he saw two flocks of birds flying in opposite directions. She was going to have to make an important choice.

I began to wonder if there would be time for my fortune when Hoja got up and went to the door, turning away a customer, flipping the sign to read "Kapali", Closed. He pulled down the shade.

"You're next," Beliz said. "However, it's his family's teatime. He's willing to read your cup in just a bit." Beliz raised an eyebrow. But, we would have to wait.

I was not about to leave. Filiz and Beliz agreed to hang around so that I, too, could get a fortune. After all, I was the guest in the country. Hoja brought us tea to sip.

As they sipped, we discussed the readings so far, and wondered how much of it was valid. He could have recognized Filiz from when she was in the spotlight. And anyone could surmise that a lovely young woman like Beliz, who wore no wedding band, might have romantic ties. But how could he have guessed that Filiz had twin sons and a daughter? Since retirement, she had kept her life private.

A dreary rain pattered against the windows. We could hear the clink and chatter of Hoja's family teatime in the back. We got up. Trying to be as unobtrusive as moths, we touched the relics on the walls: old poems in Turkish, pictures of people who had visited the teahouse, articles about Turkish history, a picture of Mustafa Kemal as a First World War hero at Gallipoli, and postcards to Rasim Hoja from admirers all over the world. He obviously took relationships personally and made people want to remember him. And he was a history buff. Adalet would like that. Maybe her spirit had indeed led us to this shop.

When Rasim Hoja returned and began again, my cup was stuck to the saucer. This had never happened to me and I couldn't guess what it meant. I pulled up the cup, turned it over, closed my eyes, and asked the silent question: "How in the world will I ever be able to write a book about Adalet now that she's gone from us?"

As Hoja raised the saucer and looked in, he gasped, grumbling as he brought a hand to his lips.

Beliz translated. "Someone's put a hex on you!"

"What? Wow," I whispered. I'd never heard a teller tell that. And, he didn't look like he was making a joke. My mind began to race. Could anyone really want to do something like that? "Someone is angry and wants something from you," Hoja continued. "And I see you have a grief."

I shifted my butt against the pressure of the pinching slats. "Ask him what I can do about the hex," I told Beliz.

When Beliz translated, Hoja rose and went to the back of the shop. I doubted that jinx business, yet believed in positive and negative forces, and for that matter, even thought-forms have power. Was this a warning?

He shuffled back with a piece of paper. On it, he wrote what Filiz informed me was a prayer. Then he folded the paper until it was only an inch wide, explaining that I was to keep it as a safeguard. Like the blue "evil eyes" that ward off harm.

"The answer to your silent question will find its own path," he said.

Rasim Hoja held the folded prayer between the index finger and thumb of one hand while he paged through a book with the other. Filiz quietly patted her hands together twice and then held them fixed at her chest. Beliz eased her shawl up onto her shoulder. I propped elbows onto the table and leaned chin onto entwined fingers. Our eyes skidded back and forth at each other. Hoja's pages turned like whispers.

"Ah-ha!" he said, laying the book down on the table and running a sharp fingernail under a line of Arabic. Neither of us moved until he withdrew his pencil from where he had parked it at the top of his ear and began to draw on an index card that he took from the book. We stretched to see the design he was sketching. After some seconds, Rasim's pink cheeks lifted as he held up his drawing and explained what it meant.

Beliz sighed lightly as she thought-out her translation. "He says," she told me, "for protection, you must buy this." She nodded toward the design. "Armut."

"For protection?" I said with a laugh. "Why, that's only a pear."

Now, here I am leaning against the rock wall on this street corner in Sultanahmet numb with realization. My mind races – prayers back at the mosque that day for Adalet's spirit, and then, discovering by accident a fortune-teller of coffee cups. And now, a fortune that has come true.

Adalet's face floats in my thoughts. I see her, as she was when I first met her in 1964. It was twelve years after she had lost everything. Her kismet, she called it.

TWENTY-SIX

To Leave Me as You Did

Adalet would never have completely abandoned Burhan. Her oldest son Nuri warned her to protest the divorce papers. But she refused. She did not believe that he would follow through on it. It clouded her mind. The heart can do that.

Adalet rubbed the florets of pink and blue tatting on the edge of the black silk, between her thumb and forefinger – one tiny loop and pearl on the other – each bloom representing the time and effort of some nameless woman, working the threads like the mothers had been taught by their mothers. The flowers added grace to the silk.

It fell from her fingers onto the top of her possessions in the suitcase on the bed. She stared at the scarf as if it had an answer. Here she was, forty-nine years old, back in her old room holding onto a present that Burhan had once upon a time bought for her. Or, was it ever actually meant for her? That was ten years ago. Since then, she'd mostly kept it tucked away.

Home, ten-years ago in 1941, was the southeastern town of Marash. The family had been assigned by the government to live there for the second time. The first time, in 1928, Deniz was born. The second time, Oznur's passing. Burhan had gone to Istanbul to take another rest. She'd been unable to contact him. Horrible. Darling Oznur, already three days' cold in the ground when he came back. After that, Burhan was even more irritable and distant. Adalet didn't care. For a long time, she didn't notice many things: her ragged nails, chapped lips, what she ate. Took to her bed, crippled. After six months passed, one afternoon, she'd found the scarf in Burhan's dresser drawer under his socks. The scarf's florets held a scent of hyacinth.

"Whose is this?" she'd asked.

"Why have you been snooping in my things?" he retorted.

"I was going to mend that hole in your socks."

"A present. For you. From Istanbul."

"A present?" she asked.

"With the situation, our child – I forgot to give it to you," he said, grasping his leather riding crop on his way to the door. Halfway, he turned. He had grown stout as an old oak tree. He waved his hand. "Anyway – now you found it. A good color for you."

"Black?" She'd sucked up straight so that the rolls on her ample body would not sag.

He held his stance and glanced at the scarf in her hand. "The pink and blue tatting. I'd like to see flowers around your face for a change."

Hadn't he mourned at all?

Now, Adalet lifted the scarf, folded and draped it over her two dresses on top of her extra pair of shoes wrapped in a cotton cloth. At the dresser, she scooped up the bottles of lemon-water and rose-lotion, carried them back to the bed, and laid them in the scuffed leather bag. She picked up the lotion and pressed it in her palms. Should she pack or unpack?

In the week's time she'd been in Kirklareli, Adalet hadn't emptied her luggage. And then, yesterday the telegraph came from Luleburgaz. Elif addressed Adalet as "Mother Dear" whenever she wanted a favor. She could almost hear her eldest daughter's sobs behind the words that followed: "Return STOP My job important STOP Who else can keep Orhan? STOP Car coming tomorrow STOP"

After the telegram arrived, she had to tell the maid, Hanifey, who had always endeared herself, more as a friend than a maid, going between Adalet and her mother to keep the peace. Hanifey's hair was more white than gray; but the deep lines in her still ruddy face hardly showed she was past seventy. The maid had tried to pry the facts from Adalet last night. Hanifey guessed what the wire said – or more than likely, the old gal had gone to the stationmaster and bribed him for the information. Hanifey wanted to know what Adalet was going to do, so as to make it a bit easier for herself in the case that she would have to pacify Brother Sukru and Adalet's father. Adalet had tossed all night long.

Adalet absently pulled the strands of her coarse dark hair and tucked them up into the bun, glancing into the mirror. Gray, already showing at the temples. Would she soon be white as Father Ahmet?

How could she disappoint her father again? In his old age, he needed her in Kirklareli to share the management of the farm work with Brother Sukru and his wife, Emine. "Adalet," Her Father had written, "You come now, and you'll have your rights of inheritance back."

Father kissed Adalet on the forehead a week ago when she came in the door. She had no doubts that she was the one to take good care of him. He said last night that her green beans with meat and tomatoes were even better than Hanifey's. She laughed out loud when she thought of that. No wonder. Hanifey had been a chambermaid up until these last few years when they had to let the cook go. Sukru's wife clearly was no accomplished hostess. Adalet's mother Zehra tried for several years to wean Emine from her peasant ways. Zehra called Emine, "Refugee bride from the Balkans." God knows the girl was born to her habits, but Sukru always seemed satisfied enough.

"What are you doing?"

Adalet jerked and dropped the lotion. How well she knew that voice.

"Mother Dearest," she whispered. In a green caftan with black zigzags down the front, the weight of Zehra's frame would fairly soak up the hazy space of a doorway. With her hands on her hips, she resembled a giant moth. Wide sleeves fluttered in the air coming from the open window.

Her demands continued. *"Adalet, I asked you a question. I wondered why you were in your room so long. Haven't you unpacked your suitcase yet?"* Zehra's tone was crystal cold. She would be aware of the telegram that Adalet received from Elif. All morning, Adalet had managed to avoid Father and Sukru. Now, still unable to know what to say and with her mouth open, she submitted the palms of her hands to the air.

Undoubtedly, Mother brushed past her, a stiff breeze wafting toward the bed to inspect her things.

"Really, Mo…" Adalet started to say.

Zehra was a whirl of wrinkled brows and forehead, hennaed hair pulled tight from her face. *"Surely you are not considering going back? Eh?"*

"I don't know," was all that Adalet could think of. Mother moved close enough that Adalet could taste onions on the breath of her.

"Child, your dear father expects tea with you in the late afternoons after his naps. You will become the source of his comfort and hope in his old age."

"About my Dear Elif," Adalet thought.

"Elif, I know, she sent for you, begging," Zehra retorted. " *That one wants you running, picking up for her all through the house. You spoiled your children."*

"She's my first born."

"One that takes care for herself."

Adalet went to the window. How she'd missed looking out this window these past twenty-eight years. This room could be hers again. The family would at last forgive her. Father didn't really want Sukru to be left with all of the land. But, little Orhan. He was the first grandchild and son of her oldest child. He was special.

"Well? How long do I wait to hear this glorious news from my willful daughter?"

"It's a difficult choice," Adalet answered.

"Tell Elif that you're needed here."

"They're sending a car from the Army post. It can arrive any

moment."

"What!" Zehra's voice shot off the walls of the room. *"Elif and her husband, Kamuran, make arrangements involving your life without telling you? And your father the generous Ahmet, who forgets the past, takes you in because you have nothing – is not consulted?"*

Adalet's eyes swept over the objects in the room. Her throat swelled to hardness.

"What were you going to do, sneak out of the house – like before?" Zehra whispered.

"I didn't promise," Adalet whispered.

"Broken hopes –that's all you offer– and your Father, him with the trusting heart."

"I'll decide when the driver comes," Adalet resolved.

"Pshaw! You should stay here." Mother's air grew sweeter. *"Daughter, why do you persist in allowing them to treat you like a servant? There is a maid here. And the Balkan Bride, Emine. In Luleburgaz, you're weighed down with the grandson, Orhan, night and day. Six children are enough to raise."*

Adalet's eyes flashed. Mother never had paused in her own projects to remember the singularity of Adalet's sorrows. She had no idea what Adalet's life was like.

More gently. *"I'm sorry. Adalet, I did not mean to forget little Oznur's death."*

Adalet lowered her eyes and stared at the faded carpet. The ache in her throat spread to her chest at the thought of that paralyzing time in Marash. Mother's observation still hung heavy after all these years.

"Come now, Adalet, it's time for a break from all this," another voice called.

As she walked to the landing, Hanifey came lumbering up the stairs. "Ah, there you are," she said, "your father and brother wait for Turkish coffee." Adalet searched back over her shoulder through the open door of her bedroom beyond the empty haze on the furniture. How could a room so crowded with echoes of a time of innocence ever again be a home to one who had traversed almost the whole of Anatolia and Thrace with the ruins of revolutions under her feet?

"Allah Knows" Hanifey said, "these past few years since our Zehra's death, your father hasn't missed a day drinking his coffee at the same time that he always did with her."

Yes, Allah Knows, Adalet thought. "It's hard for me to believe that my mother is gone," she answered, following Hanifey down the stairway to the parlor. "If only she'd relent, she could go to her rest."

Ahmet, Sukru, and Adalet had finished slurping the bittersweet coffee from the demitasse cups. With Adalet home, Sukru's wife had taken the opportunity to go visit her sister in a local village. Sukru turned his cup open end down to cool in the saucer. Adalet, like Zehra before, could read fortunes in the muddy dregs.

The black Dodge passed in front of the sheer curtains of the wide window and stopped. Adalet rose slowly, folding one hand at her neck on the other. A tingling under her palms passed up to her ears. Her underarms grew suddenly dank.

Ahmet spoke calmly. "Send the chauffeur away. Adalet, my dear, sit down."

"No, no, I promised myself that I would…" Adalet began. She stopped when Mother's words came to her shrill as a migraine: *What do you know of promise?"*

Adalet jumped up and scurried to the window and peered out. The chauffeur was coming toward the door.

Avoiding Father Ahmet's eyes, Adalet finished her sentence quickly. "–Would decide after I've spoken with the driver–" She hurried for the door before Hanifey could answer the knock. Sukru rose to his feet with a haughty grunt.

Adalet let the man into the darkened foyer. Although they

spoke softly, she knew that Ahmet, Sukru and the maid in the kitchen heard.

"…A difficult position," Adalet told the chauffeur. "My son-in-law Captain Kamuran and my daughter Elif know my father's wishes."

"They send you love," he answered, repeating the message he'd been told to deliver. "Whatever your decision, you should know that little Grandson Orhan has cried for you all week, and they fear he'll get sick. No one can replace you. The captain's wife, your Elif, has taken to bed with her nerves."

Adalet paused and searched up the stairwell. She studied the hard looks coming from the parlor. The choice had to be made quickly. Adalet took a step forward and called toward the kitchen. "Hanifey!" The weight in her chest pulled at her face, so that she struggled to mouth the words. "Please escort the driver upstairs and let him bring my bags at once." Adalet's own ragged voice sounded false to her.

In seconds, Father and Sukru were beside Adalet in the foyer, Brother's face swelled with arrogance, Ahmet's stoic with anger. Zehra's words slammed through her head in between the words of her father and brother. She could hardly suck breath.

"Look at your life's decisions, woman."

"We give you a chance!"

"Well, nothing is what you will own!"

"Elif and Kamuran could make other arrangements."

"To be a slave –"

Hanifey charged into the foyer from the kitchen. Using her strong arms, the maid stepped between Adalet and the men and began hugging and giving Adalet tearful kisses on both cheeks while the others continued. Adalet's throat ached. She had missed the nurturing Hanifey. One could never repay such a gentle hand. She looked the maid in the eyes and knew that she would never see her again once she walked out the door.

"And after everything –to divorce our family's daughter–"

Father raised a pointing finger. "Adalet, on this threshold you leave good fortune."

"Let her go," Sukru said. "We have my wife." Brother didn't need to read the fortune in his cup to know that the events that had just unfolded doubled his estate.

Adalet nodded, regarding Father's face. He always meant his words. Sucking her lip, she passed through the doorway. Adalet trundled across the yard as if wild dogs barked at her heels.

"– Shame, do you hear? No inheritance –"

"Nothing."

From her place in the black Dodge, Adalet did not look back; but the furious air of her mother tried to close in around her. *"You never achieved anything except how to be a servant!"* The very sweat on Adalet's body seemed fetid with the words that had just been exchanged. Thirty-two years and seven children and back to where she had begun; and still accused of betrayal. The willful marriage made without family arrangement. The girl "running to the husband." In truth, the girl, Adalet, had been confused about her family's reactions, with her Mother having been abducted, too. So were Mother's two sisters, Azime and Gulifer. But Mother's marriage to Father prospered. Whether one had made a good choice or not seemed all to often to hinge on the affluence that came into the marriage.

She envisioned once again her mother's infamous public show of disdain. The story had since been repeated in mythic proportions of how the servants of the manor brought all of young Adalet's clothing, books, and personals and heaped them onto the front lawn, and how Zehra sent it all to blazes while the town people crept out to watch, a bonfire reaching up to the stars, symbolizing a family's wrath toward a willful daughter.

Even so, Adalet didn't back then have as heavy a heart as she did in that back seat of the Dodge. She no longer possessed the strength of youth. Back when she was that girl of fifteen, she sat in Burhan's cousin's home and felt protected. Azime was managing. The news of Mother's raging storm warmed the ears of the whole town. Yet, all the while, Adalet had pictured herself in the center of a romantic drama that would have a happy ending. She had still been naive enough to believe the tales of what she had heard about the love between a man and a woman, and how it could overcome anything. The country's wars continued to rumble and gave no hope of good solutions. While the empire flailed in continuous confusion, Adalet chose to wish upon the brightest star in her skies, believing in the surge of her heart.

As the Dodge picked up speed on the open highway, Adalet rolled down her window. The onrush of fresh air immediately began to cool her flesh. After all, she told herself, the years had shown that her parents' harsh judgment of Burhan had some base. Yes, indeed.

On the other hand, the path she took offered life, rewards – such as her children. She wouldn't have them otherwise. She could have been like Sister Nefise in her secluded mansion. She reminded herself that President Ataturk twice praised her. Even though her husband let Ataturk think that it was he who prepared that cheese. "Teachers are the one and only people who save nations," Ataturk said. Pasha had rewarded her for getting that school going in Hakkari. There had even been talk of making Adalet a deputy in the Parliament. But, then, there was Burhan to look out for, his job; there was her own children who had been through enough.

The tears came and then she breathed quietly. The driver kept his face to the road. The wind beat its muffled flap against her ears until she no longer felt the noise of anger. She closed her eyes, exhausted, curling into her comfortable self in the corner of the dark, wide seat.

The tires scattered the gravel as the Dodge pulled up in front of the two-bedroom stucco cottage. The peonies on the fat bush by the walk inside the yard were in full bloom. A good omen, Adalet told herself. She had watered them every day last month, carrying a bucket from the rain barrel behind the house.

The driver opened the door and stood with his heels together, waiting for her to get out. His eyes glanced off above her shoulders, not to see her legs.

When the black door shut at her back, the door of Elif's house opened. Adalet reached out her hands. Orhan, her precious one, hopped into the sunlight and ran out the path, striking the peony bush with his tan skinny arms. A full blossom broke apart into the air. The fuchsia-tinged petals scattered in the dirt yard. Her heart fluttered.

Orhan stopped after he came through the gate. Wiry legs spread wide, toes wiggling in his sandals; he scowled up at her, and then cast around in a hurry until he found his long stick by the fence. He raced to pick it up and came at his grandmother, swiping near her legs, and shouting, "Bad Grandmother, bad Grandmother, to have left me so!"

Elif swooped down behind and caught him up in her arms. The stick fell to the ground. "Have you ever known such a devoted four-year old?" she asked, her eyes full and bright. Her smile lifted rouged cheeks. Her curls were pulled up on top with the Western style. She put the child down, calling him a rascal. She was laughing.

"Tell your grandmother welcome, Orhan," Elif said to him. "He is showing his grief for your absence, Mother." Elif was holding Orhan's hand and trying to bring him around. But he would not say it and ran into the house without looking back.

"It will take a few days for him to forgive you," Elif said in a whiney tone. She bent and kissed her mother on both cheeks. Adalet coldly kissed the air at the sides of Elif's face.

"That will pass," Adalet told her, looking at her daughter with interest to see that she was so quickly recovered. "However," Adalet continued, "if I'm to keep him, I'll teach him some manners."

Elif didn't answer, but shrugged her shoulders. She hooked her arm into Adalet's and they went to the house while Elif informed her mother how hard the past week had been with Adalet gone to Kirklareli.

Elif and her husband Kamuran, and Adalet sat in the kitchen, as it was still too hot with the sun coming into the living room. How cozy it was to sit around the table with the smell of steaming tea. Unfortunately, Orhan could not be persuaded to stop play-ing with his wooden train in the other room. He did not come to them, despite his father's urging.

Adalet tried to leave her sad feeling about Orhan's pouting and began focusing on Kamuran, who sat across from her. The man had a resonant voice, was stout and muscular, even when he wasn't donning his brass buttons and bars. This afternoon, he wore his leather scuffs and undershirt with his brown pants. Still, he was always the erect soldier, even now at his small kitchen ta-ble. Elif was lucky. Adalet had never heard him curse her, either. His hickory bark knuckles pedaled as he turned his fluted glass of tea. Kamuran spoke directly into his mother-in-law's eyes, telling her how glad he was to see her face again. "You will always have a place in my house, Adalet," he said. Kamuran gathered the fingers of his other hand to the thin lips of his cleanly shaved face, kissed them, and flung the salute on to Adalet with the flair of an actor.

Adalet brought her hand across her mouth and smiled. But then, she heaved a breath and released it as she dropped the hand onto the other in her lap. They had not even yet asked her how she was holding up. Orhan's thin voice was singing bits of a song as he played in the sitting room. Adalet raised her hand again and let it fall with a dull smack onto the other. They watched her. When she began to speak, she focused on their hands resting on the table. His were manicured, and Elif's, polished with dark red like Azime's. Aunt used to be proud of her long nails. Kamuran and Elif had matching rings on their fingers.

"I've lost my inheritance for the fourth time," Adalet stated flatly. "Hardly have a lira left."

Kamuran took Elif's hand and squeezed it.

"Shall I be hired as a teacher or a maid at my age? Elif, your fa-ther and his bride will live a rosy life on his pension." All of those years! Adalet should have divorced Burhan – and in doing so, she would have been entitled to receive money from his govern-ment allowance. He had threatened to divorce her many times. Adalet's breath came short. She never thought that he would car-ry out a permanent separation from her. That's why she didn't dispute the divorce. Protesting it, plus all of those years at his side and the seven children, would have gotten her a good settlement. It wasn't pride, as her children thought. She simply believed that he was bluffing again. She steadied her breath. In their marriage, and not unlike society as a whole, there had been so much of just surviving to do. And, if truth were known, Adalet had just never quite figured out how to give him whatever it was that he needed. Then, too, Adalet hadn't guessed about the young secretary, about the pregnancy.

Neither Elif nor Kamuran answered, and the pocket of silence shamed her. Adalet studied her own hands as she continued. "Burhan would have never managed to remain governor all those years without me staying by his side. To be a governor means someone has to be reliable!" A panic closed in around the edges of her skin. "Now, what I am to do – with my oldest son on a basic university scholarship and hardly able to feed himself?" Raising her head, she stared into frozen expressions. "Perhaps, I could buy a bucket and charcoal and sell chestnuts on some corner!" Her voice was sharper and louder than she intended. Her eyes darted to the open door to see if she had startled Orhan. The boy was still humming to himself.

Elif reached across the table and patted her mother's arm. "You will never need a penny if you stay with us, Mother Dear," she said brightly. "Besides, your food and lodgings are taken care of by us. With my job, I need you. Keeping Orhan requires your particular skills."

Kamuran laughed. "And, for myself, I can't wait for your meals." He leaned over and placed his broad hand on his wife's shoulder. "Elif, my bride, you are not a very good cook or house cleaner, either." He stood and scraped back his chair.

"You know I don't like housework, Kamuran." Elif withdrew her hand from the table, scooted up from her chair and faced him.

"– And cooking," she continued, "well, it can be done, though your cousin who was going to keep Orhan if Mother didn't come back –"

"She has a name," Kamuran interjected.

"– Your cousin, whoever –would not have made the fine meals you prefer. Your cousin's plates would have made even mine taste delicious– so!"

This revelation that someone else could have kept Orhan shocked Adalet to the core. A cousin? She grabbed the table's rim. They had said that there was no one else to keep Orhan! Adalet bolted up in a spin, knocking over her tea glass. The tiny spoon in the tumbler jingled.

She spat out a bitter taste of disgust. "Selfish, thoughtless –you!" The defeating realization raged through her neck into her head. Flushed by it, she was not able to utter all she felt. Instead, she stood there trembling.

Elif and Kamuran exchanged glances, realizing their slip. Elif stiffened her face and looked at her mother. Instead of trying to explain, the daughter eased out of the room with the finesse of a street cat and disappeared beyond the door. Kamuran propped his hands on his hips. His lips were drawn tight as a blade across his lean jaws.

Adalet moaned and then yelled. "What did I ever do to that child that she would rob me of inheritance for my old age?"

As if he could not unsheathe his words, Kamuran remained silent. After a few dull seconds, he shrugged. Half smiling, he dismissed himself, saying, "It will all work out." Running his hand across his nearly baldhead, he strode toward his wife and son in the other room. He turned to nod at Adalet again as if she were senile, and then closed the door softly.

Adalet stayed for some moments in that same spot. Her anger burst against the rough white walls like so many soap bubbles. She was damp all over, and empty on the inside. From the sitting room, she heard them banter on, as if nothing were amiss. An older man like Kamuran was always eager to please a young wife.

Why should they be concerned? They had what they wanted. It was her who must adjust. Elif knew that her mother would soon calm down and contend with reality. Going back to Kirklareli? Out of the question. Adalet didn't even have the money to spare to send a telegram or hire a car and driver – even if she would. To return to the past was futile.

Absently, she slouched to her chair and flopped down in it. Her feet were cold and numb as the sun lowered its light. The walls seemed to shrink. Adalet could only blame herself. She was Elif's Mother. Adalet had always let Elif have her own way, gave her preference as the first-born, and never made her think she had to give concern to her mother's needs. She was so young when Elif was born. Adalet didn't know any better, always behind Elif's every step – exactly as Mother Zehra had said many times. Why should Elif think anything else except that she deserved Adalet's sacrifices? Adalet only hoped that Zehra's spirit would leave her be until the shock settled.

"The heart must not rule the mind, Adalet." Father, the wise man who had memorized the whole Koran, would say that. Both his community and the Holy Book told him that children must be made to submit to their elders. For goodness sakes! Why had she been so strong-willed? Why hadn't she chosen to wait for a husband of their choice? She knew why.

Adalet thought that her heart must have smothered her mind at times. Nevertheless, she had stuck with her mistakes and made the best of them. She took pride in that, which was foolishness, again. She sighed. The dim kitchen walls sighed back. A wry Burhan smirk turned over and pulled on her lips. Actions, emotions and consequences. Ah yes – nothing more.

Several hours later, after her final prayer of the day, Adalet lay on one of the cots in the room where Orhan breathed peacefully in his sleep. She was remembering a voice of years before: *I go out into the morning to see what fate has written on my forehead.* Words of Aunt Azime. Well, that sly matchmaker, that mischief-maker, wrote Burhan on my forehead like a jinni, or I'm a fool, she thought. And I've been stricken by his illusive character for forty years.

She listened to the rhythm of Orhan's dream-slumber on the other side of the filmy space between them. Somehow, she had to believe that Allah understood the whole picture and that a higher presence was still with her. Even though she felt no power. In what else to hope? Ataturk was her savior once, but the Pasha was as gone as Mother's bonfire. Only the stories live on.

Little Oznur. She had only been seven years old. So much promise. Oznur was like watching her own self. Adalet shuddered at the thought of what had scattered her brood.

Look at what happened to her seventeen-year-old poet. She pictured her youngest son, Sedat, squatting by a small fire near a river somewhere on the plains of Anatolia. Maybe even Cyprus. Perhaps, Sedat wandered off after the divorce seeking a more reasonable life. "Consider me dead," his note had said. Nuri and Vedat had been combing the area of Antalya where Burhan had settled. No trace. Thus far.

In her heart, she truly believed that young Sedat was not dead. Adalet mumbled a prayer for his nomadic soul, and asked that he would come back to take her with him when he found a peaceful place. On the other hand, that boy was the seed of Mehmet Nuri the Blacksmith. For whatever reason, Mehmet Nuri had left his family in Tashkent, Uzbekistan. Neither she nor Burhan had ever known why. Mehmet Nuri had kept going west. When his first wife died, he trekked further west. Adalet and Burhan taught their children that the republic's vision was to take up the ways of the West while keeping a foot in ancient heritage. It was the legendary "Gray Wolf," after all, that had led the Turks from the Asian Steppes to Anatolia. Perhaps the family was searching in the wrong places for Sedat. Perhaps he had gone to Canada, Alaska or even Hawaii.

In the custom that had survived for hundreds of years, when a young man would leave home – whether to the army and foreign fields or to another country for venture or trade – he, in his obligation to fulfill the hope of his mother would tell her that she would not hear from him unless he made good of his life. It was common to receive a note from such a one who began, Mother, *I am not dead yet!* And then, the letter would describe the son's feats. Mehmet Nuri became profitable enough – perhaps not quite enough for the daughter of an Aga and a wealthy landowner, but more than satisfactory to most. As far as Adalet knew, Mehmet Nuri never reached back to his parents in Uzbekistan. After all of these years, Adalet could see that there was really nothing romantic in a journey that ended like that.

Why didn't children know that all a mother needed was to hear that her child was safe and well? Adalet longed to believe that the desire for that assurance was why Zehra had wanted Adalet to marry wealth. Would Mother's heart have been less cold if that had happened? What did the answer matter now? But, she knew the answer. It was a matter of values.

TWENTY-SEVEN

Raki

Istanbul, 1981

"Adalet, I have not been able to forgive him, to have left me so."

When she first heard their "Oooh, ohhhh," burring into her sleep, Adalet thought it was one of her babies. She stirred her head slightly on the goose down pillow trying to remember which one of the seven it could be, and in which city or town she might be; and whether she was alone with the children or not. Then, there again, coated in the mucilage of suspended time, another muffled, "Oooh, ohhh," what might be uttered while sipping creamy white orchid root sahlep in shivering Kars.

The sharp Istanbul morning light coming from the parlor's big window, used for looking out on the street, assumed its claim on the pale-green of her bedroom. She rubbed her jaw and brow once more into the soft furrow, and then reluctantly from the Ralph Lauren pillowcase brought from Virginia, she stretched her eyes open to a thick wall of her apartment. Her doves urged the awakening from that window and its rising sun, lighting on the outside ledge to eat the pieces of stale bread that she placed there last night.

She rolled over onto her back and brought her hands to her face and then wiped her eyes and the corners of her mouth with the sheet. Not having teeth made a niggling drool at night. She glanced up at the ceiling and said thanks for another day, and next remembered why she slept here in the sewing room instead of her own bed.

In her mind, she re-lived the moment that Sister arrived last evening. Nefise, having ridden nine hours by bus from the Chorum province northeast of Ankara, stood exhausted from the trip, and furthermore breathless from the climb up the flights of stairs to the flat. The taxi driver followed her, toting by wooden handles the two large bags sewn from kilim rugs. Sister, come to visit at last, stood with her face still as smooth as Adalet's because of the thick skin both had inherited from their mother. Nefise, still a bit shorter than Adalet, looked to be almost but not quite as wide through the hips. But not in the bust. Her legs showing below the dark blue coat that fell to her calves were still slender with trim ankles, unlike Adalet's, that had been a source of pain and swelling for years, plaguing her daily, as did her back and hips.

After Adalet hurriedly washed her face and arms in lemon water, she said quick prayers for her children, grandchildren, and living relatives wherever on this earth they may be – asking blessings from all the prophets including Mother Mary and all her angel hosts. She asked Allah to send comforts to those of her dead beloved ones, and pushed to her feet. Once that was taken care of, she folded up her prayer rug and pulled her brown sweater around her shoulders across the false-silk white blouse with the little brown flowers that she had bought on her third trip to America last year. After adjusting the coffee-colored jersey skirt across her thighs, she tugged on the cotton stockings, rolled the tops down just below her knees, and slipped her feet into the brown leather slippers that her son Vedat had bought for himself but gave to her because they were too small for him. Adalet particularly liked them. They were handmade by a fine Kurdish man whose father used to make slippers for the sultan. The slippers had no backs, so that she could just step her feet into them and shift forward when she had things to prepare, as now.

The small kitchen was a blessing. Adalet was able to strike the match and light the oven and the burner on the top with the same fire, and then lift the pots and turn to the sink by moving only a step. Doctor Nuri, her son in America, told her last trip there, that it was important she continue moving in order to keep strong bones. Some days, the arthritis, rheumatism and osteoporosis bothered her all at the same time. Swelling in her legs brought on aching that held her to her chair or bed. But, as much as possible when she could, she made an effort to walk and bend.

When Adalet set the water on to boil, she opened the refrigerator and took out the pan of stuffed pastry that she made yesterday afternoon for their breakfast this morning. She cut four large pieces of the thin dough layered with white cheese and spinach, placed them into a round pan, and stuck them into a hot oven.

Nefise was up, running water in the bathroom. Adalet had laid out towels along with the favored olive oil soap from the Aegean town of Ayvalik. Nefise would take her leisure with her toilet. By the time she came into the living room, Adalet would have the round wooden table set with the cloth and napkins that Nefise gave to her back when Adalet and Burhan were in Bilecik. The set matched the rose pattern china Nuri had bought when she lived with him in Kargi in the early Fifties. After his military service, Nuri was sent to the northeastern village of Kargi for almost four years as a required payback for his medical scholarship. Adalet had gone to live with him in one side of a rented duplex. The other side was the medical office. Not only was Nuri the general doctor, but often malaria control physician, public health officer and coroner. For transportation, Nuri rented horses. He joked that the horses were paid more than him. Elif had sent her three-year old daughter to live with them for their duration there, as Kamuran was stationed in Kars and she decided to take Orhan and join him.

Adalet would take out the delicate but solid small sterling forks and spoons for their meal. She'd had these since Kars. Nefise was used to nice things, and her first day with Adalet should be special. Sister was planning to stay as long as the both of them desired it. They had decided last night that it would be all winter – since neither of them had anyone to need their services. At ages seventy-nine and eighty-four, they could act like girls in a harem

– and keep their own hours as they pleased. While Adalet worked at the table, the October sun filled the whole living room. She glanced across to the window's ledge. A good omen: The doves had eaten every scrap of the bread.

"The taxi driver not only knew this section of the city, but he has an old mother who lives only several block from here," Nefise answered, untying the blue from her white hair and letting the scarf fall onto her shoulders. The flowers in Sister's cotton dress were the exact shade of the navy blue in the scarf. The tiny sapphire in the small gold knobs of her pierced earrings matched as well. A white muslin scarf wrapped Adalet's head turban-style, knotted at the top.

"Will the servants be watching over your big house while you are gone, Sister?" Adalet asked as she tucked strands of hair back under her scarf. Nefise's hair was cut into a stylish halo of ringlets. No doubt she had gotten permanent curls for herself. Adalet's long hair was salt and pepper. She kept it twisted back into a bun.

"Servants?" Nefise answered, waving the hand with the gold band and small diamond. Apparently, Sister did not wish to flaunt the large diamond that Ali Fuat bought her when they were engaged. "Servants?" she repeated, laughing, her cackle reminding Adalet of Aunt Azime, now dead, bless her soul, for twenty-eight years. "There have not been servants the five years since my husband was laid into the ground, no one, except the young girl who comes twice a week to clean and cook some dishes for me so that I will have something to eat besides eggs and salads."

"You always cared less for cooking. Did you never learn, Sister?" Adalet asked, seeing that she had eaten the second portion of the moist pastry. Nefise always told everyone that Adalet was the only real cook in the family.

"Would I have learned cooking? My no! It's not a problem for me since I eat so little."

"And the lands and workers? Who does the overseeing of them?" Adalet asked.

Nefise widened her eyes, scooted her chair back from the table, crossed her legs, and wiggled the red velvet slipper so that the glass chips on the toe of it sparkled. "Adalet Dearest – I thought you knew!" She stared at her younger sister, who did know. Deniz and her husband had brought the news from their trip to Nefise after Ali Fuat died; but Adalet wanted to hear Sister tell her story.

"Ah –I can see that you have heard– and yes, it is true," Nefise said. "This husband whom I followed day and night, seeing to his every whim, and thinking, regardless of his strange behaviors, that he did care enough for me to see to it that I would be secure in my old age –this prince of a man– up and died out at a tea-house one evening after gagging on a puff of smoke from the water pipe, falling over onto the floor like a fish on a rock – and me, not knowing that he had left every parcel of his lands, except that which spread around the house, for erecting a mosque with his name on it!"

Nefise flipped one leg off the other with the energy of one of those modern teenagers on the television. She stood and swept around toward the coffee table in front of the couch. For Nefise's arrival, Adalet had removed the protective coverlet that she generally kept tucked across the couch to keep it like new. Nefise paused, looking down to the floor at the marble swan with the red plastic roses from America in its back. Adalet glanced over at the amber prayer beads on top of her worn handbook of Koranic prayers that lay on the table on top of the Bible that was written in Turkish. Adalet didn't speak, knowing that Sister would continue when she was ready.

Nefise turned around, one hand delicately onto the palm of the other. Her eyes flashed. "Adalet, I have not yet been able to forgive him, to leave me so. Do you realize that I have sold most of my jewelry? Only one room on my first floor still has furniture. The things of my house have become the means of my support these five years since that man had the audacity to die and give my rightful inheritance to a mosque."

Adalet pushed up and came around the table, holding out her arms. Nefise did not move. Adalet gently took Nefise in her arms and hugged her into her bosom. Sister sniffed and heaved a breath. After a few seconds, Adalet felt her stiffen.

"It's all right," Nefise said, pulling back, "I can take care of myself."

Nefise fooled with the curls at her temple and turned and crossed to the table and settled into her chair again. Adalet padded off to the refrigerator and brought back two diced wedges of honey melon that Vedat had brought from the Mediterranean area of Antalya where he invested in fields and orchards whose harvest he brought to Istanbul, and which she had already prepared on their little rind boats. As they lingered together, Nefise ate the melon, and then gracefully placed the fork down on the plate and spoke with a quiet voice. "Little it is that I require in my old age, Sister."

"You still have the big house," Adalet said, rubbing her hand onto the linen cloth to feel the texture. "Did you not inherit something from our father?"

"A trifle, almost nothing, only enough to pay the girl who comes twice a week. My father surely thought me well off and left everything to Sukru. Father did not have a great amount at the end, you realize."

Adalet shook her head. "I wouldn't be aware, for I was disinherited, as you know."

"But, Sister," Nefise said, raising her voice, "at least you have children to care for you, take you in – look at this nice little place your sons have provided for you – and you can go to any of your daughters nearby whenever you wish!"

"I supposed that you were clever – knowing how not to have babies," Adalet said. "I never learned until I had them all. You had the life of a princess, and I, the maid. Our mother used to remind me of that all of the time."

"I'm sorry for that." Nefise looked sad. "Shall I tell you what I hid from our mother? She was so proud to be the mother of a daughter who had married two Ottoman princes."

"What you hid?"

"When you lived in Kargi with Nuri those years, you witnessed for yourself, with Ali Fuat and I living only in the next province, that my husband was merely allowed to practice at the level of a paralegal. His meager training in law meant nothing to the standards of the republic." Adalet acknowledged with the slight lifting of her head and brows, and Nefise continued. "So, there was never much money to come from my husband's profession. Whatever we took in came mostly from the wheat and the animals." Adalet shook her head and wrinkled her brow and did a "tisk-tisk" through her teeth as Nefise went on. "But it was enough, although we had to each sell precious things regularly for taxes. The villagers in Chorum worked for us almost like the serfs back in Emin Aga's Bedre. The poor people serving us seemed content enough to have provisions. It was Ali Fuat's drinking and gambling that I could not abide."

"Drinking? Gambling? Thank your lucky stars that you did not choose to have children," Adalet exclaimed, bringing her hands to her chest. Although this, she had also heard whispered back in Kargi. Nuri's friend, the judge, had heard the tale about Ali Fuat being jailed for coming to court drunk.

"Choose? Did you say choose?" Nefise said, raising her voice again. "There was no choosing about it. Once the Ottoman Empire completely collapsed and he saw how our lives were to change, the man began to drink wine every evening. The wine took to bed all of his desire for my body and laid him into a sound sleep. Later, the wine drinking became all day long. There was hardly a chance to know if we could have had a child, Sister." Nefise studied the rings on her hand. "At the end, I think the wine flowed in his veins instead of blood; and he had gambled away so much of what was to be mine, leaving me a widow with no children." She raised her head. Her face looked suddenly old. Adalet had no idea that it had been that bad. Adalet shook her head and shrugged with a sigh.

"Forgive him," Nefise hoarsely scolded, "I will not! To save his pitiful soul from rotting in hell for his sins, he gave the land away from under my feet –security, for which I suffered in order to have something in my old age! – The religious order, indeed!"

Adalet sat back from the force of her words. She was in truth a bit delighted to see so much passion come from her older sister. It was about time. "And the law," Adalet added, "Don't forget that it's not better any for a widow with heirs – most of the property goes to the children. The mother is left to haggle for mercy and hand-outs from the ones that she birthed, fed and raised – getting only a fourth of what's left."

In the silence that fell between them, Adalet reflected on the irony of being a woman. While it was true that Ataturk's laws let women air domestic violence and patriarchal oppression, by and large, the majority of Turkish women couldn't take advantage of what was on the books. Most women still worked the land and lived under the control of men and community. The freedom and justice she'd so hoped for had only partially come to pass – and that was usually for the rich and educated. But, she thought: Look at Nefise – hardly better off than a woman like my childhood friend, Zeyneb. Poor little Zeyneb. Adalet heard years ago when she last lived in Kirklareli that Zeyneb had died of an infection after the birth of her fifth daughter.

Quietly, Adalet began to finish her melon. After, they ate the grapes on her plate. They sat back and smiled at each other. "Nefise Dear," Adalet said, "I'm so pleased to have you here with me all winter. Some of your story, I had heard told; but I did not realize how sorry it had been for you, also." Nefise placed a hand onto Adalet's. "You have been an unlucky wife the same as me," Adalet continued, "and Allah has let us both survive difficult husbands –who somehow didn't manage to spoil our spirits– even though Allah Knows they tried." They had a good laugh at that.

"How many years has Burhan been dead, Adalet?"

"He died at only age sixty-three." She sucked her tongue to the roof of her mouth to make the quick wet rasp again, saying, "Burhan was a man with a good heart – but not a strong enough heart to bear his vices into old age."

Adalet silently reflected on the difficult years that followed the second time of living in Marash. After Oznur's death, Burhan got fired from his job. Adalet appealed to Congressman Doctor Fuat, who had for the sake of her and the children, gotten Burhan re-assigned up to Sivas in central Anatolia for a year; and then, Burhan was sent over to Kastamonu north of Ankara for another year, where she and the children followed. In the meantime, the children were all growing up while Burhan's bad habits got worse. He stayed away from the home more and more. When he was in the house, things were not pleasant between him and Adalet and he often harangued the children. After about a year in Kastamonu, Burhan, outraged with the governor of the province, Burhan had a physical altercation with him. When he lost his job there in 1944, it was just too much. Adalet was ashamed to appeal to Fuat's kind nature again. She packed up her kids and left him for the last time, saying she'd never travel back to him as long as he drank – and she knew that could mean forever. In Kirklareli, that time, she and her brood had to stay at an inn. The house was rented. Sabiha was given to the ground, and the family didn't make room. Nuri was desperately trying to win that scholarship to Istanbul University.

"Raki. Trying to keep up with younger women," Nefise added, eyeing Adalet knowingly.

"They had the son, Nefise," Adalet answered with a monitored calmness. "Did you know that Burhan named that baby Ertugrul Sedat – when the man and I already had a son named Sedat?" Adalet figured that Nefise had wondered at the time it happened if Burhan had learned for sure that Adalet's youngest son had died. It was a custom to name a baby after a dead child. Everybody knew that Sedat had been Burhan's favorite child.

"Have you any news on your lost Sedat?"

Adalet pulled her handkerchief from her elastic waistband where she'd tucked it. "We heard that someone saw him in Cyprus, but it has been years. Poor Sedat. He was such a delight." She dabbed at the edges of her eyes as a memory came to her of Burhan and four-year-old Sedat jumping and laughing together after Burhan had gotten the boy to pee on his lottery ticket. "This will bring me luck to win big," Burhan was telling the amused

Nuri. But, their father never did win big, and not for lack of trying everything – except perhaps temperance.

"Sedat and Vedat went with Burhan when I left him," she said. She wadded the damp handkerchief in her lap. "It wasn't long before Burhan was trying to get us to join him in Ankara. But I would not go. I no longer had the energy for what it took to move across the plains of Anatolia to an uncertain future. All three of my daughters had found husbands."

Adalet raised her hands and laid them over her heart and continued. "After Ankara, Sedat was with Burhan on the Mediterranean when Burhan was doing some secretarial job, trying to earn his pension – when he lived with that woman and then divorced me." Nefise clucked and at the same time jerked her head back in a gesture of disgust. Adalet acknowledged it, and continued. "It didn't take long for Sedat to know he couldn't take being with them. Before he ran away, he sent a letter asking Nuri to come take him. Being saved was not his kismet. Nuri couldn't go pick him up until he finished taking his last year medical school examinations. By the time he got there, Sedat had vanished."

"Why do you think Burhan named his baby Sedat?"

"Not because he knew our son was dead – as you may think! If Sedat was dead, I would know it in the same way that I feel Oznur's being gone from this world; and I don't feel that separation from him." Adalet paused, trying to envision her children's youthful faces.

"No, Burhan could not bear to think that his son could be alive and yet rejecting him. That misguided man simply did not know how to understand other people's needs."

"Did you ever talk to Burhan again after the divorce?"

"Burhan came to Kamuran and Elif's house in Luleburgaz one evening. He was married by then, and had that baby. He wanted my pardon. I told him forgiveness would have to come from Allah, for in what he did, he insulted the Almighty more than the children and me, that he had ruined what would have been a wonderful family, had failed the dream of the revolution. We would not have lost the love and support of Doctor Fuat if

Burhan's attachment to raki was not stronger than his love for his family."

"Did you, really? What did he say?"

"He cried. And then, I did forgive him, and touched his hand. I asked him to forgive me for hurtful things that I had said and done to him." Adalet had seen from the early years that Burhan was a nervous, restless soul. She hoped he found satisfaction before he died.

"Sister," Nefise said leaning across to her, "You were a saint."

"No, Nefise, you remember I was going to trick him into divorce. You were there."

Nefise sat back and blushed. She pulled forward and answered. "Perhaps it was all for the best, after all. But, never mind that now. What did he say when you asked him to forgive you?"

"Well, to tell you the truth, he laid his other hand on mine and looked into my eyes like a would-be suitor. Imagine that. I withdrew my hand, of course. 'Leave me be,' I said. Go to your harem wife!' The mystery between us was cold; and our riverbed was dry. I left the room and didn't return. Burhan sat up half the night talking with Orhan's father, Kamuran; and then he left before breakfast."

"Did you never hear from him again?"

"Before I went to join Nuri in America the first time –and that would have been the year Burhan died in 1958– Vedat told me that his father was so proud of Nuri, and that Burhan said, 'I'll get my family together and we will all go to America as one big clan. We will start anew."

"No!" Nefise said, covering her mouth with her scarf, for it was rather humorous to picture. "Was that man going to go to America with two wives and with children from each? Did Burhan think he was still an Ottoman?"

They both laughed and giggled like girls. "And our mother, father and our Brother Sabri are all resting in heaven now; and no doubt smiling with us right this minute," Adalet said, coming to her self. "In the hands of Allah. And Sister, will you have more tea?"

"Another cup. And with some honey if you have it." Adalet got up to get the tea while Nefise told her that she took honey for the arthritis in her hands. "And those materials I brought to you are the last of my handiwork," she added. "Created several years ago, for my fingers do not permit my doing it these days."

"I will make pillows of them," Adalet answered, pouring her tea, and not able with all this talk to stop remembering how Vedat said that Burhan had asked to see her when he lay in the hospital on his last pillow. If they had come for me, I might have gone – if the other woman was kept out of my sight, she thought.

"At least, our mother did not suffer long and never had to contend with the pains of old age," Nefise said.

"No," Adalet answered, sitting down and pouring herself tea and adding two spoonfuls of sugar. "Mother Zehra was also only sixty-three – the same as Burhan. Pain in her leg one day and gone from us the next. 1939.

"Those were the years of my sorrows," Adalet said flatly. "One onto the other: first our Kemal Pasha; and then, the following year, Mother. And the next year took Darling Oznur. After that, things fell apart."

Nefise sipped her Rize tea and returned the cup to the saucer with a chink. She kept her eyes on the steaming cup as Adalet continued. "And within the next five years, the divorce hit me; and after, Sedat seemed to become a part of the shifting winds."

They sat in stillness for a while, as if to allow the tilling of the soil of their lives time to take in freshness. Regardless of what they'd been through, there was always hope for a new harvest.

After several moments, Adalet mused in her mind that maybe Sedat went to find Blacksmith Mehmet Nuri's family in Tashkent. After all, she'd learned that the wind blows back and forth in all directions. Like a wheel.

TWENTY-EIGHT

The Bottom of the Cup

Those moments with Sedat were when she had become aware of how futile it was to lie in that dark pit.

Nefise reached across the table with the crisp linen cloth and the breakfast remnants. She draped a tatted edge napkin across her sister's palm so that Sister could sponge up her spill of tears. It would be a shame to have her eyes bloated and red, a pity to mar this, their first full day alone together in years. All of this talk about the difficult past was enough to make anyone wail to realize what she had lived through. It was the irony of women in society that ultimately made it interesting – if not down right humorous, in a very private way, of course. While historians bragged that the Constitution of the Turkish Republic stood solidly within the frame of equality for all, and equal rights for women, the sad reality through the years was that old men still married thirteen-year-old girls and too many males still killed their women in the name of an honor that demanded the female's being a physical and emotional slave. Though the law held up five years of education as mandatory for both sexes, a paltry percentage of poor girls could read and write. Sure, lucky upper class and elite women received professional degrees. However, these same women most often found themselves unemployed as soon as they gave birth to a child. Dependable childcare remained almost nil. Mothers-in-law rarely liked their sons' wives and one's own mother too often favored her daughter's staying home with children in the traditional manner. And thus, even mothers were often uncooperative when it came to a young woman taking her wings to the air of the future in the spirit of Ataturk's adopted and oft sited daughter, Sabiha Gokcen. The Republic enabled Sabiha as the world's first combat pilot in 1936. Yet, when "true democracy", that is, when those of conservative values took over in the late forties, women became all but grounded.

Nefise fingered the tablecloth. It was obviously one of those new linen blends. It could no doubt be washed with little ironing. This had come from Adalet's last trip to America. Good for a sister who always withstood the efforts of traveling. Burhan's father had traveled from Uzbekistan to Saudi Arabia and then across Anatolia and into Thrace. Mehmet Nuri's grandson had simply continued going west as soon as he was able.

"Sister," Nefise asked, "Did Nuri go to America before or after the first military coup of 1960?"

Adalet laughed. "My Nuri?" she answered with some delight to be able to speak of his emigration, her son, who earned the name "Cowboy" when he practiced in Kargi because of his hats and belts. Everybody knew that Doctor Nuri wanted to go to America. "That boy of mine took off for Chicago in 1958, hardly speaking any English and with only fifty dollars in his pocket."

"Sounds a bit foolish to me," Nefise said. She couldn't imagine doing a thing like that.

"Nuri had to get out," Adalet told her gravely. "After Ismet Pasha's party gave way to the conservatives, Nuri had a thirst for progressive democracy." She sat back in her chair and nodded her head before continuing. "He wasn't foolhardy. He had a job lined up there."

"Yeah," Nefise said thoughtfully, "I, for one, wasn't sorry when they got rid of those who tried to tear down all we had struggle to build." There had been a recent coup in 1980. The world seemed amazed that a military machine would be determined to protect a democracy, but not these two sisters. The duty of the nation's youth was to protect the republic.

The two sat sipping their tea for a spell. Then, Nefise reached for Adalet's hand again. "Adalet, would that I could have been with you when Oznur died," she said. "How were you able to bear it and go on?"

Adalet's throat hardened to a hurt as she thought about that awful second time in Marash 1941: *She, alone with the children, and Burhan sent to Istanbul for three months because the doctor said he needed another rest for his nerves. To think that Oznur had gotten sick after she had just given a performance for the school festival – her spindly legs and feet tap-tapping and twirling on the stage with the dance she had invented herself, swishing in the red dress that Adalet made for her, in the little black shoes that made a snapping on the stage as quick and full of energy as her spirit; and then afterwards, everybody telling Adalet how proud she must be to have such a daughter; and Adalet, so happy, thinking that no matter how kismet with Burhan had turned out to be, that Oznur was her own heart, a second chance.*

Adalet brought both hands to her face and swept the grief off and then held her palms out shoulder-height like an offering. That memory always came down like a flood.

"Open your heart, Sister," Nefise said, getting up and coming around to place her hands on her sister's cheeks. Adalet looked up into her eyes.

"She had danced so beautifully that day," Adalet told her. "Later, the sun was bright and we were all in the home. With Burhan gone to Istanbul, there was no quarreling. Toward evening, Oznur was not feeling well. I thought she had overworked herself with the performance, so I boiled a chicken and made some broth. Oznur would not take but a bit of the soup. I added lemon juice. She had begun to run a fever and have diarrhea. We thought she had a cold."

Adalet stood, and Nefise stepped back to let her walk away

from the table toward the window. Adalet looked through the veil of curtains. The day's sunshine had changed without their notice to a sudden autumn rain – beading down the pane, hitting softly on the ledge, the patting like the ticking of a clock, like blood drumming against a vein, a pulse and time, a time and no pulse pulsing – *and for several days, Oznur laid around, eating not much because of the throbbing, the pain in her stomach because her bowels had blown out, could not swallow fruit or drink, even a tea tumbler's spoon of olive oil. And then, the fever's getting higher, and she, sleeping, and when awake, delirious. Thirteen-year-old Leyla's voice: "Her stomach is swollen, too swollen!" And when Adalet looked and saw the brown blotches, she called for the doctor. Elif opening all of the windows and doors to let the breeze blow in, to cool her, and Nuri and Sedat taking turns fanning her as she lay, head in Adalet's arms, gently easing her back onto the pillow for Doctor to examine, each breath she took, Adalet's own breath. She wished to have the pain for Oznur but could not – the typhoid fever, he said, and asked if she had eaten anything that wasn't washed or had she drunk water that was not clean. Adalet did not know what to answer, she did not know, and when Vedat began to cry, Adalet did also, and would not stop. No reply from Oznur, and Adalet paced the room and prayed Allah and all the angels to heal. Oznur was dry, even with the constant washing over her thin body, and she was alternately wet with sweat then singed with fever, and her lips and cheeks were parched. Doctor left, they played her music on the gramophone to make her wake but she did not. It seemed morbid to play the music with Oznur so ill, and so they stopped, and continued on through the night with Adalet not sleeping and each of the six children taking turns getting up with Adalet to care for Oznur until the morning.*

They watched Doctor fill the big needle with the medicine he sent for, hold it up toward the light bulb that hung down from the long black cord, and inject it into her stomach. She didn't flinch, although Adalet felt it pierce her gut. Another night, no sleep, and Adalet held her head, and Nuri took her lips in his hands and opened them, and Elif poured in a little water, and Nuri massaged her jaw and throat so that the water went down. Her short curly dark blonde hair was matted from the bed and sweat, and Adalet was remembering that head caught in the bright stage, the spot of her shining like the young actress, that Shirley Temple.

The next morning, Deniz tried the gramophone again. Oznur moaned on the couch and they all ran to help her sit. Good morning, she said, and when Leyla brought tea and lemon, she drank it down, and all were so happy, the doctor's shot had done its work. The darling girl was going to be all right. When she finished her tea, she stood and began to lift her arms and slowly turn about the room, her head held back and her eyes closed as if she was in a dream, and she was floating around the couch and the samovar. And then she stopped, and smiled, and took a bow; and all clapped. Then, when she said she would go to the toilet, Leyla followed and waited at the door, and the rest held back.

Oznur opened the door and walked quickly to Adalet. At first, Adalet thought she was telling a joke: Mother, listen to me; I'm going to die. Oznur had seen what was going to happen to her. She had the vision. When Adalet tried to stop her telling that, Oznur placed her hand on her mother's cheek. It's true, she said, only two minutes left, she said – don't worry, she said. She was not in pain. I am being taken, she said, Big wings protect me. Adalet stooped, lifted her in her arms, and told her not to speak such nonsense. She went limp in Adalet's arms. Adalet tried to stand, but fell, screaming.

Sedat ran out the door with Nuri for Doctor, already on his way across the yard, and by the time he rushed in the door, she was again on the couch where Doctor grabbed her arms and held his head onto her chest to hear the pat, the pat, the pat, pat – again, again, and slapped her face. But she was lost. Her name, Adalet kept calling her name as if she could call her back from wherever she'd gone. She did not come. Leyla was making the angel's face wet with tears as she kissed her forehead and cheeks. And when Leyla fell upon the small chest and gave a wail too heavy for a fifteen-year-old girl, Adalet knew the worst loss she'd ever have.

Doctor pulled Leyla back and drew the white sheet until it was up over Oznur's bony form – and then, it was like she vanished from their hands.

Adalet turned away from the October rain and the window, and looked at her sister again. Nefise stood with her hands clasped in front of her, waiting for Adalet to share the rest, but she couldn't speak the details to her. "When I saw Oznur's body covered with the white sheet on the couch, I fell to my knees. After that, I didn't stand up," she told her. "Right after that, the religious ministers came and carried her out, wrapped in that sheet."

"It must have been terrible to bear," Nefise said, coming to her and leading her to sit on the couch. Adalet's mind was running in circles. They could let only fourteen-year-old Nuri go to bury her because they were all in such distress and disbelief. When he came back later, and said that it was done, Adalet had already begun her fall into a dark well. Nuri later told her about his experience with the awful burial. It was hard for her to believe today that she had let him do it himself then; but, she was in that long shock and his father could not be reached. He was the oldest son. It was not proper for the girls to oversee a burial. The body had to go into the ground immediately. Nuri went from the house with the men. No one gave him instructions on what was to be done:

Nuri trailed behind the pious holy men, the hojas, who followed four neighborhood men who took up the small wooden coffin onto their shoulders. His whole body felt bloated with sadness. Three times, the coffin was passed to four other shoulders, men who quit hoeing their gardens, mending wagons, tending shops, all left off to carry the common burden of death, the community loss, shouldering grief in a brief lull from regular things.

In a short while, the two workers and the holy men and Nuri trundled over the sandy hill and down a path at the edge of the town onto the plain where the ragged blue and yellow wildflowers blossomed among the tombstones.

When the men set the coffin down, Nuri sidled up to it and tried to look as if he knew what he was supposed to do. His eyes skimmed across the deep hole with the mounds of loose dirt beside it.

Then suddenly, the men took the lid off the coffin. Nuri stared in horror at the small form of his sister swathed in thin, white gauze.

Before he could speak, the men lifted Oznur out and placed her on the ground. The ministers began a dirge. Nuri pulled at one of their sleeves, but the man paid him no mind. One of the gravediggers jumped into the hole. The other lifted Oznur, and then handed her to the man in the pit, who laid her down.

Nuri screamed at the men. "They have stolen her coffin from her!" They stopped chanting and scowled at him.

"They have taken it!" he shouted louder.

When Nuri saw the shovels of dirt flung into the hole, he ran around to the other side of it and bent over the opening and began to flog one of the men across the head. "Hey, what the Devil is wrong with this crazy one?" The digger called out. He dodged Nuri's hands. Tears were gushing from the boy and he could hardly breathe. He did not know that coffins were used over and over, and that the body must be laid into the earth.

Tears and sandy dirt clogged his sight and filled his nose and throat but he lunged around the edge of the grave to the ministers, feeling like he was more than one person. He could hear himself sobbing and screaming words that did not seem to be his own: "Don't let them – she can't breathe!"

Both men held him back, and finally brought him to his knees while the two men kept filling up the hole. "You are dense, Boy," one said. He was speaking while standing over Nuri. The other agreed, "Nothing like his father. Has no manner." Nuri was not able to do anything but swab at his face.

When the men finished with the shovels, grabbed the coffin, and took off over the hill back toward the town, the holy men finally released the boy.

The two ministers took Nuri back to the mosque with them. They said they were afraid if they left him at the grave, he might try to dig up his sister with his hands. They told him to wash his face in the fountain in the courtyard. "Make yourself decent," one said. "Go home to your poor mother. I don't know what your father will say of your behavior."

He wandered home. Weary. Wretched.

In a few days, his father came home, and Nuri found him in the garden, seated on the ground, with his amber prayer beads threading through his fingers. An unaccustomed white skullcap covered Burhan's head, and his voice sounded rough and low. With his eyes closed, Burhan was reciting a mourning chant from the Koran. Nuri *was surprised that Burhan could chant the Koran. But, Burhan had been taught by his father, and could before the revolution recite the entire holy book from memory. Nuri cautiously stepped across the yard, so as not to snap a branch or make a disturbance as he came to Burhan's side.*

"Allahmercifulmmm –"

"Father, it's me, Nuri. I was scared, forgive me, I –"

"… Those who believe, and do deeds of righteousness –"

"Father Dear, I took care of Oznur, Father. They put her –"

"… Them, we shall admit to gardens underneath which rivers flow –"

"The hole, they, they covered –"

Burhan stopped and stared at him vacantly. His eyes hung bleary and heavy and filled with a heat that seemed to burn Nuri's face." Why, Boy, why do you disturb my only solace to this miserable life?"

"Father! She –"

"I'm mourning, can't you see that? She was my precious. You have to grow up, be a man." Burhan had been crying, which shocked Nuri almost as much as anything else.

When Nuri wandered off and sat down in the gravel at the side of the house, he tried to pray for Oznur and for himself; but he had gone to secular schools and did not know the proper words.

"Tell me, Sister."

Adalet turned her head to Nefise and spoke in a whisper. "Like a pit out of which I could not raise myself. I was unable to move my legs when Burhan came back from Istanbul a few days later – and I stayed like that for three months."

"Why were you unable to contact him in Istanbul?"

"He was somewhere on the road toward home," Adalet told her.

But it would not have mattered if he had been with them. Oznur's fate could not be changed. She had been shown her kismet minutes before it happened. But somehow it seemed to Adalet that Oznur's death must have been her failure as a mother. For the only time in her life, everything went black in Adalet's soul. Allah was gone from her spirit. Through the years, Adalet always kept hearth fires burning no matter how bad things got. With the wars of her life, she had seen so much blood and ash, but there was always something to make her think life would go on. Oznur's death was the death of her youth and future at the same time. Were evil jinni cursing her willfulness? She and Burhan had no solace to give each other for three months. Finally, he was transferred to another city. He went alone.

"After all, Sister," Adalet said, looking Nefise in the eyes, "I was the mother, and it was up to me to keep their lives going, to be the strong one, to protect them."

"I am certain that you did everything you could," Nefise answered.

"But, I had not protected them against the wars that raged between Burhan and me. Why had I kept coming back to Burhan time after time with nothing changing except for the worse? We needed help to know how to live together."

"But, if you hadn't come back," she said, "Deniz, Oznur or Sedat – my dear, you would not have them."

"Oznur was taken from me anyway. Sedat took himself from me." Adalet sat with her head on Nefise's shoulder, lost in Marash. The first time in Marash, it was with Deniz's birth. The second, Oznur's death. Adalet had stayed in bed the rest of that summer and even after Elif and Leyla went back to school in Istanbul in the fall. The younger children took care of her. She was at the bottom, paralyzed, and couldn't walk. Say her prayers? Prayers had not helped Oznur. To be forgiven? She would not ask. She wanted to die in her pit.

"But how did you hold on, Sister? Did Burhan help you?" Nefise asked.

"We were like strangers," she answered.

"Then, what?" Nefise urged.

Adalet sat forward and began to rub the palms of her hands on her thighs as she thought of how her child had helped her. "One day," she said quietly, "Sedat came into my bedroom with morning tea. He stood there looking at me with those big black eyes. I asked him what did he want; and he said he wanted to ask me a question, and I answered, 'What?'"

"Adalet Girl." Nefise said, bringing her hand onto her sister's, which was tediously caressing the top of her brown jersey skirt. "Is your leg hurting you?" Adalet stopped the rubbing, clicked her tongue and jerked her head negative.

Adalet continued to tell the story without looking at Nefise. "It was Sedat. He asked me that day why I didn't love him anymore. He told me I was acting as if all of my children were dead."

"The child was only eight-years old. How could he think to say that?" Nefise asked.

"Sedat always thought deeply and quietly about life. That's why he had to leave us all. It was too painful for him."

"How did you feel when he said that to you?" Adalet paused to think before she answered. Nefise's face was pinched with distress.

"I stroked Sedat's head," Adalet told her, "shaved almost bald, as it was, for his school – saying how much I loved him and his insightful mind." Sister brought a hand to her lips. "Sedat told me that he had missed me," Adalet said to herself. "He kissed my hand and brought it to his forehead; and then with that smile, he backed out of the room."

Adalet pushed up from the couch. "I'll be back in a minute," she said. Nefise watched her with a mild concern that Adalet rather cherished.

In the bathroom, she splashed her face and arms. As she dried with the towel, she studied her round form in the mirror. Her face was as oval as her sagging breasts, as her shoulders and hips. Life had molded her into an oblong circle. She held the towel still; and fused her old eyes with those staring back from the well of the mirror. She let herself be kindled by what those almond eyes had gazed upon since Oznur's passing: They had seen five of her children in adulthood working strong and trying to make sense of what life had handed to them, had absorbed the scenes of America three times, seen grandchildren on two shores, and assessed a foreign daughter-in-law, and found her a kindred spirit. Her eyes had witnessed how the love of one child drew her body back from the despair brought on by the loss of the other.

Adalet pondered again the miracle of her youngest son's words. After Sedat had left her that morning, she lay for a long while, trying to feel Allah's light. Gradually, she began to see a vision of her inner self in that awful time of death −as if she were lying in the bottom of a vessel, a cave or a cup− *as if she were but dregs of coffee, which had been consumed. Coarse and dry and dark. In that cup, what was left of her were still signs for the future, and she read into it, and saw wings and mountains and writings and roads and much more, her self, like a large house. On her chimney was a stork on a nest as extravagant as a wagon overloaded with hay, her house, sitting out in some rolling valley where the changing leaves blew across her yard, and the wind rustled against her shutters, which she had closed.*

And after a while, she heaved open those shutters. Light speared through and breezes dusted her many rooms. She became again all the places she'd lived and traveled and survived.

Her voice came whispering, telling her now she must make her own hope; and Azime chimed in −make the nest− to Oznur's rhythm tap tapping across her abdomen in a swish and a slide. And laughter rang through the corridors of her legs − which were swaying like a river, a river within a river of people on the move, fleeing invaders, or gathering for a celebration or boarding a transport. She was pressing toward safety. Her hands were alive with the need to reach, and do, and make something of little. Her Mustafa Kemal Pasha's breath thundered into her lungs and bid her turn and face the grief that threw her into the pit, telling, Take up the song of yourself and

*dance, find the creative, continue your journey, light the hearth for
as long as you may.*

Adalet pulled back out of that remembered vision welled in the
bathroom's glass. Laying the towel across its hook, she nodded her
head with what had been shown her so long before – when she had
understood that her time to die was not up to her. She had realized
also that there was no bringing Oznur back; but there were others alive who still needed her. After that vision, she had told herself that it was not time to lie down deep as a tulip bulb yet. Oznur
would always be alive in her the same as her own spirit, and would
live on in her grandchildren – the same as her mother's vision and
fortitude. Pasha's work had just begun. With a new strength and
inch by inch, she forced herself to where her legs hung over the side
of that crippling bed, and soon enough she was standing, calling
for her children, and washing Burhan's socks.

Adalet came out of the bathroom, went into the bedroom, and
opened a hand-carved wooden box someone in Marash had giv-
en to her. She searched through the contents and found the poem.

When she came back to the living room, Sister had cleared
the breakfast plates and set the swan with the roses onto the table. The rain had stopped. Nefise had opened the window to let
in the fresh air.

Nefise spun from the kitchen, saying, "Sister, I'm happy to see
that you're better. I was feeling guilty that I brought up a sad part
of your life."

Adalet opened her left hand where she had been holding the
paper, and unfolded it. "I brought you the poem I wrote about
four months after Oznur's death," she said.

Sister took it with surprise. "Adalet, I did not know you wrote
poems."

"Sometimes I wrote poems when I was happy and sometimes
when I was sad."

Nefise read it aloud:

Yikildi, neseli dunyam	*My joyful world is torn apart*
Cekildi bi-kenar oldu	*Shrunken on its axis*
Muhabbet kandili sondu	*A candle lights the darkness*
Gonlum turbedar oldu	*I bury your heart in mine*

Nefise's eyes glistened. "Thank you for sharing this with me," she said. "Only one who had survived loss would know."

"Writing that feeling down onto paper helped," Adalet told her. "After that, I did revive, as if I were a cup filled with spring water. My paralysis left me." Adalet had continued to survive in good spirits. *One day, before the family left Marash for good, Burhan took her in the buggy to Oznur's grave. The two of them sat there for a long time, talking about what they had known, and the hopes they held for the future of their children and nation. He promised he would try to do better, said he wanted to do better, and that she had been a good wife and helpmate to him; and that he knew he had made things difficult for her at times. She told him that she knew he always meant to do well, and that he had accomplished much that was admirable.*

"Adalet, there's many things I don't understand; but I know I loved you, and that I had to have you for my wife. There was no other who had your spunk and spirit —"

"I could not resist you," Adalet admitted. That night, he held her in his arms until she drifted into a tranquil sleep. As well as she could remember, it was the last time that peace ever lay between them.

"Adalet, come. The postman has brought you a letter!" Nefise called. "Come out of the bedroom if you've finished your noonday prayers."

"Thank You!" Adalet called after the postman, who waved as he turned. What a nice man, who had no requirement to climb the stairs to place the mail in her hand except that he was a good human being who believed in helping single old women.

The man who'd caught Adalet's fancy for those forty years, and for whom she'd wandered the vast stretches of Anatolia, lay in his tomb. All of that traveling in search of his shadow. She had no husband, dead or alive. Those divorce papers. She'd refused to deal with them, as if Burhan's fate included hers, forever. And then, separation. All of those miles. His leaving the marriage was not the worst. The shock was that he'd leave his flesh and blood to buoy in a sea without handing them so much as a life jacket. Sedat disappeared. Vedat floundered. The daughters married. Nuri was lucky. As for her, she'd learned to swim alone – with help from her children. And, she won the wisdom of self-reliance.

Nefise handed her the oversized white envelope.

"It's from America!" Adalet said, seeing the handwriting and stamp. They went to the table. At the seams, she pulled open the packet. "Look," she said, showing Nefise the photo of her son the doctor, with his wife and children. The little black-haired daughter sparkled in a pink ballet costume. "This is their new house," she said, pointing. "Friends tell me their house is like a hunting lodge." Adalet began silently to scan over Nuri's letter, holding it almost to her nose, for her glasses were over on the hutch. She would have to read the daughter-in-law Lee's letter later, using the English-Turkish dictionary for almost every word. Adalet did not mind translating her letters piece by piece, for it used her time well. "They invite Vedat and me to come next summer," she said, looking up.

"The little daughter reminds me of you, Adalet – when you were that age." Nefise took her arm. "But how is it to have a foreigner, a stranger, for a daughter-in-law?"

"She seems more like a daughter," Adalet answered, looking again at the photo. "Lee is a teacher like me, a poet. Our attachment is easy. I love to learn new things. She likes my cooking and stories."

"But then, you must speak English very well."

"Some. We jumble our Turkish and English together. We do hand language too."

"She must come from an engaging family."

"I visited them, and they like me." Adalet leaned her head to Nefise and lowered her voice, as if someone could hear them. "You remember how Mother was determined to disown me because I married Burhan?" Nefise nodded slowly. She pointed to her daughter-in-law standing on the steps of her home with her son, their children and that dog – which they even permitted to run through the house. "When this girl married my son, her father disowned her, too – because of Nuri's being a foreigner." They looked at each other secretly.

"But our family has such prestigious roots," Nefise said, shaking her head. It was interesting how kismet placed you with the people in your life. Adalet knew it was puzzling for Nefise to comprehend how a foreign bride and she could have so much in common; and that Lee could understand her. Love her as they would, her own children could view Adalet only as their mother. She had made herself a servant to them, and furthermore, the submissive wife of their father. The unbeliever in the photo – perhaps she could envision Adalet differently.

"Come, I'll show you," Adalet said as they walked into the bedroom. They put themselves down on the bed on either side of the wooden box from Marash; and Adalet took out the bundle of letters and cards, some of which were tied together by a hemp twine.

"All of these are from America," she told Nefise, loosening the string and ruffling through the stack, taking out several from her son's bride. "Her letters are long," Adalet said. "Orhan translates them for me. You know, he lived two years with them in America," Adalet added proudly. Nefise nodded and patted her on the shoulder. "Listen to this one," Adalet said. She did not require her glasses, for she knew all of her letters. *"March 24, 1976. Dear Mother Adalet, Thank you again for your faithful letters. We here send our love to you. Kurt is doing well in school. We just received the grade cards and he has improved continuously this year. Three-year-old Sara Ayla is full of herself – singing and dancing..."*

"Oh, I see," Nefise said, peering over at the letter. "You wrote the Turkish on top of the English words."

"Sure. I do it. Someday, I'll tell Lee all the deeds of my life and she'll record them."

Nefise laughed at the suggestion. "Who could want to read about *your* life, Sister? We've had small and average lives."

"Nations come from wombs like mine," Adalet answered, feeling again like the teacher. "Our hands keep fires while wars rage. We clean the burnt homes, help re-stack the rocks, gather the suffering ruin to our breasts and hide what we can." She held up a finger – "milk the goats, milk the cows, milk the mules if necessary! – Whatever is at hand to give us cheese and yogurt. We interpret the signs and let our people learn to read their destiny, Sister."

Nefise gaped at her, as if she did not realize that Adalet had so many confident words inside. "You have lived the name that was given you, Adalet."

"And you, too, Dearest – still living 'Excellent' as our parents named you!"

"Perhaps we could have been a bit smarter along the way," she answered, with a twinkle dancing in her hazel eyes.

"Inshallah, we inherited some wisdom from the Asian Steppes," Adalet added.

"Maybe you're right," Nefise said, thoughtfully. "People need a common story like ours – not to forget the reasons why we stay with the struggle for better times right up to the end."

"Women," Adalet answered. "And men," she added firmly. Sister agreed that those words, also, were true. And then, they set about preparing lunch, for the fall day was going strong into the early afternoon.

After lunch, Sister gave Adalet a present in a pouch, a token that felt like no more than a ferry coin. Mother Zehra had kept it tied by its drawstrings in the small maroon velvet bag. Nefise said that she reckoned the piece inside could not be opened, or perhaps Mother had saved the gold for those sure-to-come hard times again. It was tucked back under her other trinkets in a black jewelry chest, an old walnut chest with ivory inlay and silver wires.

Adalet pulled thumbs to forefingers on the drawstring. "Gold?" she asked.

When Mother Zehra died, Nefise explained, she found the chest among some things she had taken from under the bed in Zehra's room. It seemed to hold nothing but broken fragments, scraps left over from other times. Nefise took the chest home with her and placed it aside until last year when she checked to see how many bits of gold there were to sell. She then recognized it. Nefise had managed to get an Armenian friend, who had a gold shop, to fix it up good as new.

Adalet shook the gold onto her palm and took in a sudden wind of breath. At first, she simply felt awe. And then, the Balkan storm rushed back, the touch of a hand, the red trees of Bedre, and the lingering question, What did her friend, the girl Zeyneb give up for her life to be married off to an old dealer, and dead by a mere twenty-four?

"But, how," she turned in amazement to Nefise, "How did this prize of mine fall into Mother's hands?" She looked at the winking piece from her youth in the palm of her hand. Her heart-shaped locket. With a finger of her other hand, she caressed its still smooth surface. "And why," she murmured, "would my mother keep such a thing hidden?"

What did it matter? After all these years, here was her treasure back in her hand. Fitting her nails at the latch, she split the heart. It opened like a butterfly. And, there she was. Just as she remembered.

ADALET

Lifting lids she pinches mint
the green of her plastic prayer beads.

Adalet laughs,
memory's young suitors fill her table.

She is in them,
the rose water in the marrow,
they share her
century.

Her hair is salt and pepper,
her family's love is dried fruit
and the gift of new teeth.

But her portions
of white beans in olive oil, stuffed eggplant
grape leaf and green pepper dolmas
run room to room
as a child to many years ago,

who, while the men rounded the house
closing the evening shutters,
was not ready.
Had she seen the softening stones, birds and hills?
Had she left them all behind?

How the young love strong flavors,
the Ottoman knots.
How the head scarf revolution
stopped outside her kitchen window.

She looks into the sun
resolving a photograph's shadows.
She peers into the black spots
left

asking:
How long have you been there?
Come in,
are you hungry?

K. Kamal Ayyildiz